MOVING MATH FORWARD THROUGH CRITICAL THINKING AND EXPLORATION

Line It Up

Focusing on Linear Relationships

M. Katherine Gavin

Linda Jensen Sheffield

Suzanne H. Chapin

Ann Marie Spinelli

Kendall Hunt

publishing company

ACKNOWLEDGMENTS

Math Innovations Writing Team

Authors
M. Katherine Gavin

Linda Jensen Sheffield

Suzanne H. Chapin

Project Manager
Janice M. Vuolo

Teacher Edition Team
Ann Marie Spinelli

Alice J. Gabbard

Jennifer M. MacPherson

Writing Assistants
Kathy Dorkin

Jane Paulin

Jacob J. Whitmore

Mathematics Editor
Kathleen G. Snook

Assessment Specialist
Nancy Anderson

Advisory Board
Jerry P. Becker

Janet Beissinger

Diane J. Briars

Ann Lawrence

Ira J. Papick

Portions of *Curriculum Focal Points* have been reprinted with the permission of the National Council of Teachers of Mathematics.

Kendall Hunt
publishing company

www.kendallhunt.com

Send all inquiries to:

4050 Westmark Drive

Dubuque, IA 52004-1840

1-800-542-6657

Printed in the United States of America

2 3 4 5 6 7 8 9 10   13 12 11 10

Line It Up:
Focusing on Linear Relationships
Table of Contents

Math INNOVATIONS
Teaching and Learning Strategies

Think Like a Mathematician Daily Record Sheet

Think Like a Mathematician is a unique feature of the Kendall Hunt *Math Innovations* program. This daily record sheet is a learning tool designed to help students organize and keep track of their daily work and notes throughout the lessons and for reference during class discussions and homework. In addition to offering students a place to record their work and the key ideas presented in each lesson, the *Think Like a Mathematician Daily Record Sheet* also provides students with easy access to important notes when studying for quizzes and tests. Organizing work and establishing productive study habits are critical skills that need to be developed in the middle school years. Using this tool daily not only encourages students to keep a record of their own innovative results, conjectures, arguments and questions, but it also provides them with notes that can be polished or refined as well as studied. It is yet another way in which *Math Innovations* helps students reflect on their thinking process as they mature mathematically.

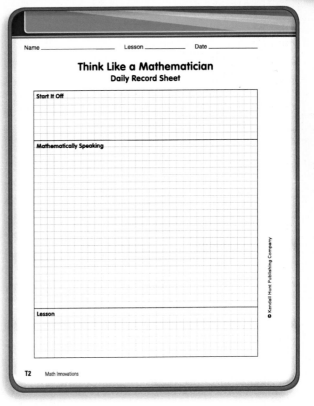

The *Think Like a Mathematician Daily Record Sheet* is partitioned into labeled sections, with one section for each component of the lesson, and has a grid paper background. Most teachers and students will use more than one *Think Like a Mathematician Daily Record Sheet* for multiple-day lessons.

An important habit of mind that this program develops in students is careful note-taking during mathematics class. Initially, teachers may need to demonstrate this to students by recording important information related to the key ideas of the lesson on the board or on an overhead for students to copy. Students should be encouraged to record other key information in their notes, such as their individual mathematical work, strategies and insights; mathematical terms and their definitions; important formulas; and examples or drawings that explain or illustrate new concepts.

It is recommended that students keep their *Think Like a Mathematician Daily Record Sheets* in a 3-ring binder. This 3-ring binder will serve as the student's mathematics notebook.

Think Like a Mathematician
Daily Record Sheet

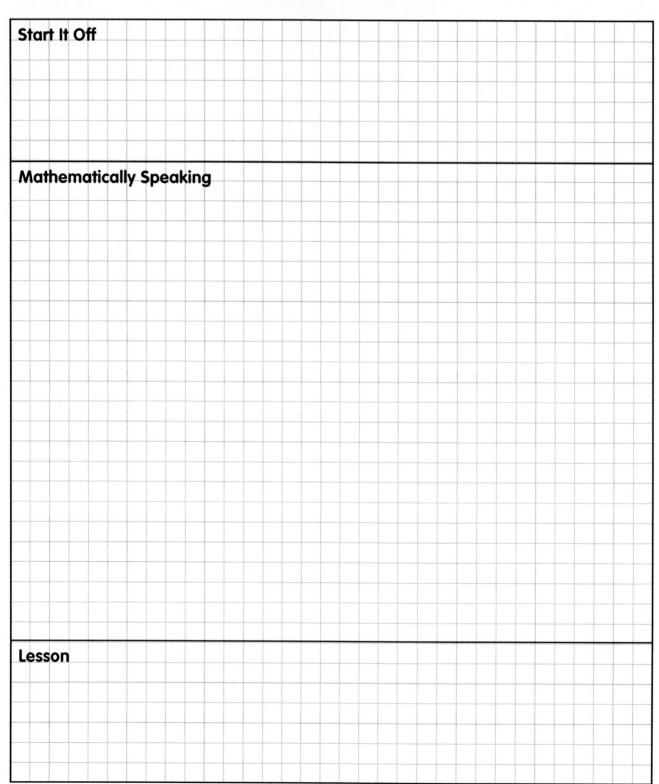

Start It Off

Mathematically Speaking

Lesson

Lesson (continued)

Wrap It Up

Start It Off

1. Identify the place value of ea
2. Determine the value of each in words.

$10^6 = 1,000,000$ Ten t

Start It Off

Start It Off is a short problem or series of problems found at the beginning of each lesson. It is designed to be a quick warm-up at the start of class that helps students build upon previous learning and connect it to new concepts that are being introduced. It usually contains a metacognitive question to help students deepen their mathematical understanding. This leads students to make connections to previous knowledge as they discover relationships among specific mathematical concepts, skills and procedures.

Using the *Start It Off* questions as a daily mathematical warm-up helps establish a classroom routine and will smooth the transition time as students enter the classroom. Students should be instructed to begin work on the *Start It Off* as soon as they enter class. This allows the teacher to take attendance, distribute materials or attend to individual students' needs. *Start It Off* problems only take a few minutes to complete, but the discussion about these problems will build skills and knowledge over time. Approximately 5–10 minutes should be used during each class to discuss the questions. For multi-day lessons, teachers may assign a part of the *Start It Off* each day.

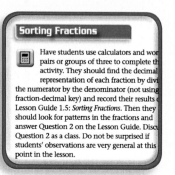

Sorting Fractions

Have students use calculators and wor
pairs or groups of three to complete th
activity. They should find the decimal
representation of each fraction by divi
the numerator by the denominator (not using
fraction-decimal key) and record their results c
Lesson Guide 1.5: *Sorting Fractions*. Then they
should look for patterns in the fractions and
answer Question 2 on the Lesson Guide. Disc
Question 2 as a class. Do not be surprised if
students' observations are very general at this
point in the lesson.

The Lesson

Guiding the Lesson

The lessons presented in *Math Innovations* have students learning mathematics using interesting, age-appropriate, hands-on investigations, tasks, problems and games. A conversational tone is used throughout the series as a motivational tool and to demonstrate respect to students' as mathematical thinkers who are capable of reading and understanding the material. Embedded in each lesson are questions that encourage students to use critical and creative thinking and mathematical reasoning as they solve problems and discover key mathematical concepts. Examples are often presented for the students to discuss and study. *Lesson Guides*, found in the Teacher's Edition, help students to record their data and organize their work as they engage in lesson activities. Using these guides will save time and enable students to focus more of their attention on developing a deeper understanding of the key mathematical concepts presented in the lesson.

Teacher notes provided in the Teacher's Edition offer assistance for the teacher in guiding and navigating students through the lesson activities. These notes include tips on teaching strategies, recommended classroom instructional arrangements, questions to further develop student understanding, key student responses and possible student misconceptions. The teacher's role during lesson exploration is to circulate, observe and ask questions, but not to explain procedures. It is important to cultivate independent student thinking during activity exploration. This provides an opportunity for students to gain self-confidence by discussing their ideas with other students as they work to gain understanding.

Guiding the Discussion

Classroom discussion is a key component in *Math Innovations*. Discussions can include the whole class, small groups or partners. Classroom discussions are especially effective in moving student thinking forward and developing students' collective understanding of key mathematical ideas. Teachers are strongly urged to allow time for students to share and discuss ideas, discoveries and solution strategies at several points throughout the lessons. Sometimes students are asked to discuss errors or incorrect procedures. While some think this will confuse students, the opposite occurs! Students clarify their understanding of the material when they have had to address their preconceived notions and misconceptions.

Teachers are also encouraged to be mindful of key vocabulary terms and symbols highlighted in the Student Edition and to emphasize their appropriate use in class discussions. Students must not only understand the meaning of these terms, but must also become fluent in the precise use of mathematical language. Teachers should expect students to use this mathematical language on a daily basis during class discussions and in their writing. As they explicitly encourage students to use this language, teachers should remind students that this helps them think and talk like mathematicians, which is a recurring goal of the *Math Innovations* program.

Talk Moves

Several strategies can be used to facilitate meaningful classroom discussions. Chapin, O'Connor, and Anderson (2009) refer to these strategies as *talk moves*. The *Math Innovations* program recommends teachers use the following six talk moves:

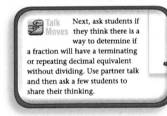

Talk Moves: Next, ask students if they think there is a way to determine if a fraction will have a terminating or repeating decimal equivalent without dividing. Use partner talk and then ask a few students to share their thinking.

Revoicing

The teacher *restates/revoices* a student's words as accurately as possible and then verifies whether the student's response was correct. This move can be used when a student's response is unclear or confusing. It also can be used when a student's contribution is unique and brilliant, but not understood by the majority of the class. For example, a teacher might ask, "You said that triangle was equilateral and scalene? Did I get that right?" The student then has a chance to restate what he or she meant. Often the next utterance is much more succinct; "No, I meant that if the triangle is equilateral, then it cannot be scalene too." This talk move helps students to clarify their thinking.

Repeat/rephrase

When using *repeat/rephrase* the teacher focuses the discussion on the main ideas of the lesson. After a student has made a particularly important point or comment, the teacher asks another student to restate the point by asking, "Would you repeat what he/she said in your own words?" It is important to use this move to highlight ideas that are foundational, no matter how small, or ideas that are not well-understood. For example, many students are confused by how the size of a denominator of a fraction affects the size of a fractional piece. This talk move can be used to ask a number of students to repeat a classmate's explanation for why $\frac{1}{8}$ is less than $\frac{1}{3}$. Do not ask students to repeat information that everyone already understands. Teachers can also follow up with the student who contributed the original thought to ensure that the idea was heard as intended. This not only validates the idea, but also gives the class another version of the idea. This talk move slows down the instruction in order to give students enough time to process what they are learning and helps students stay engaged and involved in the lesson. Many teachers have found that the use of this talk move especially benefits English language learners.

Agree/disagree and why

Agree/disagree and why is the most important talk move, as it asks students to reason about another's contribution. It is used after the teacher makes sure that students heard and had time to process the mathematical idea. By posing questions like, "Do you agree or disagree with that idea? Why?" teachers can draw out student thinking by having them apply their understanding to someone else's thoughts. It is important that teachers do not offer their positions, but instead allow students to wrestle with their own ideas. Teachers can help students focus on the correct concepts after they have had the chance to develop their own reasoning.

Adding on

Teachers encourage students to participate further in a class discussion by using *adding on*. Posing a question like "Would someone like to add on to what was just said?" solicits more input to the discussion. Surprisingly, students are not bored when more than one student contributes the same information. In fact, for many students hearing the same information a number of times helps them fully process the new content. Students also learn new approaches and problem-solving strategies when teachers elicit additional contributions. When students have to make sense of different solution methods, they must consider how these methods are similar or different from their own.

Wait time

Wait time involves waiting at least ten seconds before calling on a student for an answer once a question has been posed. This move gives students an opportunity to think about and organize their ideas. It also serves to encourage all students to contribute, not just those who process their thoughts quickly. Wait time should also be used once a student has been called upon to share an idea or respond to a question. A comment like, "We'll wait...take your time," usually serves this purpose. It is important for all students to become active in class discussions to reap the learning benefits.

Partner talk

Partner talk enables students to put their thoughts into words by discussing their ideas with a partner. It provides an opportunity for hesitant or unsure learners to clarify and practice their contribution with just one person before sharing with the whole class. Partner talk is also helpful when students do not fully understand an idea. Students can raise their questions to their partners and together decide on the best way to pose them to the rest of the class. Teachers have found that this is an effective move when few students volunteer to answer a question; asking students to discuss the question with their partner increases the likelihood of their contributions in the future!

In addition to promoting a deeper understanding of important and significant mathematical ideas, these classroom discussion strategies encourage more active student listening, enhance the quality of verbal discourse, build students' vocabulary, help students view problems from different perspectives, and foster student appreciation for a variety of thinking and problem-solving styles.

Questioning Techniques

A variety of questions designed to stimulate rich class discussions in the *Math Innovations* program are listed in the Student Edition as well as in the teacher notes found in the Teacher's Edition. These questions encourage students to delve deeply into important mathematical ideas. Students are often called upon to make and explore mathematical conjectures, analyze patterns and formulate generalizations, develop and evaluate mathematical arguments, select and apply a variety of representations, use and make connections among mathematical ideas, and reflect on their thinking and problem-solving strategies. Teachers should be aware of the type of questions they ask, and avoid *funneling* questions, which may elicit their own predetermined, restrictive answer. A better questioning strategy is the use of *focusing* questions. These allow students to explain their thinking and to develop creative solutions and understanding for internalization of concepts (Herbel-Eisenmann & Breyfogle, 2005).

- Examples of **funneling** questions (less effective for supporting deeper student thinking):

  "How many sides does that shape have?"

  "Which angle is larger?"

  "What is the product?"

- Examples of **focusing** questions (more effective to guide student thinking):

  "What have you figured out?"

  "Why do you think that?"

  "Does that always work?"

  "Is there another way?"

  "How are these two methods different? How are they similar?"

Five Ws and an H Mathematical Questions

While the focusing questions encourage students to become investigative mathematicians as they explore problems and new mathematics concepts, students may also find the following question types helpful in nudging their thinking forward and deepening their mathematical understanding. Just as students answer questions of "who, what, when, where, why and how" in writing articles for the school newspaper, they can answer these same questions as they investigate and extend mathematical problems (Sheffield, 2006). As students begin to think like mathematicians, they will realize that the most interesting mathematical concepts often begin after they answer the initial question.

- **Who?**
  Who has another method? Who has another solution? Who is right?

- **What or what if?**
  What sense can I make of this problem? What is the answer? What are the essential elements of this problem? What is the important mathematical concept? What patterns do I see in this data? What generalizations might I make from these patterns? What if I change part of the problem? What if I use a different representation?

- **When?**
  When does this work? When does this not work?

- **Where?**
  Where did that come from? Where should I start? Where might I go next? Where might I find additional information?

- **Why or why not?**
  Why does that work? If it does not work, why not?

- **How?**
  How is this like other mathematical problems or patterns that I have seen? How does it differ? How does this relate to "real-life" situations or models? How many solutions are possible? How do I know that I have found all the possible solutions? In how many ways can I represent, simulate, model, or visualize these ideas? In how many ways can I sort, organize, and present this information?

Differentiation

Think Differently

Math Innovations recognizes the importance and challenge of differentiated instruction in today's diverse middle school classroom. As a result, this program not only includes differentiated teaching strategies and tips, but also provides some ready-made tools that will meet the needs of students at different levels of learning. Where appropriate, these differentiated strategies and tools can be found in the teacher notes labeled *Differentiation: Think Differently*. Two unique features, *Accommodation Guides* and *Think Beyond Questions*, are specific to the content of the lesson and provide teachers with alternative strategies and differentiation materials that will make mathematics meaningful for all students.

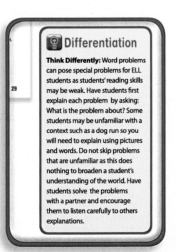

Differentiation

Think Differently: Word problems can pose special problems for ELL students as students' reading skills may be weak. Have students first explain each problem by asking: What is the problem about? Some students may be unfamiliar with a context such as a dog run so you will need to explain using pictures and words. Do not skip problems that are unfamiliar as this does nothing to broaden a student's understanding of the world. Have students solve the problems with a partner and encourage them to listen carefully to others explanations.

29

Accommodation Guides, found at the end of a lesson in the Teacher Guide, are designed to provide additional support for those students experiencing difficulty with a lesson activity. These accommodation guides often consist of ready-made tables and other graphic organizers that help student structure and organize their work. Some guides may offer different problem-solving approaches or strategies. Accommodation Guides are those Lesson Guides which contain an A after the number.

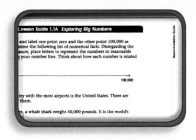

Think Beyond Questions, found in the On Your Own sections of the Student Edition, are extension questions for students that have a firm grasp of the concepts presented in the lesson and are ready for further challenge. Think Beyond Questions expand students' knowledge by asking questions that require more complex reasoning, or by asking students to conduct research or create materials.

Meeting the Needs of English Language Learners (ELL)

Today there are millions of students in mathematics classrooms who are English language learners (ELL). Research indicates that one of the most effective ways to help ELLs learn mathematics is to provide them with a discussion-rich classroom. Kersaint and colleagues (2009) state "It is through language that ELLs come to understand not only mathematics but English as well. Such classrooms are environments in which teachers and students have built a climate of trust and respect in which everyone's contributions are valued" (p. xii).

Math Innovations' emphasis on discussion and vocabulary will help your ELL students learn. To get started, you and your students need to discuss the rules for how you will talk together respectfully. If students think they might be teased or laughed at, they will be unwilling to participate. Go over body language, actions and words that are not allowed such as rolling one's eyes or tapping one's foot impatiently. Remind everyone how difficult it is to learn mathematics in a different language and how important it is to give individuals time to compose an answer. In addition, work to include all students, especially English language learners, in the mathematical conversations. When you pose a question, first have students turn and talk to a partner so they can vocalize their ideas in a safe way. Then open up the conversation to the whole class. Many English language learners have attended elementary school in another country and can enrich discussions by sharing a variety of mathematics algorithms and strategies that they learned in their home countries.

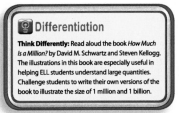

Differentiation

Think Differently: Read aloud the book *How Much Is a Million?* by David M. Schwartz and Steven Kellogg. The illustrations in this book are especially useful in helping ELL students understand large quantities. Challenge students to write their own versions of the book to illustrate the size of 1 million and 1 billion.

There are many strategies you can use to enhance the learning experience for ELLs. When possible, use visuals, physical models, manipulative materials, drawings, charts, tables and graphs to support the communication in the classroom. Write important words on the board and/or create a word wall, and link these terms with drawings and materials. Take a minute to explain idiomatic expressions or culturally based terms (e.g., blue ribbon job) and to identify important features of the text. Also help connect the mathematics of the lesson to real life, even if it means taking the time to explain a particular context. Provide opportunities for students to work with others to solve problems and use talk moves, especially revoice and repeat/rephrase discussed in this section, to enable students to hear something explained more than one time. ELLs benefit from being able to practice articulating their understanding in mathematics. A related strategy involves having students explain to their partners their solution methods prior to having to present them in front of the whole class. Dramatic gestures, speaking and enunciating clearly, and providing support around note taking will also help ELLs.

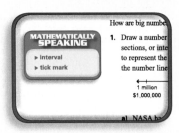

Vocabulary is especially important in mathematics and receives significant attention in *Math Innovations*. Make vocabulary learning part of every lesson by regularly discussing words, their meanings, and how we use them in a sentence. *Math Innovations* provides students with easy access to new vocabulary by highlighting new terms when they are introduced in the student text and by listing new vocabulary terms at the end of each section and lesson. Every time you discuss a Wrap It Up question, help students to use the correct terms, referring to these terms in the Mathematically Speaking section. A word wall containing these terms prominently placed in the classroom will benefit all students in speaking and writing like mathematicians using correct and precise vocabulary.

Be sure to explain the difference between the social meaning and the mathematical meaning of many words (e.g., some and sum) and ask students to draw comparisons among terms such as perimeter, area and volume. Many mathematical terms are similar in other languages and students may benefit from translating terms to their native language, especially if it is a concept that is well-understood and only the English word that is new. We have found that if students keep a personal dictionary (word, definition, picture, application or examples and non-examples), they refer to their dictionaries when confused. It also may be useful for students to have a dictionary with translations from English to their native language, especially if one is available with mathematical terms. Remember also that it is through the sustained use of these strategies that achievement gains are realized. These and additional strategies are elaborated upon in the Think Differently sections of the Teacher Edition.

Student Snapshot—Lesson Observation Tool

The Student Snapshot observational tool is another unique feature of *Math Innovations*. It is designed to be used during lesson activities in which students work in groups to explore key mathematical ideas and solve problems. One of the teacher's roles as a facilitator is to move from group to group and listen in on student conversations. This provides an opportunity to determine which students to call on for contributions during class discussions. It also enables the teacher to observe and informally assess students' depth of knowledge and understanding of major mathematical concepts; their mathematical communication skills, including the appropriate use of key mathematical terms; the forms of representation students are using; and student problem-solving and reasoning skills. As teachers observe and listen to group conversations, short anecdotal notes can be recorded to provide a snapshot of student learning. These snapshots will be helpful in assessing students' mathematical understanding and will provide insight that will be useful in guiding future instruction.

Unit _____

Student Snapshot

Name	Major Concepts/ Connections	Communication	Problem Solving

It is recommended that teachers focus on a few students per lesson (not necessarily from the same group) when using the Student Snapshot observational tool. Having a clipboard and a pad of sticky-notes handy is helpful when attempting to record anecdotal observations as the teacher moves from group to group. It is important to date the notes and to file them at the end of the class period or school day using the Student Snapshot sheet provided on page T11 or a teacher's grade book.

Wrap It Up

Each lesson contains Wrap It Up discussion questions, which provide an opportunity for the entire class to reflect on the major mathematical concepts presented in the lesson. A Wrap It Up discussion may include students sharing their discoveries from the lesson or may focus on the summary questions. During the Wrap It Up section, teachers should encourage students to use talk moves (explained above) as they share their thinking with other students. The *Think Like a Mathematician Daily Record Sheet* provides space for students to record important ideas offered during the Wrap It Up class discussions. In the beginning of the year, teachers may need to model how to record Wrap It Up comments and responses, but with daily practice students will become more independent note takers. It is important that students record their own insights and problem-solving strategies as well as those offered by their classmates or the teacher. Following each Wrap It Up discussion, students will have an opportunity to write about their mathematical understanding individually as they respond to a similar reflective question located at the beginning of each *On Your Own* section. This question is labeled *Write About It*, and provides accountability to each student for their learning, as well as a method for teachers to assess students' understanding of the major concepts of the lesson.

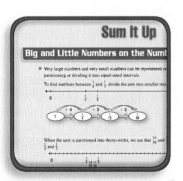

Sum It Up/Study Guide

The *Sum It Up* feature provides students with a resource for reviewing and summarizing their learning at the end of each section. This feature consists of an outline of the major mathematics concepts that students have learned within a given section and includes examples of procedures and skills. *Study Guides* located in the student book provide students with questions and exercises to review the concepts and skills presented in the section. This is another example of how *Math Innovations* helps students develop study skills and encourages them to take ownership of their learning as well as to prepare for the quizzes on each section. There also is a unit Study Guide to help students prepare for the unit test. Students might use the Sum It Up section along with the Study Guide when they have missed a mathematics class or when they want to share what they are learning with their family members or guardians.

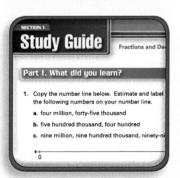

Mathematically Speaking

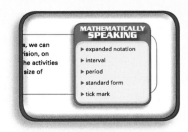

Mathematically Speaking emphasizes vocabulary words that are important mathematical concept anchors that students should use to develop their mathematical proficiency and communication skills. Students are encouraged to think about and use the new vocabulary words that are introduced and highlighted in each lesson. As students work on their homework, they can then refer to the vocabulary words that are organized for emphasis in the Mathematically Speaking box at the end of each lesson. Teachers should guide students to develop an understanding of the Mathematically Speaking terms before referring students to the glossary at the end of each unit. They should also make sure that students use their new vocabulary terms with precision as they explore the important mathematical ideas and relationships in each unit.

Word Wall

Teachers can post the Mathematically Speaking vocabulary words on a word wall so that students will have access to the words they learn throughout the unit. Words can be written in large print on sentence strips and affixed with magnet tape for posting on a magnetic surface. Magnetic posting allows for flexibility in word grouping and removal, as needed for individual or group use.

Vocabulary Activities

Motivational activities can be incorporated into lessons to make students more comfortable with the vocabulary words in Mathematically Speaking.

- **Vocabulary Scramble:** Write each word and its definition on separate cards. Shuffle the cards and give one to each student. Students then walk around the room, looking at other students' cards, trying to find their match.

- **Word/Definition Game:** "I have _____. Who has _____?" Give each student a card that has a word and a definition to a different word. Each student listens for the definition that matches his or her word, and then reads the next definition as a prompt for another student. For example, Student One: "I have <u>parallel</u>. Who has <u>the word that means a five-sided figure?</u>" Student Two: "I have <u>pentagon</u>. Who has the <u>word that means all sides have the same length?</u>"

  The rest of the class continues to read the cards, each containing a vocabulary word answer and a definition prompt for a different vocabulary word held by another student.

- Have students illustrate the Mathematically Speaking words using drawings, graphs and symbols and place these next to the vocabulary word on the word wall.

- Use free online services or software to create paper and pencil games such as crossword puzzles, word finds and word scrambles. Helpful websites include *puzzlemaker.school.discovery.com* and *www. crosswordpuzzlegames.com/create.html*.

- **Twenty Questions:** Let one student think of a Mathematically Speaking vocabulary word and answer yes and no questions from the class as they try to guess the word.

- **Pictionary:** Divide the class into two teams. Teams take turns sending students to the board. These students view vocabulary word and attempt to draw images that prompt their teams' correct guesses.

On Your Own

Each lesson concludes with an On Your Own section that includes independent work that reinforces, reviews and extends that day's learning experience. The On Your Own questions were written to be completed as homework, but a teacher may want students to start on these exercises at the end of class. If class time is limited, teachers may prefer to ask students which questions they had trouble with, or to focus on the most engaging On Your Own problems, as suggested in the Teacher Edition.

 ### Write About It

The first question of the On Your Own section has a prompt for reflective writing. This allows students to organize and consolidate the exploration and discussion of the day's lesson. Students can use the notes they recorded during the Wrap It Up section of the lesson as they reflect and respond to the Write About It journal prompts. The Write About It prompts focus on the important mathematical ideas that students should have gleaned from the lesson.

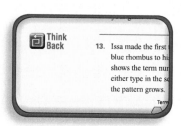

 ### Think Back

The On Your Own section includes practice problems that use concepts and skills from previous lessons and/or prior courses. In this way, *Math Innovations* spirals to continually require students to Think Back and reinforce their prior knowledge. This feature is provided to meet the recognized need for students to become mathematically literate and fluent in problem solving and computation. Think Back questions are often presented in formats similar to those found on many standardized tests, including state assessments.

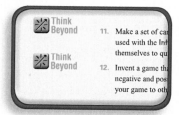

 ### Think Beyond

The On Your Own section gives students challenging opportunities to Think Beyond the material covered in the day's lesson. Teachers are encouraged to differentiate the homework assignment by giving these problems to the students who require more challenge.

Reflect

In recognition of the importance of teacher reflection for enhancing instruction and improving student achievement, *Math Innovations* has incorporated a series of reflective questions designed to support teachers in assessing their instruction and their students' learning for each lesson. The *Reflect* questions are located in the Teacher's Edition following the Wrap It Up discussion notes. These questions not only guide teachers in assessing students' understanding of key concepts in the lesson, but can help them in planning and guiding instruction for future lessons as well. Developing metacognitive habits is an essential component of Math Innovations for teachers and students alike.

Assessments

The word *assessment* is derived from the Latin phrase "to sit beside". The assessment components in the *Math Innovations* program invite the teacher "to sit beside" each student as a guide along his or her mathematics journey. The assessment data gives teachers information about how each student is progressing. The teacher can use this data to adjust the course of study so that each student continues to progress towards achieving the mathematical goals of the unit.

The following assessment components are included in each Math Innovations unit:

Questions

Each lesson in *Math Innovations* ends with Wrap It Up questions that measure students' understanding of the mathematical objectives of that lesson. Discussing these questions prepares students to respond to the On Your Own questions, and helps the teacher plan for future instruction. Study Guide questions help students to connect and reflect on the mathematics they have learned within and across sections.

Study Guide

The Study Guide in each unit in the Student Edition bridges the unit activities and discussions with the unit quizzes and test. The questions in the Study Guide will enable students to target the skills, concepts, and vocabulary terms that they need to review prior to more formal assessments.

Quizzes

Section quizzes measure a student's ability to transfer what they have learned from the problems posed in the section to extensions or modifications of these problems. Each quiz includes a question similar to the Write About It questions at the end of each lesson. Other quiz question formats include short answer, multiple-choice, true/false, and open response. Quizzes are located in the Assessment Resources.

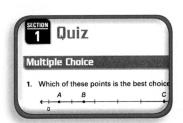

Tests

Located in the Assessment Resources, each unit test includes multiple-choice, short-answer, Write About It and open-response items. Test items vary in difficulty as well as in required depth of knowledge. For example, test items will include those that measure students' recall and reproduction, comprehension of skills and concepts and strategic and complex mathematical reasoning.

Student Self-Assessment

At the end of each Math Innovations unit, students will reflect on their performance prior to, as well as after, the unit test. Students will measure their reasoning, problem solving, and communication skills, identify areas in which they are in need of improvement, and write about *how* they will improve those areas in future study. The Student Self-Assessments are in the Assessment Resources.

Projects

The projects in *Math Innovations* allow students to develop mathematical understanding through independent exploration. Students will think creatively, make decisions, and write about the mathematical concepts explored during a particular unit. A rubric specific to each project is provided to assess students' work. Projects and rubrics are located in the Assessment Resources.

Student Snapshot

As students work through a *Math Innovations* unit, the teacher is encouraged to observe students' depth of comprehension, communication, and representations, as well as their problem-solving and reasoning skills. The teacher can write observations on 1.5" × 2" sticky notes to place on Student Snapshot sheets in a 3-ring binder as an authentic assessment of each student's long-term progress. The Student Snapshot sheet is on page T11 in the Teacher Guide.

References

Chapin, S.H., C. O'Connor, and N.C. Anderson. 2009. *Classroom discussions: Using math talk to help students learn, grades 1–6*. Sausalito, CA: Math Solutions Publications.

Herbel-Eisenmann, B.A. and L.M. Breyfogle. 2005. "Questioning our patterns of questioning." *Mathematics Teaching in the Middle School*, NCTM, Vol. 10, No. 9.

Kersaint, G., D. Thompson, and M. Petkova. 2009. *Teaching Mathematics to English Language Learners*. New York: Routledge Publishers.

Sheffield, L.J. 2006. "Developing mathematical promise and creativity," *Journal of the Korea Society of Mathematical Education, Series D, Research in Mathematics Education,* Vol. 10, No. 1: 1–11.

Line It Up:
Focusing on Linear Relationships

Goals of the Unit

In *Line It Up: Focusing on Linear Relationships*, students will

- ▶ Represent and analyze linear functions using words, equations, tables and graphs.

- ▶ Understand the concepts of slope and *y*-intercept, and use these to interpret situations and to compare and contrast linear functions.

- ▶ Find the solution to a system of linear equations graphically.

- ▶ Graph points on a Cartesian plane and recognize linear relationships.

Unit Overview

In *Line It Up: Focusing on Linear Relationships*, students build upon the foundation of algebraic concepts they learned in Grades 6 and 7 to integrate the ideas of function and related variables. They make connections between various representations of these relationships. The emphasis is on linear relationships; examining the behavior of these relationships as presented graphically, in tables, and with symbolic notation. The Grade 8 Curriculum Focal Points from the NCTM *Principles & Standards for School Mathematics* serve as a guide in stating the following:

Students use linear functions, linear equations, and systems of linear equations to represent, analyze, and solve a variety of problems. They recognize a proportion $\left(\frac{y}{x} = k, \text{ or } y = kx\right)$ as a special case of a linear equation of the form $y = mx + b$, understanding that the constant of proportionality (k) is the slope and the resulting graph is a line through the origin. Students understand that the slope (m) of a line is a constant rate of change, so if the input, or x-coordinate, changes by a specific amount (a), the output, or y-coordinate, changes by the amount ma. Students translate among verbal, tabular, graphical, and algebraic representations of functions (recognizing that tabular and graphical representations are usually only partial representations), and they describe how such aspects of a function as slope and y-intercept appear in different representations. Students solve systems of two linear equations in two variables and relate the systems to pairs of lines that intersect, are parallel, or are the same line in the plane. Students use linear equations, systems of linear equations, linear functions, and their understanding of the slope of a line to analyze situations and solve problems. (www.nctm.org)

Reprinted with permission from *Curriculum Focal Points for Prekindergarten through Grade 8 Mathematics: A Quest for Coherence*, copyright 2006 by the National Council of Teachers of Mathematics. All rights reserved.

The study of algebraic thought and processes at this level serves three purposes. First, students further review basic algebra concepts such as variable and representation, as introduced in Grades 6 and 7. The following content expectations from the NCTM *Principles & Standards* (initially set in Grades 6 and 7) link to the Grade 8 Focal Points and state that students will:

- Develop an initial conceptual understanding of different uses of variables.
- Use symbolic algebra to represent situations and to solve problems, especially those that involve linear relationships.
- Represent, analyze, and generalize a variety of patterns with tables, graphs, words, and, when possible, symbolic rules.
- Model and solve contextualized problems using various representations, such as graphs, tables, and equations.

The second purpose is to have students develop an understanding of linear functions, with a specific focus on the concept of change (and rate of change). Students analyze and solve problems involving linear relationships, as well as situations involving systems of linear equations. The following content expectations from the NCTM *Principles & Standards* link to the Grade 8 Focal Points and state students will:

- Identify functions as linear or nonlinear and contrast their properties from tables, graphs, or equations.
- Explore relationships between symbolic expressions and graphs of lines, paying particular attention to the meaning of intercept and slope.
- Use graphs to analyze the nature of changes in quantities in linear relationships.

Third and finally, students address topics in the representations of discrete data. Students explore scatter plots of data. The following content expectations from the NCTM *Principles & Standards* link to the Grade 8 Focal Points and state that student will:

- Select, create, and use appropriate graphical representations of data including histograms, box plots, and scatter plots.
- Discuss and understand the correspondence between data sets and their graphical representations, especially histograms, stem-and-leaf plots, box plots, and scatter plots.

This unit focuses on linear functions to further students' understanding of algebraic concepts. After an initial review of algebraic ideas, students analyze characteristics of linear functions and their graphs, including slope and rate of change. Students learn about direct variation relationships and examine systems of linear equations.

Section Summaries

 SECTION 1 **Relationships on the Coordinate Plane**

Students build concept maps to organize their knowledge of algebra to this point. They consider relationships between independent (input) and dependent (output) variables as shown in tables and on graphs. They analyze the behavior of these relationships and begin to use the term "function" to describe them.

 SECTION 2 **Analyzing Change**

Students look at tables and graphs to determine the rate of change of linear relationships. They then integrate the idea of steepness of a line with the ratio of changes in each variable, the rate of change, and the formula of "rise over run." Students determine the slope from given equations, tables, and graphs, and explore both positive and negative slope. They distinguish between a scatterplot and a line graph. Students identify where a function is increasing or decreasing.

 SECTION 3 **Analyzing Linear Functions**

Students explore the slope-intercept form of a line, $y = mx + b$, and recognize direct variation linear functions. They find the slope and the y-intercept from an equation of a line. Students examine several linear equations simultaneously as a system of equations, solve for points of intersection graphically, and identify when two lines are parallel.

Unit Mathematics

Algebra is a branch of mathematics that uses symbols to represent numbers and express mathematical relationships. Algebra is also known as generalized arithmetic. The word *algebra* is derived from the word *al-jabr* meaning "restoration." Al-jabr is actually one of two operations used to solve quadratic equations as described in a book by Muhammad ibn Musa al-Khwarizmı, an Arab mathematician from the 9th century who is considered to be the father of algebra.

In ancient Egypt and Babylon, over two thousand years earlier than al-Khwarizmı, people solved linear and quadratic equations using methods similar to those we use today. They also solved multivariable equations. The ancient methods of solving equations were studied in the Islamic world and became known as the science of restoration and balance. In Course 1 and Course 2, students began the study of algebra with the idea of balance, focusing on equivalence as presented symbolically in expressions and equations. In Course 3 we continue the study of algebra with a focus on analyzing, modeling, and solving problems.

Early algebra, however, was different than what we know today, as operations were written out in Latin, Arabic or Greek. It wasn't until much later that the numbers, symbols, and notations that modern students use today were developed. In the late 16th century, a French mathematician, François Viète, developed the symbolism of using letters for unknown quantities. Later, in the early 17th century, René Descartes began the convention of using letters at the beginning of the alphabet to stand for constants and letters at the end of the alphabet to stand for unknowns. Descartes was instrumental in combining geometry and algebra to form what is today known as analytic geometry. We recognize an example of this work in the Cartesian coordinate system that Descartes invented to describe the location of an object in space.

In as much as most middle school math curricula continue to integrate all five of the NCTM Content Standards, algebra is certainly very prominent. During the middle school years, students transition from arithmetic to algebra. The Supporting the Transition from Arithmetic to Algebraic Reasoning (STAAR) project out of the Wisconsin Center for Education Research (WCER) involves a group of interdisciplinary researchers looking at middle school students' transitions in this area. In a 2007 article, this group identified three main focus areas for addressing student learning in middle school algebra: equivalence, variable, and representation. These three areas are emphasized throughout the algebra sections of this program at all grade levels.

Equivalence

According to many researchers, student understanding of the concept of equivalence is often impeded by their misinterpretation of the equal sign. To many students, the equal sign is an instruction to "do something." Students are accustomed to arithmetic problems that contain an operation, or several operations, followed by an equal sign. From the student perspective, the equal sign indicates that he or she should carry out the operations (on the left of the equal sign) and then write the answer (to the right of the equal sign). As students transition to algebra, the equal sign must take on a relational interpretation. This is to say that the equal sign indicates that the expression on the left of the equal sign is related to the expression on the right of the equal sign. And, furthermore, the relationship between the two sides is one of equivalence.

The following are a few examples of relational interpretations of the equal sign in mathematical sentences.

- The equal sign relates two different calculations that result in the same number or quantity when evaluated.

$$2 + 5 = 3 + 4$$
$$2(2 + 4) = 4 + 8$$

- The equal sign relates the value of an expression with another expression that can be used to compute that same value.

$$8 + 2 = 2(x + 4)$$
$$2 + 6x = 6 + x + x^2$$

- The equal sign relates two different symbolic expressions that represent the same number and quantity:

$$x^2 = x \cdot x$$
$$2l + 2w = l + l + w + w$$

In order to understand the relational interpretation of the equal sign, students should address a variety of equations within a variety of contexts where there are operational expressions on both sides of the equal signs.

Variable

Descartes instituted the convention that letters at the beginning of the alphabet usually stand for constants, while letters at the end of the alphabet stand for variables. Following this convention, we often use the variables x and y and set up our graphical coordinate system with x as the independent variable, plotted along the horizontal axis, and y as the dependent variable, plotted along the vertical axis. Often a and b are used in formulas to represent constants. And, we use lowercase letters as variables that represent numbers or functions and uppercase letters to represent sets. Additionally, we normally put all variables in italics.

As you know, the mathematics community does not strictly follow the symbolic "conventions" above. Many times we want the variable to have some meaning within the context of our problem, so we may use b to represent the number of boxes, t to represent a time in minutes, d to represent a distance in miles, or C to represent a total cost in dollars. It is important that students understand that they can use any letter or symbol ($\square$ or $\diamond$ or even ☺) as a variable. One essential, but often overlooked, aspect of solving a problem is that whenever we introduce a variable, we should define the variable and indicate its units (e.g., t is the time traveled in hours). Students should develop the habit of always defining their variables as they algebraically model problems.

We use variables in different ways for different reasons. The following are examples of three primary uses of variables:

- The variable represents one or more specific value(s). Many equations have one variable and when we solve the equation, we find the value(s) for this variable that makes the statement true.

$3.00 = 0.25x + 2.00$ The ice cream shop sells a large cup of ice cream for $2.00. You can add more ice cream to your cup for $0.25 per ounce. If you want to spend $3.00 for ice cream, how many more ounces of ice cream, x, can you add to a large cup?

- The variables represent related varying quantities. Many times we want to write an equation that will describe a relationship between two or more varying quantities. Each variable can take on many values, but once one variable takes on a particular value, the other variables in the equation take on values according to the relationship.

$C = 1.25x$

If an item costs $1.25, then there is a relationship between the number of items purchased, x, and the total cost to purchase these items, C. Once I determine how many items I want to purchase, I can use this equation to determine the total cost.

- The variable represents many quantities and is not related to another variable. When describing mathematical properties, for example, we often use variables to indicate that the property will hold regardless of the value assigned to the variable. Here a variable represents many numbers that will make the equation true.

$a + b = b + a$

The commutative property of addition uses a and b as variables to show a generalized property that is true for any real numbers a and b.

When two variables represent varying related quantities, one variable is usually dependent upon the other: as one varies the other one must vary according to a defined relationship. Given a real world situation, it is usually straightforward to see which variable is independent (free to take on any acceptable value) and which variable is dependent (its value determined by the choice of the independent variable value). These are also called the input (independent) and output (dependent) variables/values. In the equation above, $C = 1.25x$, the independent variable is x, the number of items I choose to purchase. Once I decide upon this number, I can determine the cost, C. The cost is dependent upon the number of items purchased. The concept of variable is one of the central ideas of middle school algebra. Students' understanding of the concept of variable is critical for their success in algebra, as well a for future mathematics studies at the high school level and beyond.

Representation

Using multiple representations allows students the opportunity to understand concepts using the representation that best suits their strengths. Additionally, by looking at algebraic problems using more than one representation, students may make connections that reinforce their algebraic reasoning.

"Representations are necessary to students' understanding of mathematical concepts and relationships. Representations allow students to communicate mathematical approaches, arguments, and understanding to themselves and to others. They allow students to recognize connections among related concepts and apply mathematics to realistic problems." (www.nctm.org)

Reprinted with permission from *Curriculum Focal Points for Prekindergarten through Grade 8 Mathematics: A Quest for Coherence,* copyright 2006 by the National Council of Teachers of Mathematics. All rights reserved.

The term "rule of three" was initially coined during the calculus reform efforts in the late 1980s to emphasize the benefits of students representing relationships graphically, numerically, and symbolically. This idea was expanded to the "rule of four" to accommodate writing as another method of representation. It is now commonplace for teachers to emphasize multiple representations of problems at all levels of mathematics education. The following describes some of the methods used to represent algebraic relationships:

Numerical/Tabular Representations

Many times we ask students to record information in a table in order to identify a pattern or relationship. The information may come from collecting data, researching information, or evaluating expressions. Students should develop the habit of structuring their table in a format that aids their understanding of the data. The following examples use two columns, but students can organize data into three or more columns to look for relationships.

=== Examples ===

Data Pairs

I collect the shoe size and height (to the nearest $\frac{1}{2}$ inch) of each student in my class. I make a table with one column for height and one column for shoe size, and then record each pair of data. In order to better analyze my data, I order the data from smallest to largest height.

Height (inches)	Shoe Size
58	5
60.5	7
62	6.5
62	6
63	7

Input/Output Table

I record the outside temperature every six hours during a 24-hour period. I make a table with one column for the time and one column for the temperature. In order to better analyze this relationship, I enter the times in sequential order.

Time	Temperature °F
4 p.m.	65
10 p.m.	55
4 p.m.	55
10 p.m.	48
4 p.m.	60

Graphical/Pictorial Representations

We often use graphs to display information and relationships. Graphical, sometimes called geometric, representations are extremely helpful to visualize patterns. Drawings and diagrams, such as flow charts or geometric figures, are also included in this category. Common forms of graphs include bar graphs, scatter plots, and line graphs. The following table compares some of the characteristics of two types of graphs that we use in this unit: scatter plots and line graphs. In selecting a representation form, students should choose one that best portrays the problem.

Type of Graph	Description	Advantages	Disadvantages
Scatter Plot **Height to Shoe Size**	A scatter plot displays ordered pairs of data. The points are not connected because the data are discrete.	• Shows exact data values (each point) and sample size • Shows trends in the data relationship	• Difficult to determine exact data values, sample size and relationships with large data sets • Provides only a trend based on data points
Line Graph **24-Hour Temperature**	A line graph displays ordered pairs of data connected by line segments. The points are connected because the data are continuous.	• Can display multiple sets of data (with several lines) • Can estimate or infer interim data from the line	• Although used to show trends with discrete data, the line segments are only valid for continuous data

It is important in drawing graphs that students choose an appropriate scale to most accurately portray information. Although the two axes on a particular graph may be scaled differently (see the example for the line graph), the intervals of each individual axis should be even. The relationship should be drawn to scale according to the set up of the axes. Students should use a compression bar to show that a portion of the axis is not used (see examples). The following are examples of some situations depicted using graphs.

Scatter Plot

After collecting data on height and shoe sizes, I set up a coordinate system with height along the horizontal axis and shoe size along the vertical axis. I did not connect the points because my data are discrete (height to the nearest $\frac{1}{2}$ inch; shoe size in whole and $\frac{1}{2}$ sizes)

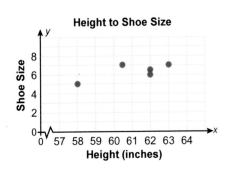

Height to Shoe Size

Line Graphe

After making a table of data values for the temperature readings, I set up a coordinate system with time along the horizontal axis and temperature along the vertical axis. I connected the data points because the line represents continuous data.

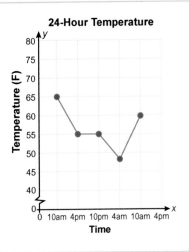

24-Hour Temperature

Symbolic/Analytic Representation

A symbolic or analytic representation uses mathematical symbols and notation to present a relationship in a concise form. In this unit, we symbolically represent relationships using both recursive and explicit rules. Recursive rules rely on a previous application of the rule to find the next value. Explicit rules find an output value directly (or explicitly) for any given input value(s). Students look for patterns in recursive rules that assist them in developing explicit rules. At this level, students also use variables to translate word problems into symbolic explicit rules in order to solve the problem. Students' understanding of the concept of variable and their ability to define variables and think algebraically are important in this translation. Students encounter many explicit rules and variables in common formulas.

Recursive Rule	I am building a walkway of stones. Each 1 foot section of the walkway is made of a rectangular stone and four triangular stones. At Stage 1 there are 5 stones and at Stage 2 there are 10 stones. The recursive rule to determine the number of stones needed at any stage is *New = Previous* + 5; or, by letting *n* be the total number of stones required in the new stage and *p* be the total number of stones required in the previous stage, the recursive rule is $n = p + 5$.
Explicit Rule— recursive relationship	To find an explicit rule for the walkway problem, I need to recognize a pattern and write a rule to determine the total number of stones needed for any given stage. Let *T* be the total number of stones needed for a walkway of length *l* feet. Noticing that at each stage the total number of stones is equal to 5 times the length of the walkway I write the explicit rule: $T = 5l$.
Explicit Rule— word problem	Consider the widely known student-professor problem. "Write an equation, using the variables *S* and *P* to represent the following statement: 'At a university, there are six times as many students as professors.' Use *S* for the number of students and *P* for the number of professors." The problem statement has defined the variables, so the explicit rule that relates the number of students to the number of professors is: $S = 6P$. This problem is well known because many students will incorrectly write the equation as $P = 6S$. An easy way to check one's equation is to substitute a value for one of the variables and see if it makes sense. With 1 professor, there would be $S = 6 \times 1 = 6$ students, which makes sense.
Explicit Rule— formulas	Formulas use variables and are explicit rules. Some examples are: • Let *A* be the area of a rectangle with sides of length *l* and *w*. $A = lw$. • Let *P* be the perimeter of a square with sides of length *x*. $P = 4x$. • Let *C* be the circumference of a circle of radius *r*. $C = 2\pi r$.

Notice that the variables are defined in each rule example. Students should note what values make sense when substituted into particular rules. In the stone walkway problem, the recursive and explicit rules use variables that must be positive integers, because these rules only make sense for whole number lengths and whole numbers of stones (1, 2, 3, ...). The student-professor rule also only makes sense when using positive integers. The formula examples, however, provide instances where the variables can be any positive real number.

Written (and Verbal) Representations

It is important that students are able to verbalize and articulate their reasoning and understandings of algebraic concepts and processes. Students do this during class discussions, as well as through specific requirements. Within each unit, the *Wrap It Up* and *Write About It* items usually ask the student to articulate their understandings verbally or in writing. It is important when listening to student discourse or reading student writing to not assume that a student is simply inarticulate or mathematically unsophisticated. Most often students mean exactly what they say and what they write. Their misunderstanding and misconceptions are evident to the careful listener and reader.

Additional Mathematics in this Unit

(Cartesian) Coordinate System

A straight line in space that has an associated direction, a selected origin point, and a unit length indicated is called a number line or axis. We know that two lines that intersect in space define a plane. Two real number axes that intersect perpendicularly at their origins define the two-dimensional Cartesian plane. The point of intersection is called the origin of the system and is designated by the coordinate pair (0, 0). The two axes are most often presented with one horizontal and one vertical number line. Often, the horizontal axis is called the x-axis, while the vertical axis is usually called the y-axis.

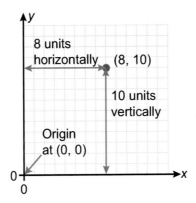

Using the Cartesian coordinate system, we can specify the location of a point in the plane using an ordered pair of coordinates. The coordinates specify the direction and the horizontal distance from the vertical axis and the direction and the vertical distance from the horizontal axis. The point (8, 10) is plotted above by moving horizontally from the y-axis 8 units and vertically 10 units. The coordinates are ordered in the sense that by convention the horizontal displacement is always first, and therefore the coordinates are written as (x, y).

Linear Functions

A function is a rule that describes how one variable is related to another variable. In a function, one variable depends on another. The function rule matches each input (independent variable) value to only one output (dependent variable) value. Students first begin to discover linear functions by plotting points from a table or from a set of points that satisfy an equation. They then connect these points and notice that they form a line.

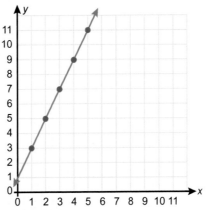

Using tables of sequence values, students look for the recursive pattern of "plus a constant" at each step of the recursion to identify a linear relationship. In the following table we see that *New = Previous* + 2. Students recognize that as long as the input column is increasing by a constant amount (in the case below, it is one unit per step) and the change at each step of the output column is a constant (in the case below, it is two units), then the relationship is linear.

Input (x)	Output (y)
1	3
2	5
3	7
4	9

+1 (between input rows), +2 (between output rows)

It is easier to determine if a relationship is linear when the input column of the table is organized in ascending order. We can determine the slope (discussed in the Rate of Change and Slope section) of any linear relationship represented by an input/output table by taking the ratio of $\left(\frac{\text{change in output}}{\text{change in input}}\right)$ between any two lines in the table. In the current example this ratio is $\left(\frac{2}{1}\right)$.

Increasing/Decreasing Functions

A function in which the value of the output increases as the value of the input increases is called an increasing function. An increasing linear function will have a positive constant slope. If the value of the output decreases as the value of the input increases, then the function is decreasing. A decreasing linear function will have a negative constant slope. The relationship shown in the graph and table above is an increasing linear function.

Slope-Intercept Form of a Line

Symbolically an equation for the relationship above is $y = 2x + 1$. This form, $y = mx + b$, is called the slope-intercept form of a line. Notice that the dependent variable, y, is on the left side of the equation by itself and has a coefficient of 1. The coefficient m of the independent variable, x, is equal to the slope of the line and the y-intercept is the point $(0, b)$. Often, we want to put linear equations into the slope-intercept form in order to "read off" the slope and the y-intercept.

Direct Variation

Direct variation is a special case of a linear function where the y-intercept and the x-intercept are both located at the point $(0, 0)$. The equation for such as line is simply $y = mx$. The relationship between the two variables in this case is one of proportionality. The two variables, x and y, are said to be proportional if their ratio, $\frac{y}{x}$ is a constant. Often, the letter k is used to indicate the constant of proportionality and the equation is written as $y = kx$. The slope of the line representing a direct variation or proportional relationship is equal to the constant of proportionality k. We can see that the value of y "directly varies" as the value of x varies.

The following is an example of an increasing linear function with a y-intercept at (0, 0). This is a direct variation or proportional relationship:

Example

I earn $8.40 per hour. The more I work, the more I earn. The amount of my weekly pay check is directly proportional to the number of hours I work. Every week the ratio of total pay to hours worked is equal to 8.40 (dollars/hour).

Let p be the amount of my paycheck in dollars and h be the number of hours worked during the pay period: $p = 8.40h$.

Hours Worked	Pay Check
0	$0.00
1	$8.40
2	$16.80
3	$25.20
4.5	$37.80
6	$50.40
10.25	$86.10

Rate of Change, Rate and Slope

Informally introduced in Course 2, the concept of slope is more formally addressed in this unit. Slope is the physical interpretation of the rate of change of a function. The idea of slope is first one of "steepness" of a straight line. Students then explore the ratio of "rise over run." They look at representative right triangles along the graph of a line to observe and calculate rise and run. Students encounter the idea of a horizontal line having slope equal to zero; no matter what the run, the rise is always zero. Students explore both positive and negative slope and determine the relationship between the several equations by looking at their slopes.

Systems of (Linear) Equations and Solutions

A collection of two or more equations of lines is called a system of linear equations. The solution to a system is the point(s) of intersection, if any, of all the lines in the system. Systems of equation either have a single solution (all lines intersect at one point), no solution (all lines are distinct and parallel or all lines are distinct with no common intersection point), or the solution is infinite (all lines are coincident, indicating that all equations are different forms of the same line).

When two lines are drawn on the same coordinate system, they will intersect (cross at a single point), be distinct and parallel (have no points in common), or be coincident (have all points in common; different forms the same line). Two distinct lines will be parallel if they have equal slopes. If the slopes of the two lines are not equal, the lines will intersect. If the slopes of the two lines are negative inverses of each other, the intersecting lines will be perpendicular.

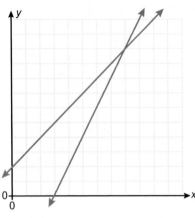

Two distinct intersecting lines:

$y_1 = x + 2$ and $y_2 = 2x - 6$

Slopes: $m_1 = 1$ and $m_2 = 2$

Point of intersection: (8, 10).

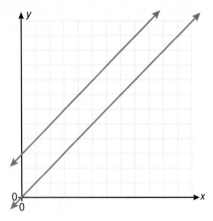

Two parallel lines:

$y_1 = x$ and $y_2 = x + 3$

Slopes: $m_1 = 1$ and $m_2 = 1$

No points of intersection.

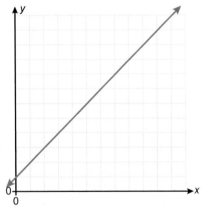

Two coincidental lines (the same line in two forms):

$y_1 = x + 1$ and $2y_2 = 2x + 2$

Slopes: $m_1 = 1$ and $m_2 = 1$

All points are the same.

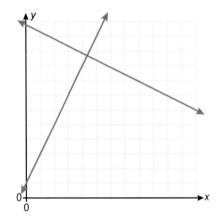

Two perpendicular lines:

$y_1 = 2x + 1$ and $y_2 = -\frac{1}{2}x + 12$

Slopes: $m_1 = 2$ and $m_2 = -\frac{1}{2}$

Point of intersection: (4.4, 9.8).

The following example demonstrates the use of a system of three linear equations:

Example

You are planning a community event and want to provide each attendee a snack. You are concerned about total cost. Company A will provide granola bar snacks for $0.15 each while Company B will charge $0.20 each. Company C charges $10 to set up a distribution booth, but then the bars will cost only $0.05 each.

Let c be the total cost of granola bars and let p be the number of people who attend the event. We write the following equations:

Company A	$c = 0.15p$
Company B	$c = 0.20p$
Company C	$c = 0.05p + 10$

 NOTE Notice that the values for p in this situation are discrete, but in the graph below we model the situation continuously to compare the three options.

p	c Co. A ($)	c Co. B ($)	c Co. C ($)
10	1.50	2.00	10.50
50	7.50	10.00	12.50
100	15.00	20.00	15.00
150	22.50	30.00	17.50
200	30.00	40.00	20.00

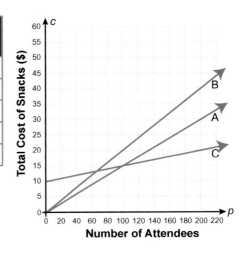

Notice that there is no solution to this system of three equations; there is not a single point where all three lines intersect. However, students can compare costs of the various companies as each pair of lines intersects. The lines for Companies A and B intersect at the origin. When these two companies provide no granola bars, the cost is $0. Also, Company A is always less expensive than Company B. The graph shows two additional points of intersection:

(100, 15)   With 100 attendees the cost for both Companies A and C will be $15. For less than 100 attendees Company A is less expensive and for more than 100 attendees Company C is less expensive.

$(66\frac{2}{3}, 13\frac{1}{3})$ The cost lines for Companies B and C will intersect between the 66th and 67th attendee with a cost of between $13 and $14. Company B is less expensive than Company C for 66 attendees or less.

Line It Up:
Focusing on Linear Relationships
Unit Planner

See Assessment Resources for Unit Test to use as Unit Pretest if desired.

Section 1: Relationships on the Coordinate Plane

Lesson 1.1: Thinking about Algebra

Pacing based on 45-minute classes

In this lesson students learn about concept maps. They then activate their prior knowledge about algebra by creating a concept map for algebra.

Pacing	Lesson Guides* (need to be duplicated)	Materials*	Essential *On Your Own* Questions	*On Your Own* Extensions	Mathematically Speaking
DAY 1	■ Lesson Guide 1.1A, *It's All about Algebra* (optional)	■ Large sheets of paper such as chart paper ■ Sticky notes ■ Internet access	On Your Own 4 Think Back 7–10		■ concept map ■ links ■ nodes
DAY 2			Write About It 1 On Your Own 2, 3, 5, 6		

* The Think Like a Mathematician Daily Record Sheet should be used daily

Lesson 1.2: Analyzing Graphs

In this lesson, students will begin to analyze points on a graph by focusing on the relationship between two variables in a given situation. They will note which axes of the coordinate grid correspond to which of the variables.

Pacing	Lesson Guides* (need to be duplicated)	Materials*	Essential *On Your Own* Questions	*On Your Own* Extensions	Mathematically Speaking
DAY 1	■ Lesson Guide 1.2, *NBA Stars* ■ Lesson 1.2, *Comparing Areas of Conference Tables*	■ Graph paper, one per student for Start it Off ■ Chart paper, one sheet per group ■ Markers, one per group ■ Internet access ■ Graph paper for Think Beyond question (optional)	Write About It 1 On Your Own 2–4 Think Back 14	Think Beyond 8, 9	■ compression bar ■ variable ■ *x*-axis ■ *y*-axis
DAY 2			On Your Own 5–7 Think Back 10–13		

* The Think Like a Mathematician Daily Record Sheet should be used daily

Lesson 1.3: Relating Tables and Graphs

In this lesson, students take a closer look at the relationship between two variables in a given situation. Students analyze tables and graphs that represent given situations and discover the advantages and disadvantages of each type of representation. Students also explore how the scale on graphs can sometimes distort the relationship between two variables, while accurately representing the data.

Pacing	Lesson Guides* (need to be duplicated)	Materials*	Essential *On Your Own* Questions	*On Your Own* Extensions	Mathematically Speaking
DAY 1	■ Lesson Guide 1.3A, *Beware of Scale* (optional) ■ Lesson Guide 1.3, *Ms. Tootyourhorn's Sales* for use with lesson Question 15 and On Your Own	■ Graph paper	Write About It 1 On Your Own 2–5 Think Back 14–15	Think Beyond 10	■ scale ■ line graph
DAY 2			On Your Own 6–9, 11 Think Back 12, 13		

* The Think Like a Mathematician Daily Record Sheet should be used daily

Lesson 1.4: Linear Functions

This lesson introduces the term function and explores linear functions. Students analyze the relationship between two variables in a linear function and learn to identify the independent and dependent variables. Students relate linear functions to their different representations: tables to graphs and equations to graphs.

Pacing	Lesson Guides* (need to be duplicated)	Materials*	Essential *On Your Own* Questions	*On Your Own* Extensions	Mathematically Speaking
DAY 1		■ Graph paper	On Your Own 2, 4, 5 Think Back 10, 11	Think Beyond 3, 8	■ dependent variable ■ function ■ independent variable ■ input variable ■ linear function ■ output variable
DAY 2			On Your Own 6, 7 Think Back 12, 13		

* The Think Like a Mathematician Daily Record Sheet should be used daily

Lesson 1.5: Using a Graphing Calculator

In this lesson students will learn to use the list and graph functions of the graphing calculator.

Pacing	Lesson Guides* (need to be duplicated)	Materials*	Essential *On Your Own* Questions	*On Your Own* Extensions	Mathematically Speaking
DAY 1		■ Graph paper ■ Graphing calculators	On Your Own 3–6, 11 Think Back 12,13		■ explicit rule ■ recursive rule
DAY 2			Write About It 1 On Your Own 2, 7–10 Think Back 14–15		

* The Think Like a Mathematician Daily Record Sheet should be used daily

Assessment Opportunities

	Student Edition	Assessment Resources	Online
Sum It Up (Student Self-Asessment)	pp. 45–46		
Student Study Guide (Self-Assessment)	pp. 47–50		
Quiz		pp. 1–5	

Section 2: Analyzing Change

Pacing based on 45-minute classes

Lesson 2.1: Exploring Rate of Change

In this lesson, students take a closer look at the relationship between independent and dependent variables. They use tables and graphs to analyze situations and determine if the relationship represents a constant rate of change.

Pacing	Lesson Guides* (need to be duplicated)	Materials*	Essential On Your Own Questions	On Your Own Extensions	Mathematically Speaking
DAY 1		■ Graph paper ■ Rulers	On Your Own 2, 3, 8, 10 Think Back 16–20	Think Beyond 15	■ discrete ■ increasing function ■ rate ■ rate of change ■ scatter plot ■ unit rate
DAY 2			Write About It 1 On Your Own 4–7, 9, 11–14		

* The Think Like a Mathematician Daily Record Sheet should be used daily

Lesson 2.2: Exploring Slope

In this lesson, students first explore slope conceptually as related to the steepness of a line. Then they investigate slope in more depth as a constant rate of change between two variables in a given situation. To compare changes in the dependent variable (y-values) to changes in the independent variable (x-values), students work with tables, graphs and equations to identify and interpret slope as it relates to real-world conference.

Pacing	Lesson Guides* (need to be duplicated)	Materials*	Essential On Your Own Questions	On Your Own Extensions	Mathematically Speaking
DAY 1		■ Graph paper ■ Rulers ■ Colored pencils or markers (optional to make multiple lines on the same graph) ■ Graphing calculators (optional)	On Your Own 2, 3, 6, 9–11 Think Back 13	Think Beyond 12	■ numerical coefficient ■ slope
DAY 2			Write About It 1 On Your Own 4, 5, 7, 8 Think Back 14, 15		

* The Think Like a Mathematician Daily Record Sheet should be used daily

Lesson 2.3: Slope as the Ratio $\frac{\text{rise}}{\text{run}}$

In this lesson, students graph the given lines, and then they discover the ratio $\frac{\text{rise}}{\text{run}}$.

Pacing	Lesson Guides* (need to be duplicated)	Materials*	Essential *On Your Own* Questions	*On Your Own* Extensions	Mathematically Speaking
DAY 1	■ Lesson Guide 2.3A, *Execustay's Conference Center* (optional) ■ Lesson Guide 2.3, *A New Situation* ■ Lesson Guide 2.3, *Creating Slope Triangles*	■ Graph paper ■ Rulers ■ Colored pencils or markers ■ Graphing calculators	On Your Own 4, 5, 7a, 7b, 9, 11–13 Think Back 14	Think Beyond 10	■ $\frac{\text{rise}}{\text{run}}$
DAY 2			Write About It 1 On Your Own 2, 3, 7c, 8, 9 Think Back 15		

* The Think Like a Mathematician Daily Record Sheet should be used daily

Lesson 2.4: Increasing and Decreasing Functions

Students will continue to explore the slope, using equations, tables and graphs. They will discover that the rate of change in some situations does not imply an increasing change in both variables. Students will explore real-world situations where the change in the *y*-values is negative while the change in *x*-values is positive. This results in a negative slope. Students will investigate and compare how positive and negative slopes are represented on a graph.

Pacing	Lesson Guides* (need to be duplicated)	Materials*	Essential *On Your Own* Questions	*On Your Own* Extensions	Mathematically Speaking
DAY 1	■ Lesson Guide 2.4A, *Scottsdale Conference* (optional)	■ Graph paper ■ Graphing calculators	Write About It 1 On Your Own 2, 5, 7–9 Think Back 11–15	Think Beyond 10	■ decreasing function
DAY 2					

* The Think Like a Mathematician Daily Record Sheet should be used daily

Optional Technology Lesson for this section available at **www.mymathinnovations.com**

Assessment Opportunities

	Student Edition	Assessment Resources	Online
Sum It Up (Student Self-Asessment)	pp. 92–94		
Student Study Guide (Self-Assessment)	pp. 95–99		
Quiz		pp. 6–11	

Lesson 3.1: More About Slope

Pacing based on 45-minute classes

In this lesson students will connect what they have already learned about direct variation and the constant of proportionality, k, to the concept of slope. Students will recognize the role of the y-intercept in linear equations and will learn the slope-intercept form, $y = mx + b$.

Pacing	Lesson Guides* (need to be duplicated)	Materials*	Essential *On Your Own* Questions	*On Your Own* Extensions	Mathematically Speaking
DAY 1	■ Lesson Guide 3.1A, *The y-intercept* (optional)	■ Graphing calculators ■ Graph paper	On Your Own 2–5, 15 Think Back 17–21	Think Beyond 16	■ constant of roportionality ■ direct variation ■ parallel ■ slope-intercept form ■ y-intercept
DAY 2			Write About It 1 On Your Own 6–14		

* The Think Like a Mathematician Daily Record Sheet should be used daily

Lesson 3.2: An Important Meeting Point

In this lesson, students should polish their ability to identify and interpret the slope and y-intercept of linear functions as they work with equations written in slope-intercept form. The activities presented are designed to deepen students' understanding of the relationship between parallel and intersecting lines, and their slopes. Students will also explore how to solve a system of equations graphically by identifying the point of intersection and interpret what that point represents in relation to a given real-world situations.

Pacing	Lesson Guides* (need to be duplicated)	Materials*	Essential *On Your Own* Questions	*On Your Own* Extensions	Mathematically Speaking
DAY 1		■ Graph paper ■ Graphing calculator	Write About It 1 On Your Own 2–9 Think Back 11–15	Think Beyond 10	■ point of intersection ■ solution to a system of equations ■ system of equations

* The Think Like a Mathematician Daily Record Sheet should be used daily

Lesson 3.3: Graphing Systems of Equations

In this lesson, students will explore a variety of linear functions with positive and negative slopes, form generalizations about lines, and consider how their graphs behave on a coordinate plane. There is less emphasis on real-world situations in this lesson. Rather, students are encouraged to focus on the mathematics behind the situations to develop a broader understanding of the key ideas that are being generalized as student mathematicians.

Pacing	Lesson Guides* (need to be duplicated)	Materials*	Essential *On Your Own* Questions	*On Your Own* Extensions	Mathematically Speaking
DAY 1		■ Graph paper ■ Graphing calculator	Write About It 1 On Your Own 2–10 Think Back 12–16	Think Beyond 11	
DAY 2					

* The Think Like a Mathematician Daily Record Sheet should be used daily

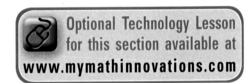

Optional Technology Lesson for this section available at **www.mymathinnovations.com**

Assessment Opportunities

	Student Edition	Assessment Resources	Online
Sum It Up (Student Self-Asessment)	pp. 127–129		
Student Study Guide(Self-Assessment)	pp. 130–145		
Quiz		pp. 12–17	
Unit Test		pp. 19–25	
Unit Reflection Form		p. 26	
Unit Project		p. 27	
Answers		pp. 29–35	

Relationships on the Coordinate Plane

LESSON 1.1

Thinking about Algebra

Suggested Pacing: 2 Days

In this lesson students learn about concept maps. They then activate their own prior knowledge about algebra by creating a concept map for algebra.

LESSON OBJECTIVES

■ Students will explore concept maps as a tool to organize their thinking and demonstrate an understanding of mathematical topics and how they relate to one another.

■ Students will create a concept map for algebra.

DAY 1	MATERIALS*	ESSENTIAL *ON YOUR OWN* QUESTIONS
A Concept Map of Shapes	**In Class** ■ Large sheets of paper such as Chart paper ■ Lesson Guide 1.1A, *It's All about Algebra* (optional) ■ Sticky notes **On Your Own** ■ Internet access	Questions 4, 7–11
DAY 2	**MATERIALS***	**ESSENTIAL *ON YOUR OWN* QUESTIONS**
A Concept Map of Algebra		Questions 1–3, 5, 6

* The Think Like a Mathematician Daily Record Sheet should be used daily

---

MATHEMATICALLY SPEAKING

▶ links   ▶ nodes

SECTION 1

Relationships on the Coordinate Plane

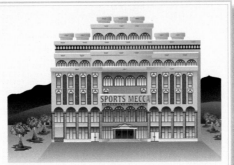

In this unit you will take on the role of a conference planner who works for Sports Mecca, a company that sells sporting goods. As the conference planner, you must find a place to host the conference, determine the cost of renting the conference center, order supplies and figure out travel costs. Graphs, tables and equations will help you make good business decisions. When you use graphs, tables, and equations, you are using algebra!

LESSON 1.1 What is Algebra?

➡ **Start It Off**

Ms. Perez posed the following question to her eighth grade class: What is algebra?

1. How would you respond to each of these students?

2. What else might you say about algebra?

Algebra is about graphing points and lines. You use variables like x and y when you are graphing, too!

Algebra is about solving equations to find values of x.

Algebra is about looking for patterns in numbers and predicting what comes next.

Section 1: Relationships on the Coordinate Plane • Lesson 1.1   **1**

➡ **Start It Off**

 Talk Moves Have pairs of students discuss the responses Ms. Perez's students gave to the question, "What is algebra?" Then have students discuss their ideas about what algebra is as a class. Use talk moves, such as adding on, agree/disagree, and why to stimulate discussion. Patterns, variables, equality and graphing on a coordinate grid are important concepts students may have had experience with in grades 6 and 7. Learn more about the "talk moves" in the Teaching and Learning Strategies on page T5.

Answers will vary. Student responses should indicate that all three students were correct. Each presented information that represented a facet of the study of algebra. Students will further explore how these and other ideas fit together as they learn more in-depth about algebra in the upcoming unit. This exercise is designed to help students recall prior knowledge about what the study of algebra entails.

DAY 1 TEACHING THE LESSON

This lesson is designed to help students activate prior knowledge about algebra in preparing them for the investigations that lie ahead in this unit. Students are first introduced to a concept map. Concept maps are valuable tools that provide teachers with useful information to assess student understanding and the effectiveness of instruction. They enable teachers to: explore students' understanding of a limited aspect of a topic, determine whether students can relate distinct topics, identify relationships that students perceive between concepts, identify which concepts students view as key ones and promote discussion (White and Gunstone, 1992). In addition, concept maps serve as a means of empowering students by inviting them to construct their own personal representation of what they know and how they know it. They encourage student self-assessment and reflection. Furthermore, concept maps provide a useful way to communicate students' mathematical accomplishments to others, especially at parent-teacher conferences.

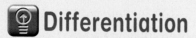

Think Differently: Concept maps are excellent graphic organizers that help students who need more support in understanding how key mathematical ideas are connected. They also provide links among mathematical terms, which supports ELL learners.

Introduce the idea of a concept map to students. Ask:

- *Have you used a concept map in another subject area?*

- *What does a concept map look like?*

- *How does a concept map help you organize your thinking?*

A Concept Map of Shapes

1. Model with students how to create a concept map for the topic "Geometric Shapes" as outlined in Parts a and b of Question 1. Distribute a piece of large paper to each pair of students. Have students work with their partner to complete Parts c and e, creating a concept map of geometric shapes using all the words from each student's list. To allow students to rephrase, replace and refine their ideas, we suggest using sticky notes when designing their maps.

A concept map is a great way for you to organize your thinking. Making a concept map will help you as a student mathematician think about how you have used algebra before. It will show how the ideas that you have learned about algebra can fit together.

A Concept Map of Shapes

1. To show how concept maps work, we are going to start with a topic you have studied since kindergarten—geometric shapes.

   a) To get you started, here is a list of ten math words or phrases related to geometric shapes. Write each word or phrase on a sticky note.

   b) Arrange these sticky notes on a large sheet of paper so that the most general terms are at the top of the paper and the most specific terms are at the bottom. For example, if you wanted to arrange the terms *quadrilaterals, parallelograms* and *two-dimensional shapes,* you would place *two-dimensional shapes* at the top of the paper, *quadrilaterals* below that, and *parallelograms* below *quadrilaterals.* You can also arrange other terms from top to bottom in this manner.

   c) Connect the terms on sticky notes with lines called links. Label each link with a brief description of why the terms are connected. For example, between *two-dimensional shapes* and *quadrilaterals* your link might read: Quadrilaterals are four-sided two-dimensional shapes.

2. Have each pair share their completed concept maps with the class and compare results. Below is a sample response with all connections made. Some students may not have made all of these connections. For example, they may have prisms and cubes as separate categories. Encourage discussion among the class about the connections between these ideas.

d) Now you are ready to transfer your arrangement of terms and links to a concept map. Write the most general term, *Geometric Shapes*, in an oval at the top of a large sheet of paper. Ovals that contain terms are called nodes.

e) Create a map with all the terms listed on the sticky notes as nodes. Include links between the nodes.

To get you started, we have put some of these nodes in order with links between them.

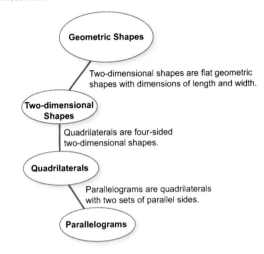

Geometric Shapes

Two-dimensional shapes are flat geometric shapes with dimensions of length and width.

Two-dimensional Shapes

Quadrilaterals are four-sided two-dimensional shapes.

Quadrilaterals

Parallelograms are quadrilaterals with two sets of parallel sides.

Parallelograms

2. Share and compare maps with a partner. How are they alike? How are they different?

3. With your partner, add five new words or phrases to your maps. Your maps will now show what both of you know about geometric shapes.

> There is usually more than one correct way to create a concept map. Your map provides a picture of how YOU organize your knowledge about a concept. It is your own personal statement as a student mathematician. It shows the ideas that you think are important about a concept and how you connect these ideas together.

3. Have students add at least five words or categories, or make at least five changes to make their original concept maps more comprehensive. For students who need a greater challenge, you can suggest that they make a larger map with more terms. For students who need support, you might suggest some terms for them to include such as pentagons, hexagons, circles, pentagons, cylinders, cones, rectangular prisms, transformations, reflections, rotations and translations.

Summarize Day 1

As a wrap it up discussion at the end of day 1, ask students to discuss how they would describe to a friend who was absent today what a concept map is and how it helps you to organize what you know about a particular concept.

Guide the discussion to include the following key ideas:

- A concept map is a graphic organizer that shows key ideas and how they relate to a particular concept.

- Placing the main concept at the top of the map, students then list categories, subcategories, and descriptions to link ideas together, showing how they relate to each other and to the main concept. This helps demonstrate what students know about a concept.

Geometric Shapes

Three-dimensional shapes are Geometric shapes that have length, width and height.

2-D Shapes

Triangles are three-sided two-dimensional shapes.

Prisms are 3-D shapes that have two parallel congruent faces that are polygons.

3-D Shapes

Pyramids are three-dimensional shapes with a base that is polygon and triangles as the other faces. The triangles meet at a point or vertex opposite the base.

Quadrilaterals

Triangles

Prisms

Cubes are prisms with six square faces.

Parallelograms

Cubes

Pyramids

Rectangles

Squares are rectangles with equilateral sides.

Squares

DAY 2 TEACHING THE LESSON

A Concept Map of Algebra

Tell students they will make a concept map illustrating what they know about the concept of algebra. As a class, brainstorm a list of words and/or phrases related to this topic and write these on the board or overhead. Use words from the accommodation guide on page 6A entitled Lesson Guide 1.1A: *It's All about Algebra* as starting points if necessary.

Tell students to order the words from the most general (or most inclusive) to the least general (or most specific or narrow). Next, students should begin creating the concept map by placing the word *Algebra* at the top of the page. Encourage students to think of how the words on their list relate to each other. This will help in deciding where to place them on their maps. Categories and subcategories should be placed as nodes and descriptions as lines/links connecting the nodes. Remind students that they will be able to add to and/or change this map as they learn more about algebra throughout this unit.

Have students share their concept maps with two or three other students. Have students work together in small groups. Distribute a piece of large paper to each group and have the groups create one concept map to share with the class. Have each group discuss their algebra concept map with the class, noting similarities and differences.

A Concept Map of Algebra

To review what you already know about algebra, we are going to create a concept map. You have already learned many important ideas about algebra in your mathematics career.

4. As a class, come up with ten mathematics words or phrases that are connected to algebra. Write these down on separate sticky notes. On your own, list at least five more mathematics words or phrases for your personal concept map.

5. Put the words or phrases in order from the most general to the most specific. Then, use this arrangement to create a concept map with *Algebra* as the top node. Write descriptions along the links that connect the nodes.

Throughout this unit you will learn more about algebra, so you will be able to add more nodes and links to your map. At the end of the unit you can compare your first map to your final one to see how much you have learned!

6. When you are done with your map, share it with two or three other class members. Combine your work to create one large concept map for your group. Put it on a large sheet of paper to share with the class. Choose someone in your group to present your concept map to the class.

Wrap It Up

Talk with your partner and discuss the question "What is algebra?" How does this compare with what you said during the Start It Off section of the lesson?

MATHEMATICALLY SPEAKING
▶ links
▶ nodes

Focus the discussion on the different major concepts of algebra—patterns and generalizations; properties such as associative, commutative, distributive; equality, equivalent expressions, and solving equations; graphing ordered pairs and equations, etc. Functions and linear relationships will be featured in this unit. Many students will not be familiar with these ideas at this point. Students will go back at the end of the unit and add these to the concept map.

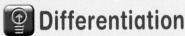

Differentiation

Think Differently: For those students experiencing difficulty getting started on the algebra concept map, the following tips may be helpful.

- Offer Lesson Guide 1.1A: It's *All About Algebra* to accommodate those students who appear frustrated generating terms when creating their concept map. *Accommodation Guides* (Lesson Guides which contain an A after the number) are designed to provide additional support for those students experiencing difficulty with a lesson activity. This is especially helpful for ELL students who may need more support with mathematical vocabulary.

- Provide a mathematics dictionary so students may look up terms related to the study of algebra.

- Have Course 1 and 2 textbooks available to refresh students' memories about previously studied concepts.

- Ask probing questions for those students who seem stuck. For example, ***"Did anyone think to include "patterns" in their concept map?"***

- The Think Back exercises found at the end of *On Your Own* may help students remember some of the things they learned about algebra in grades 6 and 7. You can refer students to this section and/or have students complete these exercises prior to creating the algebra concept map.

 **W**rap It Up

Guide the discussion to help students see how much they have added to the ideas they presented in the Start It Off. This will help them see the value of the concept map, especially in making links between categories. Make sure you discuss the following words or phrases: patterns, generalizations or rules, equality, solving equations and graphing equations. Students should be familiar with these ideas and should have studied them in previous grades.

Reflect

Use these questions to help you reflect on the lesson and plan for future instruction.

- How detailed or comprehensive were students' algebra concept maps?

- How well did they link ideas together and communicate connections on their concept maps?

- What are some misconceptions that students included in the concept maps?

- What are some key ideas related to algebra that students omitted from their concept maps that need to be addressed as students work through this unit?

References

White, R. and R. Gunstone. 1992. *Probing Understanding*. Philadelphia, PA: Falmer Press.

On Your Own

1. **Write About It** Answers will vary.

2. Answers will vary.

3. Both Kalene and Jolene are correct. Variables can be used in both expressions and equations.

NOTE Note that variables in expressions can represent many values or quantities, while variables in equations usually represent a specific unknown. The node for variables may have a link to the node for expressions *and* another link to the node for equations.

---

4. **a)** Answers will vary. Possible solution: line, equation, ordered pair, table, the origin

   b) Answers will vary. Possible solution using the words given above:

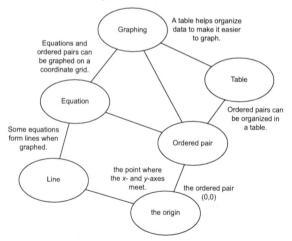

5. Answers will vary. Here is one reference from http://www.und.nodak.edu/instruct/lgeller/algebra.html.

   The word *algebra* is a Latin variant of the Arabic word *al-jabr*. This came from the title of a book, *Hidab al-jabr wal-muqubala*, written in Baghdad about 825 A.D. by the Arab mathematician *Mohammed ibn-Musa al-Khowarizmi*.

The words *jabr* (JAH-ber) and *muqubalah* (moo-KAH-ba-lah) were used by al-Khowarizmi to designate two basic operations in solving equations. *Jabr* was to transpose subtracted terms to the other side of the equation. *Muqubalah* was to cancel like terms on opposite sides of the equation. In fact, the title has been translated to mean "science of restoration (or reunion) and opposition" or "science of transposition and cancellation" and "The Book of Completion and Cancellation" or "The Book of Restoration and Balancing."

Jabr is used in the step where $x - 2 = 12$ becomes $x = 14$. The left-side of the first equation, where x is lessened by 2, is "restored" or "completed" back to x in the second equation.

Muqabalah takes us from $x + y = y + 7$ to $x = 7$ by "cancelling" or "balancing" the two sides of the equation.

Eventually the *muqabalah* was left behind, and this type of math became known as algebra in many languages.

It is interesting to note that the word *al-jabr* used non-mathematically made its way into Europe through the Moors of Spain. There an *algebrista* is a bonesetter, or "restorer" of bones. A barber of medieval times called himself an algebrista since barbers often did bone-setting and bloodletting on the side. Hence the red and white striped barber poles of today.

6. Answers will vary.

NOTE Note that since students will be using operations with integers throughout eighth grade, it is important to review the concepts and skills associated with integers now. These concepts include understanding positive and negative numbers, zero, computing with signed numbers, and graphing signed numbers on a number line.

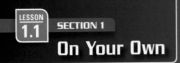
Write About It

1. Select a term or phrase on your algebra concept map that you think you know a lot about and write several things about it.

2. Select a term or phrase on your algebra concept map that you think you don't know much about and make a list of questions you would ask to learn more about it.

3. On her concept map of algebra, Kalene put *variables* in a node under *expressions*. Jolene put variables in a node under *equations*. Are their maps correct? Explain your reasoning.

4. a) Name five words, phrases, or ideas that you relate to the term *graphing*.

   b) Create nodes that link to *graphing* using your five words. Write descriptions along the links that connect the nodes to show how they are related.

5. Use the Internet to research the origin of the word *algebra*. Report on your findings. How is this related to some of the nodes and links in your concept map?

6. Make a concept map for the term *integers*. Include at least five nodes and links.

Think Back

7. **a)** 0

NOTE Students do not need to write out steps but should be able to name properties.

associative property, commutative property, and the inverse property of addition

$(\frac{1}{2}a - \frac{1}{2}a) + (21 - 21)$
$\quad 0 \quad + \quad 0$
$\qquad\qquad 0$

b) 55

commutative property, associative property, inverse property, and identity property of multiplication

$(\frac{2}{5})(\frac{5}{2})$ (55)

$((\frac{2}{5})(\frac{5}{2}))(55)$

$(1)(55)$

55

c) 1

inverse property of addition and multiplication, and identity property of addition

$d + (-d) + \frac{1}{12} \cdot 12$
$\qquad 0 + 1$
$\qquad\qquad 1$

d) $3n + 37$

commutative property and associative property of addition

$n + 2n + 6 + 31$

$(n + 2n) + (6 + 31)$

$3n + 37$

e) $2x + 12.25$

distributive property, commutative property, and associative property of addition

$3x + 12 + 0.25 - x$

$(3x - x) + (12 + 0.25)$

$2x + 12.25$

8. a) $t = 0.10d$ (Students may choose different variables for their equation.)

b) d represents the number of dollars made on Valentine's Day at the Good Foods Store.

t represents the total amount of money that will be donated to the National Heart Association.

9. a) $x = -26$

b) $d = 42.6$

c) $a = 0.6$

d) $c = 3$

e) $n = 39.5$

f) $b = -4$

10. a) $a = \$4.13$;

Real-life situations will vary.
Possible response:

Mr. Cole's class and Ms. Burbank's class were collecting money for a local charity. Mr. Cole's class collected $3.98 on Monday and $4.15 on Tuesday. Ms. Burbank's class collected $4.00 on Tuesday, but forgot to write down the amount that was collected on Monday. If both classes collected the same amount of money in two days, how much money did Ms. Burbank's class collect on Monday?

Think Back

7. Simplify the following expressions. State which properties you used: commutative, associative, distributive, identity for addition or multiplication, or inverse for addition or multiplication.

a) $\frac{1}{2}a + 21 - 21 - \frac{1}{2}a$

b) $\left(\frac{2}{5}\right)(55)\left(\frac{5}{2}\right)$

c) $d + (-d) + \frac{1}{12} \cdot 12$

d) $n + 6 + 2n + 31$

e) $3(x + 4) + 0.25 - x$

8. **a)** The Good Foods store is holding a fund-raiser. The store will donate 10¢ to the National Heart Association for every dollar it makes on Valentine's Day. Write an equation to represent this situation.

b) What do the variables in your equation represent?

9. Solve the following equations.

a) $x + 36 = 10$

b) $-12.2 + d = 30.4$

c) $2a = 1.2$

d) $\frac{c}{4} = \frac{3}{4}$

e) $2n - 4 = 75$

f) $6 - 3b = 18$

10. For each of the following open sentences, write a real-life situation it could represent. Solve the equation, and then explain what the solution means for the situation you described.

a) $\$3.98 + \$4.15 = a + \$4.00$

b) $17 \cdot 29 = c$

11. Evaluate the following expressions.

a) $3 + 42 - 5 \cdot 3 + 4$

b) $3 + 42 - 5 \cdot (3 + 4)$

c) $3 + (42 - 5) \cdot 3 + 4$

---

b) $c = 493$ Real-life situations will vary. Possible response:

There were 17 classrooms in Flanders School. Each classroom had 29 desks. How many desks were there in Flanders School in all?

11. a) 34

b) 10

c) 118

Lesson Guide 1.1A *It's All About Algebra*

Use the words listed below to create a concept map for algebra.

- Think about how these words and ideas relate to each other. This will help you decide where to place them on your concept map.
- Remember to describe on your concept map how these words and ideas are linked or connected to each other.

Algebra

Associative Property

Commutative Property

Coordinate Grid

Distributive Property

Equality

Equations

Expressions

Formula

Generalization

General Rule

Graphing

Identity Property

Input Variable

Inverse Operations

Making Predictions

Ordered Pair

Origin

Output Variable

Patterns

Quadrant

Variables

x-axis

y-axis

LESSON 1.2 Analyzing Graphs

Suggested Pacing: 2 Days

In this lesson, students will begin to analyze points on a graph by focusing on the relationship between two variables in a given situation. They will note which axes of the coordinate grid correspond to which of the variables.

LESSON OBJECTIVES

■ Students will explore the relationship between two variables in a given situation.

■ Students will identify the variables in a given situation and indicate on which axes the variables should be represented on a coordinate grid.

■ Students will identify and interpret points on a graph by describing the points in terms of the relationship between the two variables in a given situation.

DAY 1	MATERIALS*	ESSENTIAL *ON YOUR OWN* QUESTIONS
Choosing NBA Stars	**In Class** ■ Graph paper ■ Lesson Guide 1.2: *NBA Stars* ■ Lesson 1.2: *Comparing Areas of Conference Tables* ■ Chart paper ■ Markers ■ Internet access **On Your Own** ■ Internet access ■ Graph paper for Think Beyond question (optional) ■ Lesson Guide 1.2: *NBA Stars*	Questions 1–4, 14
DAY 2	**MATERIALS***	**ESSENTIAL *ON YOUR OWN* QUESTIONS**
Comparing Areas of Conference Tables		Questions 5–13

* The Think Like a Mathematician Daily Record Sheet should be used daily

---

MATHEMATICALLY SPEAKING

▶ compression bar ▶ variable ▶ x-axis ▶ y-axis

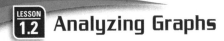

Start It Off

Plot the points below on a coordinate grid. Then connect them in the given order to find the answer to this riddle:

What do you call an angle that has been run over by a truck?

$(-3, 3), (0, 3), (6, 3), (6, 0), (6, -1), (2, -1), (-1, -1), (-3, -1), (-3, 1), (-3, 3)$

What clues in the given coordinate pairs can help you to visualize the shape of the figure they will form before you actually plot the points?

MATHEMATICALLY SPEAKING

▶ variable
▶ x-axis
▶ y-axis

In the next few lessons, you will look at relationships between variables. You will learn how lines on graphs can represent relationships between two variables. You will use graphs, tables, and equations as mathematical models to represent real situations. These tools will help you to make smart business decisions as you assume the role of a conference planner.

Let's Review Remember that a graph is a representation of a situation described by two variables. It displays how one variable is related to the other. The x-axis and the y-axis on the coordinate grid each represent one of the two variables in the situation. It is very important to understand the meaning of each variable in order to place points on a graph accurately and to interpret correctly what these points represent.

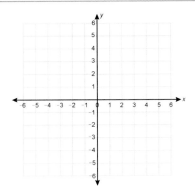

Answers will vary. Possible response:

The first three points are aligned horizontally since the y-coordinates of the ordered pairs are 3. The x-values of the points are increasing, so the horizontal line extends to the right. The next two points are aligned vertically to (6, 3) since the x-coordinates of these points are also 6. The y-values are decreasing, so the vertical line extends downwards. The next two points are aligned horizontally to the point (6, −1) since they also have y-coordinates of −1. The x-values of these points are decreasing, so the horizontal line extends to the left. The last two points have the same x-value as the point (−3, −1), so they are aligned vertically. Since the y-values are increasing, the vertical line extends upwards. The last point given in the list is the same as the first point, creating a closed polygon that has 4 sides and 4 right angles when the points are connected.

Start It Off

Answers: An angle that got run over by a truck is a wrecked angle: A rectangle (that is, a "wrecked angle").

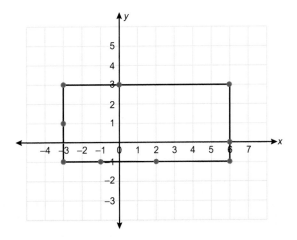

DAY 1 TEACHING THE LESSON

Students will explore how graphs can be used to represent a given situation. In this lesson, students will begin to analyze points on a graph by focusing on the relationship between two variables in a given situation, noting which axes of the coordinate grid correspond to which variables. This is an important skill to develop in order to accurately place points on a graph and successfully interpret what the graph represents.

Distribute Lesson Guide 1.2: *NBA Stars*, to students. Have students work independently on Question 1, and then share their responses with a partner. Discuss any discrepancies as a class. Encourage students to share strategies for how they determined which player goes with each point.

 Differentiation

Think Differently: This graph was specifically designed so that the variable height would be labeled on the *x*-axis. You should emphasize to students the need to pay careful attention to the labels of the graph in order to interpret the points appropriately. Students may initially think that height is represented along the *y*-axis. Students may also consider only one of the variables when interpreting the points. It is important to remind students to pay attention to both variables when identifying points on the graph. To support students that are experiencing difficulty, ask the following questions to scaffold learning and redirect thinking:

• *On which axis is height labeled?*

• *What does a point located to the far right on the graph represent?*

• *What is the label for the y-axis?*

• *What does a point located towards the top of the graph represent?*

Your company is planning to feature NBA players from past seasons at the conference this year. Your job is to create posters of the players in action. Ms. Sarina, your boss, has given you a graph titled "NBA Stars." She wants you to choose three of the players from the 2005–2006 season to appear on the posters. First, you will need to interpret the graph.

1. Examine the graph below. Use the information given to determine which player is represented by each point on the graph.

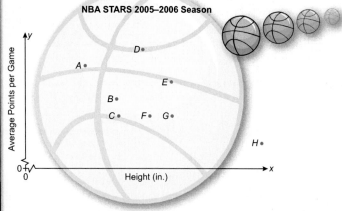

NBA STARS 2005–2006 Season

y — Average Points per Game · *x* — Height (in.)

I. Kobe Bryant, a 6-foot-6-inch-tall guard, was the leading scorer during the season with an average of 35 points per game.

II. LeBron James and Carmelo Anthony, who are both 6 feet 8 inches tall, scored an average of 31 points and 27 points per game, respectively.

III. Paul Pierce, who is an inch taller than Kobe Bryant, scored an average of 27 points per game, as did Dwyane Wade, who is 6 feet 4 inches tall.

IV. Gilbert Arenas, at 6 feet 4 inches tall, averaged 29 points per game.
V. Allen Iverson, the shortest player on the list, scored on average 33 points per game!

V. Yao Ming, the first NBA player of Chinese origin, is a whopping 7 feet 6 inches tall and scored 22 points per game on average for the season.

 Talk Moves Have students work independently on Questions 1–8. When finished, discuss the solutions as a class. Use talk moves, such as repeat/rephrase and adding on, to further the discussion and enhance understanding.

1. Answers:
    A. Allen Iverson
    B. Gilbert Arenas
    C. Dwyane Wade
    D. Kobe Bryant
    E. LeBron James
    F. Paul Pierce
    G. Carmelo Anthony
    H. Yao Ming

2. **a)** Identify the variables represented by each axis on the graph.

   b) Explain how increases in the value of each variable would be represented on the graph. Use two different examples from the graph in your explanation.

3. Why is point *B* directly above point *C*?

4. Explain why points *C*, *F* and *G* lie along the same horizontal line.

5. We have used a **compression bar** (⌁) on both the *x*-axis and *y*-axis. Each bar indicates that we have removed a piece of that axis from the graph.

   a) What do you think the purpose of the compression bar is?

   b) Why do you think we used a compression bar for this particular graph?

6. **a)** Using the graph and the information in Question 1, estimate the height of Allen Iverson.

   b) Go online at www.nba.com to find Iverson's actual height. How close were you?

   c) What aspects of the graph helped you to determine his height?

7. Shaquille O'Neal, a 7-foot-1-inch-tall player, scored an average of 20 points per game for the 2005–2006 season. Plot a new point on the graph corresponding to his statistics.

8. Use the graph to determine what relationship, if any, there is between the two variables. Explain your answer.

2. **a)** The variable represented on the *x*-axis is height. The variable represented on the *y*-axis is the average number of points scored per game.

   b) An increase in height is shown moving horizontally to the right on the *x*-axis. An increase in the number of points scored per game is shown moving vertically up the *y*-axis. Examples will vary. Possible response: Yao Ming is the tallest player so he is represented on the graph at point *H*, which is the farthest point to the right along the *x*-axis. Kobe Bryant scores the most points per game (35) among the

players listed. He is represented on the graph at point *D*, which is the highest point along the *y*-axis.

3. Point *B* is directly above point *C* because they represent players that are the same height. Gilbert Arenas and Dwyane Wade are both 6 feet 4 inches tall.

4. Points *C*, *F* and *G* are directly across from each other because they represent players that have scored the same number of average points per game. Dwyane Wade, Paul Pierce and Carmelo Anthony all scored an average of 27 points per game.

5. Answers will vary. Possible response: The compression bar indicates that a nonessential piece of the graph has been removed, allowing more focus on the data being presented. Since the featured basketball players were at least 6 feet or taller, it wasn't necessary to include heights less than 6 feet on the graph along the *x*-axis. Also, the players averaged more than 20 points per game, so it isn't necessary to include points less than 20 on the graph along the *y*-axis.

6. **a)** Estimates for Allen Iverson's height will vary. Accept a reasonable estimate that is approximately 6 feet.

   b) Allen Iverson's actual height is 6 feet. If there is no internet access in the classroom, you can inform students of this fact.

c) Answers will vary. Possible response: Point *C* (Dwyane Wade) represents a height of 6'4" and point *G* (Carmelo Anthony) represents a height of 6'8". The difference between those two heights along the *x*-axis is 4 inches. The distance along the *x*-axis between point *A* (Allen Iverson) and point *C* appears to be about the distance along the *x*-axis between point *C* and point *F*. Therefore, Allen's height must be approximately 4 inches less than Dwyane Wade's height. Allen's height is 6 feet.

7.

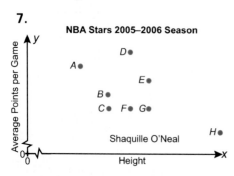

Summarize Day 1

Question 8 can be used as a discussion question to wrap up day 1. Have students discuss in pairs and then share.

8. Student responses should indicate that there doesn't seem to be a relationship between the two variables; height doesn't seem to relate to the number of points scored per game. For example, Yao Ming is the tallest, but he scored the least number of points per game. Gilbert Arenas and Dwyane Wade are the same height, but Arenas scored more points per game than Wade. Also, Allen Iverson is the shortest player featured, but he did not score the least or greatest number of points per game. The number of points scored per game does not seem to depend on a player's height.

Comparing Areas of Conference Tables

9. Examine the shapes on the grid below. These are scale drawings of the top surfaces of rectangular tables at the conference. Registration materials will be placed on these tables.

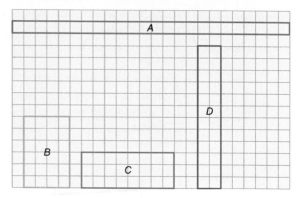

a) What is the area in square units of each of the four tabletops?

b) Label four of the points on the graph with the letters *A*, *B*, *C*, and *D* to correspond with the four shapes.

Shapes

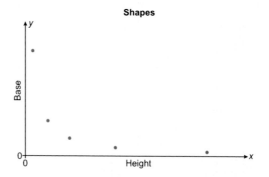

c) Draw a fifth tabletop that corresponds to the remaining point on the graph.

d) Why might you want tabletops with different shapes for the conference?

DAY 2 TEACHING THE LESSON

Comparing Areas of Conference Tables

Pass out Lesson Guide 1.2: *Comparing Areas of Conference Tables*. You may want to review the concept of area for some students. The areas of the given rectangles are all the same, but the relationship between the height and the base is quite different. Students match the shapes to points on the graph, indicating height on the *x*-axis and base on the *y*-axis. This activity goes beyond the NBA Star Stats because they have to

Think Beyond

10. Create a graph whose points correspond to every possible rectangle that has an area of 24 square units. First, graph all possible whole number values for the base and height. Put a numerical scale on the x- and y-axes. Then, think about possible fractional and decimal values. How does this graph compare to the one above?

⬆ Wrap It Up

Explain why it is important to pay attention to the labels on the x- and y-axes when creating or interpreting graphs.

MATHEMATICALLY SPEAKING

▸ compression bar
▸ variable
▸ x-axis
▸ y-axis

create a new rectangle that corresponds to a new point. Question 7 in On Your Own asks for similar mathematical thinking on the part of students.

9. **a)** The area of Shape A is 24 square units.
   The area of Shape B is 24 squares units.
   The area of Shape C is 24 square units.
   The area of Shape D is 24 square units.

b)

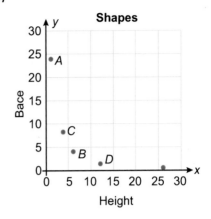

c) The last point is (24, 1). Since the x-value is 24, the height of the shape is 24 units. The y-value is 1, so the base is 1 unit. The last point represents a rectangle with a height of 24 units and a base of 1 unit.

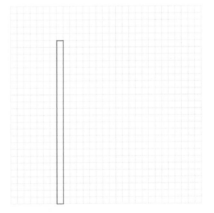

d) The tables may serve various purposes. A long narrow table might have name tags or conference packets displayed. No one will have to sit or work at this table so it can be narrow. A short wide table may have chairs around it so that conference attendees can sit down and fill out registration forms.

Think

Beyond This question will be appropriate for your more advanced students.

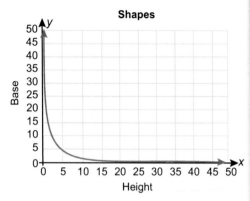

Shapes

This graph connects the dots from the scatter plot in Question 6. This means that for every point (x, y) along the line, $xy = 24$ square units.

If there is sufficient class time, have students do Question 7 in On Your Own in class.

W rap It Up

Student responses should indicate the following key ideas:

• A graph is a representation of a situation and shows how one variable is related to another.

• In order to create and interpret a graph accurately when representing a given situation, it is important to know which variable is represented along each axis. This is done by labeling each axis.

Reflect

Use these questions to help you reflect on the lesson and plan for future instruction.

• How easily were students able to interpret the points on the graph?

• Are students able to recognize which variables are represented on the axes of the graph?

LESSON 1.2 **SECTION 1**

On Your Own

Write About It

1. Why might the NBA Stars graph be challenging for someone to interpret? What errors might a student make? Why?

2. Vince Carter averaged 24 points per game in the 2005–2006 season. He is $6\frac{1}{2}$ feet tall. Where would you place a point on the NBA Stars graph to represent his statistics? Choose the letter of the correct response.

   A. directly to the left of C.

   B. directly above H

   C. lined up vertically with D

3. Add points to the NBA Stars graph to represent the height and the points scored per game for each of the following players. Write which points represent which players.

   a) Dirk Nowitch: 7 feet tall, 27 points scored per game

   b) Ray Allen: 6 feet 5 inches tall, 25 points scored per game

4. Choose three players to feature at the conference. Explain your reasons and how they relate to the graph.

5. At the Vermont Country Store there is a cheese corner where they sell several varieties of cheddar. Each point on the graph below represents packages of cheese that were sold one Saturday morning.

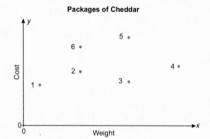

Packages of Cheddar

   a) Which package weighs the least?

   b) Which package costs the most?

   c) Which packages, if any, are the same weight?

• What were some strategies students used to successfully identify NBA players on the graph?

On Your Own

Write About It Answers will vary. Student response should include the following key ideas as to why the graph is challenging to interpret:

1.

• Someone may not pay attention to the labels along the x- and y-axes and automatically think height is represented along the y-axis.

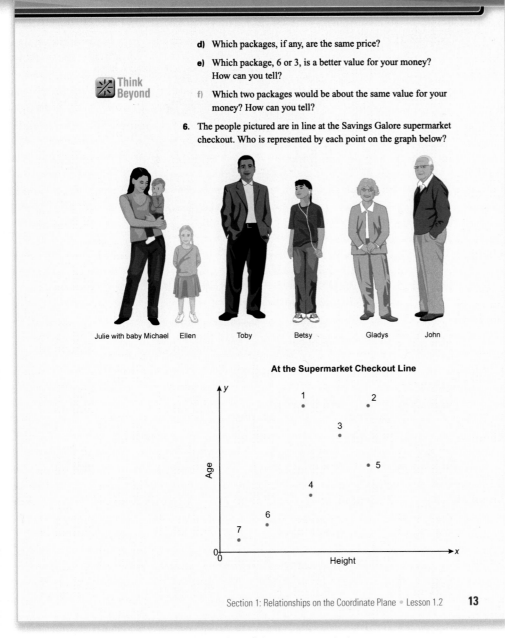

d) Which packages, if any, are the same price?

e) Which package, 6 or 3, is a better value for your money? How can you tell?

f) Which two packages would be about the same value for your money? How can you tell?

Think Beyond

6. The people pictured are in line at the Savings Galore supermarket checkout. Who is represented by each point on the graph below?

Julie with baby Michael   Ellen   Toby   Betsy   Gladys   John

At the Supermarket Checkout Line

2. **C.** lined up vertically with *D*

3. a) Dirk Nowitch: Point *I*

   b) Ray Allen: Point *J*

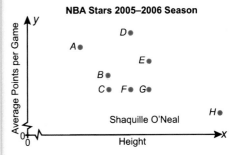

4. Most likely students will choose the top three scorers, Kobe Bryant, Alan Iverson and Lebron James. However, some may choose well known players such as Yao Ming and Shaquille O'Neal that participants would recognize more easily.

5. a) Package 1

   b) Package 5

   c) Packages 2 and 6; Packages 3 and 5

   d) None of the packages have the same cost.

   e) Package 3 is a better value for the money. Package 3 weighs more than Package 6 and costs less. You get more cheese for less money.

- The scales are not listed on the axes so it is more difficult to interpret the coordinates of the points given.

- Someone may not understand what a compression bar represents.

- A student might make an error when interpreting the graph. They may confuse the variables by thinking the higher points on the graph represent the taller players or that the points farther to the right represent the greater number of points scored per game.

- Students may focus only on one variable when identifying players on the graph.

f). **Think Beyond** Packages 2 and 5 give the same value for the money. They are located the same distance away from the *x*- and *y*-axes, approximately along the line $y = x$. This means that as the weight increases, the cost increases at the same rate for both packages.

6. Point 7 Baby Michael

Point 6 Ellen

Point 4 Betsy

Point 1 Gladys

Point 3 Julie

Point 5 Alex

Point 2 John

7. a)

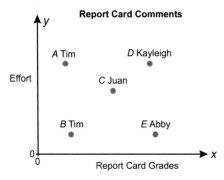

b) Answers will vary. One possible report:

Tyler has shown a great deal of effort this marking period. He is working extremely hard. However, he is still experiencing difficulty with many math concepts. His test and quiz grades do not reflect the effort he is putting forth.

8. **Think Beyond** There are many ways points can be positioned to show a similar relationship between two variables at each point. For example, as one variable increases, the other variable decreases; or as one variable increases, the other variable increases. When there is a relationship, usually points appear to form a trendline.

7. The following comments about math grades were sent home on the report cards of Kayleigh, Tim, Abby, and Juan.

a) Label four of the points on the graph with the appropriate names.

b) Create a report for the fifth point.

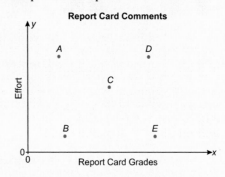

 Think Beyond

 Think Beyond

8. Make up a situation where there is always the same relationship between the *x* and *y* variables for every point. Give specific points to illustrate your explanation. Create a graph to show this relationship.

9. Look up the average number of points scored per game and the heights of some of the leading scorers in the Women's National Basketball Association (WNBA). Create a WNBA Stars graph with clues and give it to a partner to complete. Compare answers.

14 Course 3: Line It Up: Focusing on Linear Relationships

Possible situation: As students progress through grade levels, the average amount of time required to complete homework increases.

Point	Grade	Time in Minutes
A	Grade 3	30
B	Grade 4	45
C	Grade 5	60
D	Grade 6	75
E	Grade 7	90
F	Grade 8	105

Think Back

You are arranging a flight from Boston to St. Louis for Ray Allen and Emeka Okafor. You check the flight options to find the best deal. There is a direct flight leaving Boston at 3:15 pm EST that arrives at St. Louis at 5:25 pm CST. Recall that Central Standard Time (CST) is an hour earlier than Eastern Standard Time (EST). There is also a connecting flight that leaves Boston at 11:00 am, and arrives in Charlotte, NC at 3:00 pm EST. The connection departs Charlotte at 3:47 pm EST, and arrives in St. Louis at 5:47 pm CST.

10. What is the total travel time from Boston to St. Louis for each option? What is the difference in flying time between the two options?

11. The distance from Boston to St. Louis is 1,042 miles if you fly non-stop. If the direct flight costs $228, what is the cost per mile of travel? What is the cost per hour?

12. The distance from Boston to Charlotte is 723 miles and the distance from Charlotte to St. Louis is 572 miles. If the connecting flights together cost $178, what is the cost per mile of travel? What is the cost per hour?

13. Which flight would you select? What factors should you consider when selecting a flight?

14. **What went wrong?** Solve $\frac{1}{4}x - 2 = 20$.

    Steffi reasoned that if she added 2 to both sides, she would have $\frac{1}{4}x = 22$, so $x = \frac{1}{4}$ of 22, or $x = 5.5$.

Assigned Homework

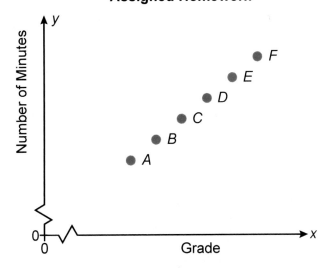

9. **Think Beyond** Answers will vary. Students should create a graph, as well as clues about each player.

 Think Back

10. Total travel time for the connecting flight is 7 hr. 47 min. Total travel time for the nonstop flight is 3 hr. 10 min. The difference in flying time is 7 hr. – 3 hr. 10 min. = 3 hr. 50 min.

11. Cost per mile = $\frac{228}{1,042}$ = $0.22 per mile

    Cost per hour = $\frac{228}{3.167}$ = $72 per hour

12. Total miles = 723 + 572 = 1,295 miles

    Cost per mile = $\frac{178}{1,295}$ = $0.14 per mile

    Cost per hour = $\frac{178}{7}$ = $25.43 per hour

13. There is no right or wrong answer. If cost was the most important thing, then they would take the longer flight to save $50. If they had to be there by a certain time or their time was limited, they would probably choose to pay extra and save time. Since there is about a four-hour travel time difference, their time is valued at $\frac{\$50}{4}$ or $12.50 per hour!

14. Steffi was fine until she got to $\frac{1}{4}x = 22$. She should have multiplied both sides by 4, instead of taking $\frac{1}{4}$ of 22, to get an answer of $x = 88$.

NBA Stars

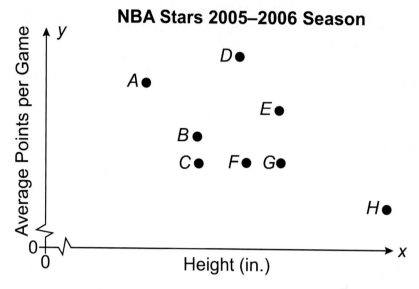

NBA Stars 2005–2006 Season

I. Kobe Bryant, a 6-foot-6-inch-tall guard, was the leading scorer during the season with an average of 35 points per game.

II. LeBron James and Carmelo Anthony, who are both 6 feet 8 inches tall, scored an average of 31 points and 27 points per game, respectively.

III. Paul Pierce, who is an inch taller than Kobe Bryant, scored an average of 27 points per game, as did Dwyane Wade, who is 6 feet 4 inches tall.

IV. Gilbert Arenas, at 6 feet 4 inches tall, averaged 29 points per game.

V. Allen Iverson, the shortest player on the list, scored on average 33 points per game!

VI. Yao Ming, the first NBA player of Chinese origin, is a whopping 7 feet 6 inches tall and scored 22 points per game on average for the season.

Comparing Areas of Conference Tables

Examine the shapes on the grid below. These are scale drawings for some rectangular table at the conference where registration materials will be displayed.

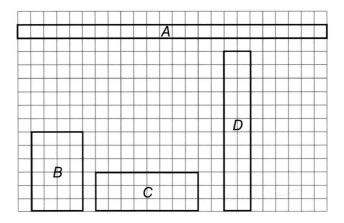

a) What is the area in square units of each of the four tabletops?

b) Label four of the points on the graph below with the letters *A*, *B*, *C*, and *D* to correspond with the four shapes.

Shapes

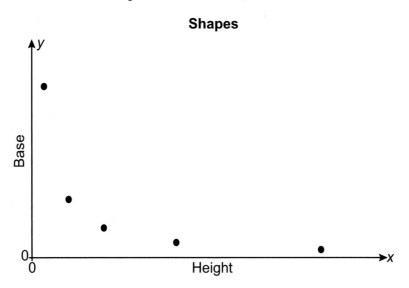

c) Draw a fifth tabletop that corresponds to the remaining point on the graph.

d) Why might you want tabletops with different shapes for the conference?

Relating Tables and Graphs

Suggested Pacing: 2 Days

In this lesson, students take a closer look at the relationship between two variables in a given situation. Students analyze tables and graphs that represent given situations and discover the advantages and disadvantages of each type of representation. Students also explore how the scale on a graph can sometimes distort the relationship between two variables, while accurately representing the data.

LESSON OBJECTIVES
- Students will continue to explore the relationship between two variables in a given situation as they analyze and compare tables and graphs.
- Students will explore whether scale affects the relationship between two variables in a given situation on a graph.
- Students will recognize the power of scale in influencing opinion and misrepresenting information.

DAY 1	MATERIALS*	ESSENTIAL *ON YOUR OWN* QUESTIONS
Relating Tables and Graphs What a Difference a Scale Makes! From Graphs to Tables	**In Class** ■ Graph paper **On Your Own** ■ Graph paper ■ Lesson Guide 1.3A: *Beware of Scale* (optional) ■ Lesson Guide 1.3: *Ms. Tootyourhorn's Sales* for use with lesson question 15 and On Your Own	Questions 1–5, 14, 15, 16;
DAY 2	**MATERIALS***	**ESSENTIAL *ON YOUR OWN* QUESTIONS**
From Tables to Graphs		Questions 6–9, 11–13

* The Think Like a Mathematician Daily Record Sheet should be used daily

---

MATHEMATICALLY SPEAKING

▶ scale (on a coordinate axes system)   ▶ line graph

LESSON 1.3 Relating Tables and Graphs

→ Start It Off

In New York City, the avenues run from south to north and the streets run from east to west, as shown in the diagram below. Jessica is staying at a hotel at 48th Street and 3rd Avenue. She needs to walk to a meeting at the United Nations building at 45th Street and 1st Avenue.

1. What is the fewest number of blocks she could walk? (A block is the distance from one intersection to the next intersection.)

2. By how many different paths could she get there in the fewest number of blocks? Draw all the possible paths on graph paper.

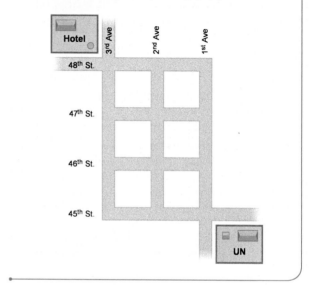

In Lesson 1.2, you looked at the relationship between two variables by analyzing points on a graph. In this lesson, you will look at the relationship between two variables as you analyze graphs and tables.

→ Start It Off

1. It would take Jessica a minimum of five blocks to get from the hotel to the United Nations; three blocks to get from 48th St. to 45th St. and two blocks to get from 3rd Ave. to 1st Ave.

2. There are 10 different possible paths Jessica could take to get from the hotel to the United Nations. Each path is outlined in the diagram on the next page.

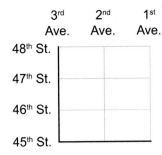

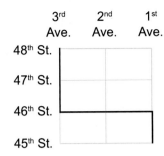

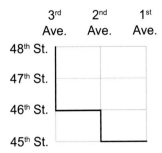

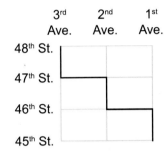

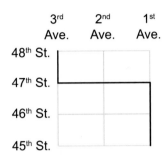

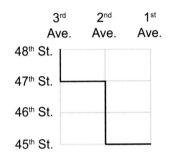

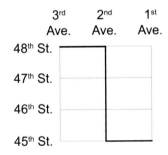

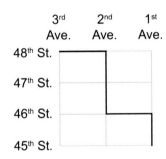

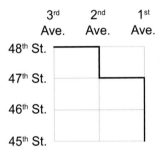

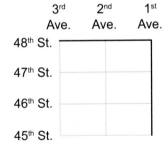

A discussion of how they found the total could elicit many strategies. One that works well is to begin at the end. There is only one way to get from 45th and 2nd or from 46th and 1st. This means that there are two ways to get from 46th and 2nd. Moving backwards, there is only one way to get from 47th and 1st. Adding that corner plus the corner of 46th and 2nd, means that there are 3 ways to get from 47th and 2nd. Similarly, there are 3 ways to get from 46th and 3rd. There is one way to get from 48th and 1st, so that and the 3 ways to get from 47th and 2nd give 4 ways from 48th and 2nd. Adding that to the 6 ways from 47th and 3rd gives you 10 ways total from 48th and 5th. This works for any size grid.

TEACHING THE LESSON

What a Difference a Scale Makes!

Begin the lesson with a short discussion about scales of graphs. Ask:

- *How do you know what scale to use when creating a graph?*
- *What helps you determine the scale to use?*

Guide the discussion to help students recognize that scales on graphs can be adjusted to make the same data look different. People who are responsible for marketing products are aware of this and often adjust scales to present their products in the most favorable light.

 Have students work with a partner to complete Question 1 by matching the given scenarios with the appropriate graphs. Discuss student responses when finished. Use talk moves, such as agree/disagree and why, to resolve any discrepancies.

Next have students work independently on Questions 2–7 and then share responses with the class.

What a Difference a Scale Makes!

Scales on the *x*- and *y*-axes can really make a difference in how a graph looks. Businesses may try to influence consumers by adjusting the scales on one or both axes of graphs that represent their products. Sometimes this can lead to misleading, though technically correct, graphs.

For example, at the Sports Mecca conference, salespeople will give presentations about their sales over the past few years.

The graphs below each show the number of treadmills that Ms. Tootyourhorn sold, *y*, over a period of time, *x*.

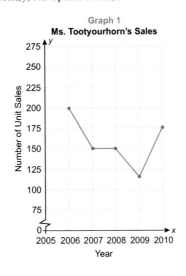

Graph 1
Ms. Tootyourhorn's Sales

Graph 2
Ms. Tootyourhorn's Sales

 Differentiation

Think Differently: Some students may think that a change in scale does affect the relationship between the two variables in a given situation. For students having difficulty with Question 2, you may want to model the same data on two graphs that have different scales. Ask students to identify specific *x*-values on each graph and note that the corresponding *y*-values are the same. Although a change in scale can appear to distort the relationship between two variables, it does not technically alter the relationship. As an option, use Lesson Guide 1.3A to help scaffold student learning.

1. Ms. Tootyourhorn: Graph 2

To measure the number of unit sales, this graph uses a scale that begins at 100 and has intervals of 15 units. This distorts the sales so that her sales appear to have had a huge increase. Also, the *x*-axis has the years 2009 and 2010 labeled with a wide space between them and omits other years.

Mr. Burstyourbubble: Graph 3

To measure the number of unit sales, this graph uses a scale that begins at 100 and has intervals of 50 units. This distorts the sales over the year so her sales appear to have only had a minimal increase. Also, the *x*-axis has the years 2009 and 2010 labeled with a wide space between them and omits other years.

Ms. Longtermplanning: Graph 1

This graph is the only one that shows more than one year's sales data. This can be seen by looking at the labels on the *x*-axis. This graph shows a trend in sales over a longer period, which illustrates a more accurate picture of the salesperson's success record.

2. Graphs 2 and 3 are similar in the following ways:

    •   Both show the same sales data for Ms. Tootyourhorn from 2009 to 2010.

    •   Both graphs show a straight, rising line.

    •   Labels on the axes are the same on both graphs.

    •   Titles on the graphs are the same.

    Graphs 2 and 3 are different in the following ways:

    •   The scales on the *y*-axes are different on the graphs.

    •   The rising line on graph 2 appears steeper than on graph 3.

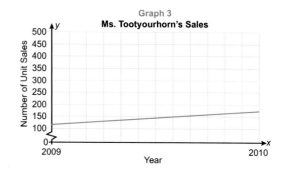

Graph 3
Ms. Tootyourhorn's Sales

- Ms. Tootyourhorn wants to show that her sales increased dramatically from 2009 to 2010.

- Mr. Burstyourbubble wants to show that Ms. Tootyourhorn's sales increase from 2009 to 2010 was not that large.

- Ms. Longtermplanning believes it is necessary to look at sales over a longer time frame to get a more accurate picture of a salesperson's success.

1. Match each graph to the person who should use it to promote his/her point of view. Explain your reasoning.

2. How are graph 2 and graph 3 alike? How are they different?

3. **a)** For the year 2010, how many treadmills did Ms. Tootyourhorn sell?

    b) Are the same values on all three graphs?

    c) Why does her increase in sales look greater on graph 2 than on graph 3?

MATHEMATICALLY SPEAKING

▶ line graph

People in business often connect points on a graph in instances where it is not mathematically correct to do so. They use a line graph in these cases to highlight patterns or trends in the data.

3. **a)** 175

    b) yes

    c) The difference in the scale on the *y*-axes, shown in increments of 15 rather than 50, allows the value 175 to be placed higher on graph 2 than graph 3. This gives the appearance of a greater number of sales on graph 2. These graphs show that a change in their scales can distort the relationship between two variables while still displaying the data in an accurate fashion.

4. a) Look at graph 1 without the line segments connecting the data points as shown below. Why do you think it is more effective for a presenter to use a line graph in this case rather than distinct, unconnected points?

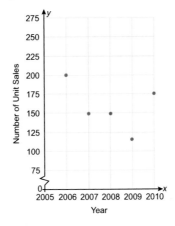

b) Why is it mathematically incorrect to connect the points on this graph?

5. Graphs also have disadvantages when representing a situation. What are some disadvantages in using a graph to describe a situation?

4. a) The data are distinct points. We only know the values for the sales year and the number of units sold for the individual discrete points given.

b) A line graph makes it easier to see the relationship between variables. The line shows that as time went on (to the next year), the number of units went up or down.

5. While graphs make it easier to see trends, it is more difficult to determine exact data values. Also, depending on the scales used, a graph can distort data that is being represented even though the data is accurately represented.

Have students complete Questions 6–9 independently or with a partner. For Question 6, encourage students to look at Graph 2 and 3 to find an exact value for year 2009.

Circulate as students work on the problems. Take note of interesting ideas and solution strategies students are using and encourage those students to share their ideas in a class discussion when finished. This is also a good time to use the Student Shapshot observation tool to record notes as you formatively assess student understanding of the ideas presented in the lesson. Focus on just a few students during one question. Pay attention to the mathematical vocabulary students are using as well as problem-solving strategies.

6. Number of unit sales for 2009 may vary slightly. Accept answers that are reasonable.

Ms. Tootyourhorn's Sales	
Year	Number of Unit Sales
2006	200
2007	150
2008	150
2009	120
2010	175

7. Ms. Tootyourhorn's unit sales decreased by 50 units from 2006 to 2007. Her sales remained the same from 2007–2008 and then decreased by 30 units from 2008 to 2009. Her sales increased from 2009 to 2010 by 55 units, ending slightly lower in sales than when she started in 2006.

8. Answers will vary. Look for student justification that is reasonable and appropriately supports their responses. For example, Ms. T's sales dropped for 3 years and in the fourth year are rising closer to her unit sales for 2006.

Summarize Day 1

Consider using Question 9 as a Wrap It Up discussion for Day 1. Students can discuss their answers with partners and then share as a class. Also discuss why it is necessary to carefully examine the scales on the *x* and *y*-axes when analyzing graphs that are in newspapers, magazines and on the Internet. Students will be doing this in the On Your Own exercises.

9. The table and graph are alike in the following ways:

- Both can represent the same data.

- It is possible to identify and determine changes in the relationship between the variables in both displays.

The table and graph are different in the following ways:

- It is easier to determine exact values for variables in the table.

- It is easier to determine the exact change in values in the table.

- It is easier to see trends or increases and decreases in the graph.

- Graphs can distort the relationship between variables depending on the scales used, even though the data is presented accurately.

Relating Graphs and Tables

6. Create a table of values for graph #1 of Ms. Tootyourhorn's (Ms. T's) sales above.

Hint
See page 155

7. Based on the table and graph, describe Ms. T's sales from 2006 to 2010.

8. If you were Ms. T's boss, how would you evaluate her performance over the past year? Over the last five years?

Hint
See page 155

9. Compare the information given in a table and a graph. How are they alike? How are they different?

The table below shows Mr. Burstyourbubble's (Mr. B's) sales record.

Year	Sales
2006	225
2007	175
2008	175
2009	100
2010	175

10. Imagine a line graph of Mr. B's sales. Predict the following:

a) Between which points would Mr. B's graph have a line segment that rises from left to right? Why? Describe the relationship between the two variables (sales and years).

b) Between which points would the graph have a line segment that falls or decreases from left to right? Why? Describe the relationship between the variables (sales and years).

c) Between which points would the graph have a horizontal line segment? Why? Describe the relationship between the variables (sales and years).

DAY 2 TEACHING THE LESSON

From Tables to Graphs

Students will now create a graph using a table. Have students complete Questions 10–12. Make sure they predict what the graph will look like before they actually complete the graph. This encourages them to look at the relationship between the variables in the table. The Wrap it Up question is very important as it is one of the more important mathematical ideas students should learn from this section.

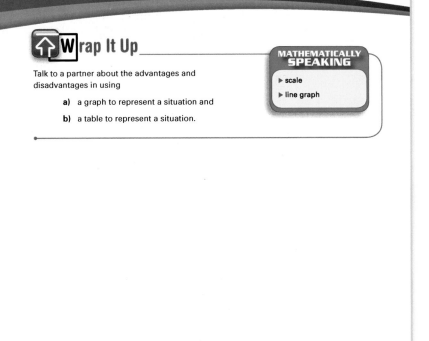

11. a) Predict how the graph of Mr. B's sales would compare to Ms. T's sales from 2009 to 2010.

   b) Graph Mr. B's sales record from 2006 to 2010 on the same coordinate grid as Ms. T's.

   c) Was your prediction correct? How do Mr. B's sales compare to Ms. T's sales?

12. If you were Mr. B's boss, how would you evaluate his performance? Would you consider him to be more successful than Ms. T? Why or why not?

⬆W︎rap It Up

Talk to a partner about the advantages and disadvantages in using

   a) a graph to represent a situation and

   b) a table to represent a situation.

MATHEMATICALLY SPEAKING

▶ scale
▶ line graph

10. a) Mr. B's graph will have a line segment that rises from left to right for 2009 to 2010, since there was an increase in sales. As time (years) increased, the number of sales increased.

   b) Mr. B's graph will have a line segment that falls from left to right for 2006 to 2007 and 2008 to 2009, since there was a decrease in sales. As time (years) increased, the number of sales decreased.

   c) Mr. B's graph will have a horizontal line segment for 2007 to 2008 since sales remained constant. As time (years) increased, the number of sales stayed the same.

11. a) Student answers will vary. Possible response:

The graph for Mr. B's sales will be similar to Ms. T's in that the line segment from year 2009 to 2010 will rise upwards from left to right. However, since Mr. B had a greater increase in sales compared to Ms. T (75 vs. 55), the line segment for Mr. B's sales will be steeper than the one on Ms. T's graph. This line segment will begin at year 2009 with a *y*-value of 100 (slightly lower than Ms. T's *y*-value of 120) and will end at year 2010 with a *y*-value of 175 (the same as Ms. T's *y*-value).

b) Pass out Lesson Guide 1.3 *Ms. Tootyourhorn's Sales* for students so students can graph Mr. B's sales.

Graph of Mr. B's sales record:

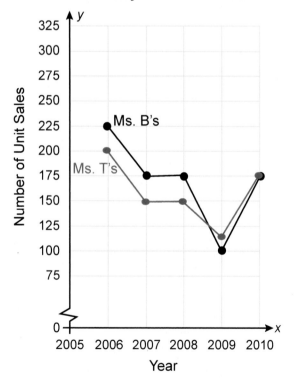

Mr. Burstyourbubble's Sales

c) Although Mr. B's sales started higher than Ms. T's sales, both had a decrease in sales from 2006 to 2007 of 50 units. From 2007 to 2008, sales did not change for either. While Mr. B and Ms. T had decreases in sales from 2008 to 2009, Mr. B's decrease was 75 units compared to Ms. T's 30 units. From 2009 to 2010, both had an increase in sales; however, Mr. B's increase was 75 units compared to Ms. T's increase of 55 units.

12. Answers will vary. Look for student justification that is reasonable and appropriately supports student responses.

Wrap It Up

Guide the discussion to emphasize the following key ideas.

a) Advantages of using graphs to represent situations include:

- Graphs make it easy to see trends and relationships between the variables.

- Graphs allow situations to be more readily compared.

  Disadvantages of using graphs to represent situations include:

- Depending on the scale being used, graphs may distort the relationship between the variables while accurately representing the data.

- Graphs make it more difficult to determine exact data values or exact changes in the relationship between the variables.

b) Advantages of using a table to represent a situation include:

- Tables make it easy to determine exact values.

- Tables make it easy to identify the exact change in the relationship between the variables.

  Disadvantages of using a table to represent a situation include:

- Tables make it more difficult to see trends in data.

- Tables make it more difficult to make comparisons between situations.

Reflect

Use these questions to help you reflect on the lesson and plan for future instruction.

- How comfortable were students in identifying the advantages and disadvantages of using tables and graphs to represent different situations?

- How successful are students in interpreting a given situation based on tables and graphs?

- Are students able to accurately describe the relationship between variables from tables and graphs?

LESSON 1.3 SECTION 1

On Your Own

MATERIALS LIST
▶ Graph Paper
▶ Lesson Guide 1.3
  Ms. Tootyourhorn's
  Sales"?

On Your Own

1. ![Write About It icon] **Write About It** Answers will vary. Possible response:

A change in the scale on one of the axes can distort the relationship between the variables even though the data is accurately represented. For example, the graphs below show the same data for a given situation. Hosting a charity clothing drive, a local middle school collected 40 coats in 2009 and 80 coats in 2010. Graph A uses a larger scale on the *y*-axis with intervals of 100 coats, which makes the amount of coats collected look very small. Graph B uses a smaller scale with intervals of 10 coats, so the amount of coats collected appears much more impressive than Graph A. Even though the graphs look different the data used is the same for both.

Write About It

1. How can changing the scale of one axis create a misleading graph? Provide an example.

2. Ms. Tootyourhorn predicts that her sales will remain steady for the next two years and then increase by 55 units in the third year. Extend Graph 1 using the Lesson Guide to include this information.

3. Spot the misleading graph in this article published by *The Times*. Explain why it is misleading.

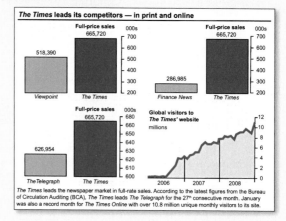

4. Find a graph in a magazine, newspaper or on the Internet that you consider to be misleading. Bring it to class, and explain why it is misleading.

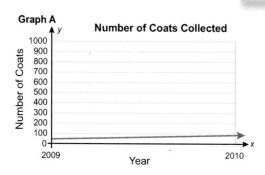

Graph A — Number of Coats Collected

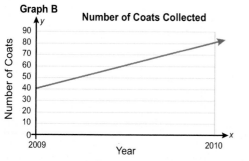

Graph B — Number of Coats Collected

2.

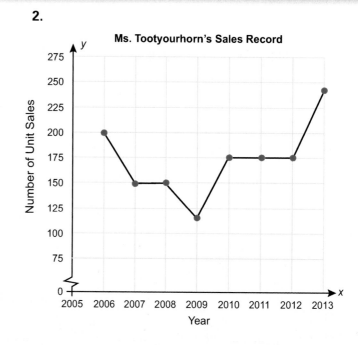

Ms. Tootyourhorn's Sales Record

5. You work at Computers-R-Us. Below is a table showing unit sales of computers, price per computer and the annual revenue (unit sales • price) for the last four years. Complete the chart by filling in the annual revenue for years 3 and 4.

	Year 1	Year 2	Year 3	Year 4
No. of Unit Sales	500	1,000	1,500	2,000
Selling Price per Unit	$2,000	$2,000	$1,500	$1,100
Annual Revenue	$1,000,000	$2,000,000		

For Questions 6 and 7 below, decide which two of the four variables shown (year, number of unit sales, selling price per unit and annual revenue) you will use on your graph. You may choose different variables for each question. Then decide on the scales for the x- and y-axes. Finally, create your graphs.

6. Suppose that you are head of sales at Computers-R-Us. Create a graph to present at the annual board meeting that will highlight the success of your sales department.

7. Suppose that you are the Chief Financial Officer (CFO) at Computers-R-Us. Create a graph to present at the annual board meeting that will show the change in annual revenues from year 1 to year 4.

a) What is the relationship between unit sales and revenue from years 1 to 3?

b) What is the relationship between unit sales and revenue from years 3 to 4?

c) A board member asks why the number of unit sales grows at a steady pace each year, but revenue figures do not. Explain to her why this is the case.

8. Why might the unit price of computers have decreased from year 3 to year 4?

9. If the company decides not to change the price of computers in year 5, how many computers will need to be sold to increase revenues by approximately $500,000? Add this information to the table and to the graph you made in Question 6.

real-life contexts. Have students discuss and compare their ideas about the graphs with each other.

5. Revenue for Year 3; $2,250,000, Revenue for Year 4; $2,200,000

6. Graphs will vary. Students should use the unit sales data to highlight the success of the department. Look for scales that magnify the increase in unit sales over the years.

Possible graph:

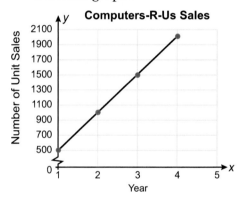

7.

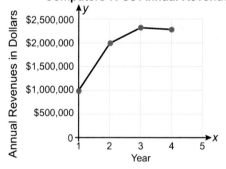

a) For Years 1 to 3, as unit sales increased, the annual revenues also increased.

b) From Year 3 to Year 4, as unit sales increased, the annual revenues decreased.

c) Although the number of unit sales increased, the price per unit decreased in Year 3 and Year 4, so the company did not gain as much revenue.

3. The bar graph comparing full-price sales of *The Times* and *The Telegraph* is misleading. The scale for the graph begins at 420,000, rather than at 0. This exaggerates the difference in sales and makes The Times's sales appear to be almost double that of the sales of *The Telegraph*. In reality, the increase in sales for The Times is only 8.7%.

4. Answers will vary. You may want to collect the graphs students find and place them at a learning center where students from other classes might have a chance to look at them and determine what is misleading about the graphs. This is a wonderful opportunity for students to apply what they are learning to

8. Answers will vary. Possible responses:

- It might have cost less to make the computers.

- Due to competition, the company may have dropped prices to encourage sales.

- The computer model may have become outdated with a new model coming out the following year.

9. A total of 2,455 computers will need to be sold to increase revenues by approximately $500,000, which is an additional 455 computers from Year 4.

	Year 1	Year 2	Year 3	Year 4
No. of Unit Sales	500	1,000	1,500	2,000
Selling Price per Unit	$2,000	$2,000	$1,500	$1,100
Annual Revenue	$1,000,000	$2,000,000		

 Think Beyond

10. If this company's annual expenses are $2 million, would you invest in this company? Why or why not?

11. Mark keeps track of his math quiz scores in the table below.

Quiz Number	Score Based on 100 Points
1	61
2	61
3	64
4	68
5	72
6	73
7	75
8	80
9	82

Create two different graphs from this table:

a) One that accurately represents the Mark's math scores.

b) One that could be misleading. Explain why your graph is misleading.

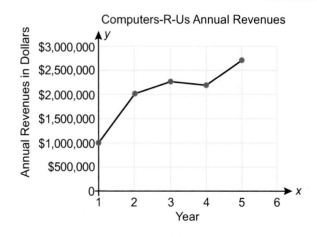

Computers-R-Us Annual Revenues

10. **Think Beyond** Answers will vary. Some students may answer no because the revenues are $2,700,500; the profit for year 5 is only $700,500. Other students may answer yes, thinking the profit signals a positive trend and profits will continue to rise. More savvy students may want to compare this company's profits to other companies in the industry before making a decision.

12. Which word, *always*, *never*, or *sometimes* correctly completes each of the following statements about integers. Give an example or examples to support your answer.

   a) A positive integer minus a positive integer
   is _____ positive.

   b) A positive integer plus a negative integer
   is _____ positive.

   c) A negative integer plus a negative integer
   is _____ positive.

   d) A negative integer minus a negative integer
   is _____ positive.

13. The total land area of the United States is 3,615,122 square miles, and the total land area of Australia is 2,967,909 square miles.

   a) Estimate the ratio of the land area of Australia to the land area of the United States as a fraction and then as a decimal rounded to the nearest hundredth without using a calculator.

   b) Write the actual ratio as a decimal rounded to the nearest hundredth. Then write this rounded decimal as a fraction in lowest terms.

   c) Compare the answer you found in Part b to your estimate. By how much do they differ? Would you say your estimate was a good one? Why or why not?

14. **a)** If the land area of the world is about 57 million square miles, what percent of the world's land area does the United States represent?

   b) What percent of the world's land area does Australia represent?

15. To find the temperature in degrees Fahrenheit, F, for a temperature given in degrees Celsius, C, use the formula $F = \frac{9}{5}C + 32$.
   The average temperature in Ulan-Bator, Mongolia is $-4.0°$ Celsius. What is this temperature in degrees Fahrenheit?

b)

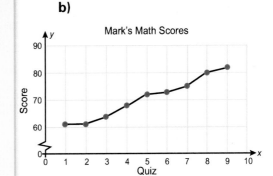

Since the *y*-axis on the bottom graph begins at 60, it makes the increase in quiz grades appear to be greater than it actually is. The graph on the top shows the actual range of quiz scores from 0–100, which represents the increase in quiz scores in a more realistic perspective.

 Think Back

12. **a)** sometimes; Answers may vary; Example:
   $5 - 3 = 2$ and
   $3 - 5 = -2$.

   b) sometimes; answers may vary; example:
   $5 + (-4) = +1$ and
   $5 + (-6) = -1$.

   c) never; answers may vary; example:
   $(-4) + (-3) = -7$.

   d) sometimes; answers may vary; example:
   $(-3) - (-4) = +1$ and
   $(-3) - (-1) = -2$.

13. **a)** Estimates will vary. Possible response: Round to the millions: 3.0 million to 3.6 million is $\frac{5}{6}$, or 0.83

   b) 0.82 or $\frac{41}{50}$

   c) Answers will vary. In the example above, the difference between the decimal estimate and exact value is 0.01. This would be considered a good estimate.

14. U.S. $\approx 6.3\%$; Australia $\approx 5.3\%$

15. $24.8°F$

11. Answers will vary. Possible graphs:

a)

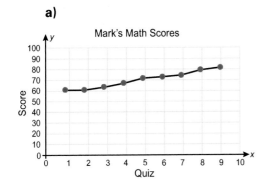

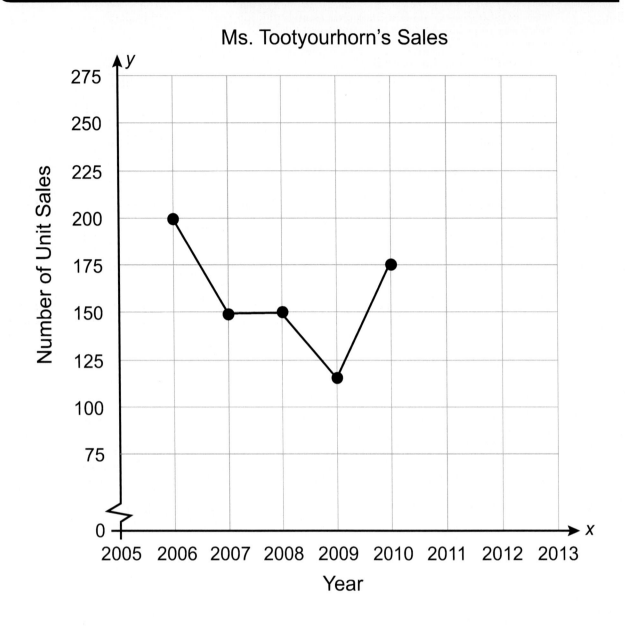

Ms. Tootyourhorn's Sales

An 8th grade class at Batchelder School held a bake sale to raise money for a class trip. Below are graphs that Kristy and Marlon created to show how many boxes of cookies their class sold each day for three days.

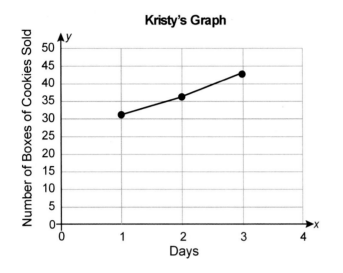

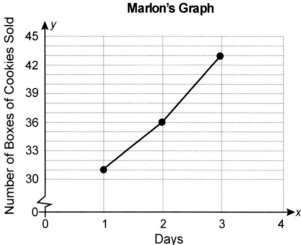

1. Use Kristy's graph to determine how many boxes of cookies were sold on Day 1 of the 8th grade bake sale.

2. Use Marlon's graph to determine how many boxes of cookies were sold on Day 1 of the 8th grade bake sale.

3. Use Kristy's graph to determine how many boxes of cookies were sold on Day 3 of the 8th grade bake sale.

4. Use Marlon's graph to determine how many boxes of cookies were sold on Day 3 of the 8th grade bake sale.

5. What is the same about the graphs?

6. What is different about the graphs?

7. Which graph should the students use to advertise the success of the bake sale?

An 8th grade class at Batchelder School held a bake sale to raise money for a class trip. Below are graphs that Kristy and Marlon created to show how many boxes of cookies their class sold each day for three days.

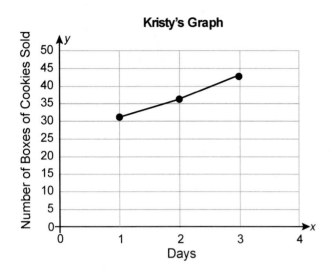

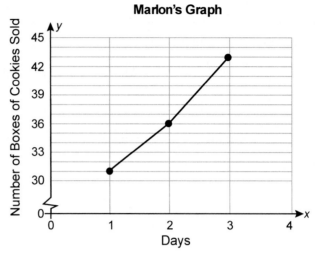

1. Use Kristy's graph to determine how many boxes of cookies were sold on Day 1 of the 8th grade bake sale.   **31 boxes**

2. Use Marlon's graph to determine how many boxes of cookies were sold on Day 1 of the 8th grade bake sale.   **31 boxes**

3. Use Kristy's graph to determine how many boxes of cookies were sold on Day 3 of the 8th grade bake sale.   **43 boxes**

4. Use Marlon's graph to determine how many boxes of cookies were sold on Day 3 of the 8th grade bake sale.   **43 boxes**

5. What is the same about the graphs?   **Kristy and Marlon accurately represented the same data on the graphs. The relationships between the x and y-values on the graphs are the same.**

6. What is different about the graphs?   **Kristy and Marlon used different scales on the y-axis for their graphs. On Marlon's graph, the increase in boxes of cookies sold over the three days appears to be greater compared to Kristy's graph. His scale did not begin at 0, so the increase is distorted.**

7. Which graph should the students use to advertise the success of the bake sale? **Marlon's graph.**

   Why?   **Marlon's graph makes the increase in sales appear more dramatic, so it would be more convincing than Kristy's graph.**

LESSON 1.4 Linear Functions

Suggested Pacing: 2 Days

This lesson introduces the term *function* and explores linear functions. Students analyze the relationship between two variables in a linear function and learn to identify the independent and dependent variables. Students relate linear functions to their different representations: tables, graphs and equations.

LESSON OBJECTIVES
- Students will explore linear functions represented in tables, graphs, and equations.
- Students will identify a function as a relationship where the value of one variable depends on the value of another variable.
- Students will be able to identify the independent and dependent variables in a given situation.
- Students will be able to identify a linear function as a relationship where the x and y variables are related in the same way across the function.
- Students will describe a linear function as a relationship whose graph is a straight line.

DAY 1	MATERIALS*	ESSENTIAL *ON YOUR OWN* QUESTIONS
Independent and Dependent Variables	In Class ■ Graph paper	Questions 2, 4, 5, 6, 10, 11
Calculating Mileage Reimbursement	On Your Own ■ Graph paper	

DAY 2	MATERIALS*	ESSENTIAL *ON YOUR OWN* QUESTIONS
Linear Functions		Questions 6, 7, 8, 12, 13, 14

* The Think Like a Mathematician Daily Record Sheet should be used daily

MATHEMATICALLY SPEAKING

- ▶ dependent variable
- ▶ function
- ▶ independent variable
- ▶ input variable
- ▶ linear function
- ▶ output variable

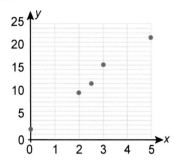

1. The point (3, 16) is the only one not on the straight line.

2. If you change the y-value of (3, 16) to 14, the point (3, 14) lies on the line.

3. If you keep the y-value at 16 and change the x-value to 3.5, the point (3.5, 16) lies on the line. (The equation is $y = 4x + 2$.)

4. Students may draw a line through the four points that *are* on the line and estimate the new points. They might notice that if the x-value increases by 1, the y-value increases by 4. They may see that if the x-value increases by 0.5, then the y-value increases by 2, and extrapolate from there.

DAY

1 TEACHING THE LESSON

Independent and Dependent Variables

Begin the lesson by discussing the meaning of the word function and introducing the term *mathematical function*. Tell students that they will begin to explore one type of function known as a linear function. Introduce the terms *independent variable* and *dependent variable*. These

---

LESSON 1.4 Linear Functions

➡ **Start It Off**

Plot the following points on graph paper: (0, 2); (2, 10); (2.5, 12); (3, 16); (5, 22).

1. Are they all on one straight line? If not, which is/are out of line with the rest?

2. If you keep the original x-value(s) of the point(s) in your answer to Part a, what new y-value would move each point onto the line?

3. If you instead keep the original y-value(s) of the point(s) in your answer to Part a, what new x-value would move each point onto the line?

4. How did you find the values in Questions 2 and 3?

What do you think of when you hear the word *function*?

• You may think of the eighth-grade dance that was held last week. Sometimes we call such social events "functions."

• You might also think of how a machine or process works, or "functions."

• There are also functions in algebra. In this section you have looked at how one variable is related to another. In a mathematical function, the value of one variable *depends on*, or "is a function of," the value of another. There are many types of mathematical functions. In this unit, you will be looking at *linear functions*.

Independent and Dependent Variables

Let's consider the conference that you are planning for Sports Mecca. At the conference, the participants will be given Sports Mecca T-shirts. Each shirt costs $10.00. The total cost of the shirts depends on the number of shirts purchased. There are two variables in this situation: The total cost of the shirts and the number of shirts purchased.

---

terms are very important since they demonstrate the relationship between the two variables in a function. Discuss the T-shirt problem and make sure students understand the relationship between the two variables. You may want to write the rule that defines this function as "total cost equals $10 times the number of T-shirts" or $C = 10n$. The cost depends on the number of T-shirts purchased. Have students complete Question 1 before moving on to ensure that they can identify the independent and dependent variables in a situation.

MATHEMATICALLY SPEAKING

▸ independent variable

▸ dependent variable

Notice that one variable depends on another: The total cost *depends* on the number of shirts purchased. The number of T-shirts that you purchase is the independent variable and their total cost is the dependent variable.

1. As a conference planner you will encounter many situations in which one variable depends on another. State the independent and dependent variables in each situation below. Explain your answers.

    a) The cost of Internet access is based on the number of minutes that are used.

    b) The number of people attending the conference determines the amount of bottled water that will be needed.

    c) The total cost of breakfast is based on the number of people attending the conference.

Calculating Mileage Reimbursement

The Sports Mecca conference will be held in Houston, Texas. You will pay each employee driving to the conference 40 cents per mile to cover part of the gas costs.

2. What are the two variables involved in determining the payment to attendees driving to the conference? State the independent and dependent variables.

MATHEMATICALLY SPEAKING

▸ function

▸ input variable

▸ output variable

Think of a function as a rule that tells us how one variable is related to another. You can think of the independent variable as the input variable and the dependent variable as the output variable. For each input variable, there is only one output variable. In this situation, you input the number of miles driven, use the rule or function to perform an operation on the input variable, and end up with the amount paid to cover the cost of driving that number of miles.

Have students talk with a partner about Question 3, to write a general rule to describe the relationship between the distance driven and the amount of money reimbursed. Have them write the rule both in words and with symbols. Have students share and discuss their responses as a class.

NOTE Students may choose any letter to represent the variables in their general rule. Emphasize with students that by convention, *x* usually represents the independent variable and *y* usually represents the dependent variable. This is important to note so that when graphing the function on a coordinate grid, students will accurately represent the variables on the appropriate axes.

Next have students complete Questions 4–7 where they complete a table and analyze the relationship between the two variables using the table.

Calculating Mileage Reimbursement

Have students discuss the independent and dependent variables in the given mileage reimbursement situation and describe how they relate to one another. Guide the discussion to help students recognize that the dependent variable depends on the independent variable. Have students do Question 2.

Next discuss the idea of function as a rule that relates two variables. Students may be familiar with function machines where they had related the variables as input and output values.

a) Write the rule in words.

b) Use letters for the variables and write the rule as an equation.

 NOTE In mathematics, it is common to use *x* to represent the independent variable and *y* to represent the dependent variable. In this case, *x* is usually shown on the horizontal axis and *y* on the vertical axis.

We can write the function rule for mileage reimbursement as the equation $y = 0.40x$, where *x* is the number of miles driven and *y* is the amount of money received.

Let's use a table to describe this function.

Mileage Reimbursement Chart	
Distance in Miles	Money Received ($)
0	0.00
1	0.40
2	0.80
3	1.20

4. Continue this table to include the reimbursement up to and including 10 miles.

5. Explain what (0, 0) means in this situation.

6. How are the two variables related?

 Hint See page 155

 **Differentiation**

Think Differently: Guide students who are experiencing difficulty with Questions 6 and 7, to focus on how the two variables in each situation relate to each other by asking:

• *Are both variables in the mileage reimbursement situation increasing? Decreasing?*

• *Are both variables in Ms. Tootyourhorn's situation increasing? Decreasing?*

 Talk Moves Encourage students to discuss Question 8a with a partner as well. Have pairs share their predictions with the class. Use talk moves, such as revoicing, and agree/disagree and why, to enrich the discussion. Encourage students to justify why they think their prediction is correct. Do not correct any predictions at this point. Have students compete Questions 8b and 8c independently and then compare the graphs to their predictions.

Summarizing Day 1

1. **a)** independent variable—number of minutes; dependent variable—cost

   b) independent variable—number of people attending the conference; dependent variable—amount of bottled water to order

   c) independent variable—number of people attending the conference; dependent variable—cost of breakfast.

2. The two variables are the distance driven and the amount of reimbursement. Since the amount of money depends on the distance driven, the dependent variable is the amount of reimbursement and the independent variable is the distance driven.

3. **a)** The number of miles driven multiplied by $0.40 equals the amount of money an attendee receives in reimbursement.

   b) $a = 0.40d$, where *a* equals the amount of money received and *d* represents the number of miles or distance traveled.

7. How does this relationship compare to the relationship between the variables in Ms. Tootyourhorn's graph from the previous lesson, shown here?

Graph 1
Ms. Tootyourhorn's Sales

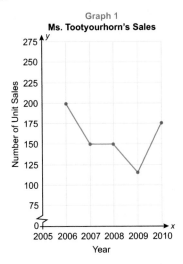

8. **a)** Look at your table of values. Predict what a graph of this function will look like.

   b) Graph the values in the table. Describe your graph.

   c) Predict how the graph will look if the driving distance increases beyond 10 miles.

9. If a conference participant drives 17 miles, how much money will he receive? Talk to your partner and answer Parts a, b, and c together.

   a) Explain how to use the function rule to find the answer.

   b) Explain how to use the table to find the answer.

   c) Explain how to use the graph to find the answer.

4.

Mileage Reimbursement Chart	
Distance in Miles (x)	**Money Received (y)**
0	$0.00
1	$0.40
2	$0.80
3	$1.20
4	$1.60
5	$2.00
6	$2.40
7	$2.80
8	$3.20
9	$3.60
10	$4.00

5. The coordinate pair (0, 0) means that for zero miles of travel, the reimbursement amount is zero dollars.

6. As the number of miles driven increases by 1, the amount of reimbursement increases by $0.40.

7. For the travel reimbursement situation, both variables increase at a steady rate. The relationship between variables in Graph 1 in Lesson 1.3 is not always the same. From 2009 to 2010, the number of unit sales increased. In other years, the number of sales remained constant or decreased. There was no consistent relationship between the variables of time and number of unit sales.

8. **a)** Answers will vary. However, the graph will look like a rising straight line from left to right, starting at the origin (0, 0). Do not tell students this at the start, but instead accept all answers and then have students create the graph and then compare the graph to their prediction.

   b) Graphs will vary depending on the scales used. Possible graph:

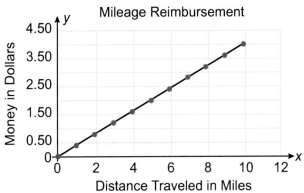

The graph is a straight line that begins at the origin (0, 0) and rises upwards from left to right.

c) The line of the graph will continue to rise from left to right in a straight line at the same steepness. So, for every 1-unit (mile) increase along the *x*-axis, there will be a $0.40 increase along the *y*-axis.

Summarize Day 1

Question 9 is a good *Wrap It Up* question for this lesson as it shows how students can use a table, a function rule, an equation or a graph to find an ordered pair in a linear relationship.

9. $6.80

  a) Substitute 17 for *d* in the rule $a = 0.40 \cdot d$ and solve the equation for *a*.

$$a = 0.40d$$
$$a = 0.40(17)$$
$$a = \$6.80$$

  b) Extend the table to 17 miles, or add the reimbursement amount for 10 miles and the reimbursement amount for 7 miles to determine the reimbursement amount for 17 miles.

  c) Extend the line on the graph. Locate 17 miles on the *x*-axis, and determine the value of the *y*-coordinate for the corresponding point on the given line.

Examining Linear Functions

MATHEMATICALLY SPEAKING
▶ linear function

The relationship used to determine travel reimbursement, $y = 0.40x$, is an example of a *linear function*. It is a function because it shows a relationship between two variables where one depends on the other, and because each input value produces only one output value. It is linear because its graph is a straight line.

Let's examine another function.

10. The cost of Internet access at the conference is $0.01 per minute.

  a) State the independent and dependent variables.

  b) Create a table and find the cost for 1, 2, 10, 20, 30, and 60 minutes of Internet access.

  c) Write a function rule using an equation to show the relationship between the variables. State what each variable in your equation represents.

  d) Predict whether or not this is a linear function. Then graph the function. Remember *x* is the independent variable and *y* is the dependent variable.

  e) Examine your graph. Was your prediction correct? Why or why not?

11. **a)** From the graph, find the approximate cost for 15, 40, and 90 minutes of Internet access.

  b) Use your rule to find the cost of 3 hours of Internet access.

  c) The conference center provides the option of paying $9.95 per day for Internet access. What discount is this compared to the per-minute charge for the same amount of Internet access?

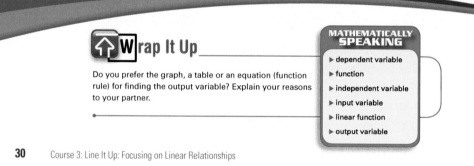

Wrap It Up

Do you prefer the graph, a table or an equation (function rule) for finding the output variable? Explain your reasons to your partner.

MATHEMATICALLY SPEAKING
▶ dependent variable
▶ function
▶ independent variable
▶ input variable
▶ linear function
▶ output variable

Linear Functions

Today's work is reinforcement of the new concepts introduced on Day 1. Students are given an opportunity to use the new concepts of dependent and independent variables, creating a table, writing an equation and graphing a function. They then use the graph, table and/or equation of a function to find additional ordered pairs. This practice, along with the On Your Own questions, is important in solidifying their understanding.

Question 10 provides another opportunity for students to explore a function graphically, using a table and using the function rule or equation. Students should be able to work independently at this point and then share answers as a class.

10. **a)** The independent variable is the number of minutes on the Internet, the dependent variable is the cost for the use of the Internet.

b)

Number of Minutes	Cost For Use of Internet
1	$0.01
2	$0.02
10	$0.10
20	$0.20
30	$0.30
60	$0.60

c) $y = 0.01x$, where x is the number of minutes of Internet access and y is the cost.

d) At this point students should be able to predict the function will be a straight line, thus a linear function.

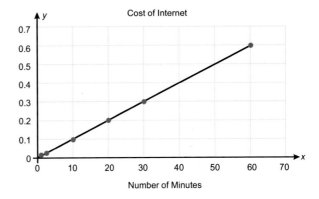

e) Yes, the graph is a straight line.

11. **a)** 15 minutes costs $0.15; 40 minutes costs $0.40; and 90 minutes costs $0.90.

b) 3 hours = 180 minutes;
$y = 0.01(180) = \$1.80$.

c) 1 day = 24 hours = 1440 minutes;
$y = 0.01(1440) = \$14.40$.

The discount is $14.40 − $9.95, or $4.45.

Wrap It Up

Student answers will vary. The most efficient method is the equation, especially if the numbers are large and the table is limited to the first few data points. Other students prefer the visual graph to find the y value.

Reflect

Use these questions to help you reflect on the lesson and plan for future instruction.

- What strategies do students use to help them identify the independent and dependent variables in a linear function?

- How comfortable are students with interpreting linear functions using tables, graphs and equations?

MATERIALS LIST
▶ Graph Paper
▶ Graphing Calculators

Write About It

1. a) Explain the difference between independent and dependent variables to a friend who was absent today.

   b) Describe a relationship that has an independent and a dependent variable. Label each variable.

2. Use the function rule you developed for travel reimbursement to answer the following:

   a) Heather will be driving 450 miles to the conference in Houston. What will be her travel reimbursement?

   b) Mike will be driving 605 miles. What will be his travel reimbursement?

Think Beyond

3. Consider the travel distances in Question 2. In which cities might Heather and Mike live?

? Hint
See page 155

4. Identify the independent and dependent variables in the following situations. Explain your answers.

   a) In a walkathon, a student collects $1.00 for every $\frac{1}{2}$ mile she walks.

   b) The number of boards used to create a fence determines the length of the fence.

   c) The number of conference attendees is related to the time of year the conference is held.

   d) The cost of an LCD projector, used to show presentations on large screens to groups, varies according to the amount of time rented.

   e) The size of a conference room determines its rental cost.

5. Create a situation and identify the independent and dependent variables.

On Your Own

1. Write About It

a) The independent variable is the input variable in a relationship and the dependent variable is the output variable. The dependent variable depends on the value of the independent variable.

b) Answers will vary but an example of such a relationship would be the number of T-shirts distributed to a soccer team depends on the number of players on the team. The independent variable is the number of players on the team and the dependent variable is the number of T-shirts.

2. a) Heather will receive
   450 • 0.40 = $180.

   b) Mike will receive
   605 • 0.40 = $242.

3. Think Beyond Answers will vary. Possible cities: Heather might live in New Orleans and Mike might live in Memphis.

4. a) The independent variable is the number of $\frac{1}{2}$-miles walked and the dependent variable is the amount of money the student collected. The amount of money collected depends on the number of $\frac{1}{2}$-miles walked.

   b) The independent variable is the number of boards used to create the fence and the dependent variable is the length of the fence. The length of the fence depends on the number of boards used.

   c) The independent variable is the time of the year the conference is held and the dependent variable is the number of people attending the conference. The number of people attending the conference depends on the time of year.

   d) The independent variable is the rental time for the LCD projector and the dependent variable is the cost for the rental. The cost of the rental depends on the amount of time the LCD projector was rented.

e) The independent variable is the size of the room and the dependent variable is the cost of the room. The cost of the room depends on its size.

5. Answers will vary. One example: the cost of lunch depends on the number of people eating lunch.

The independent variable is the number of people eating lunch and the dependent variable is the cost of the lunches.

6. Both *a* and *b* are linear relationships. (*c* represents a nonlinear relationship $y = x^3$.)

a)

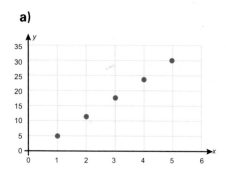

b)

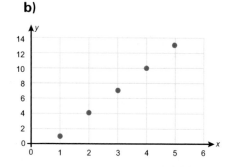

c)

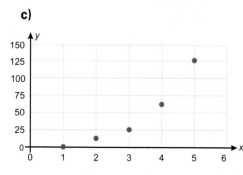

This is not linear, but rather forms a curve.

6. Predict which relationships are linear functions. Graph each relationship to check your predictions.

a)

x	y
1	6
2	12
3	18
4	24
5	30

b)

x	y
1	1
2	4
3	7
4	10
5	13

c)

x	y
1	1
2	8
3	27
4	64
5	125

7. a) The number of minutes, *m*, required to bake *n* medium-sized potatoes is equal to 3 minutes times the number of potatoes being baked plus an additional 2 minutes.

b) The independent variable is the number of potatoes being baked.

The dependent variable is the total number of minutes required to bake the potatoes.

c) No. A value of 0 for *n* (number of potatoes needed to bake) would not make sense. You would only want to determine the baking time if you were cooking one or more potatoes.

7. A microwave cooking guide indicates that the number of minutes, *m*, required to bake medium-sized potatoes at one time is given by the equation $m = 3n + 2$, (*n* represents the number of potatoes).

   a) Explain this function rule in words.

   b) Identify the independent and dependent variables for this function.

   c) Does it make sense to use a value of 0 for *n*? Explain.

   d) Does it make sense to use a value of $n = 8$ for this function? Explain.

   e) Create a table of values for this function. Does this relationship appear to be linear?

   f) Graph the function. From the graph, does this relationship appear to be linear?

8. The 8th grade trip this year will be to Quebec, Canada. Students know that the temperature in Canada is given in Celsius degrees. The linear functions $F = \frac{9}{5}C + 32$ and $C = \frac{5}{9}(F - 32)$ can be used to convert between degrees Fahrenheit, *F*, and degrees Celsius, *C*.

   a) Which function would be easiest to use to translate 70° Fahrenheit to the equivalent temperature in Celsius degrees?

   b) Identify the independent and dependent variables in the function you named in Part a.

   c) When they get to Quebec, the students see a sign that states that the temperature is 18° Celsius. Which function would be easiest to use to find this temperature in Fahrenheit degrees?

   d) What are the independent and dependent variables in the function you named in Part c?

   e) Use the appropriate function rule and determine the Celsius equivalent of 70°F and the Fahrenheit equivalent of 18°C.

 Think Beyond

9. a) With a partner, graph each of the functions in Question 7.

   b) What similarities or differences do you notice about these graphs?

f) Yes, this relationship is linear. The graph shows this function as a straight line.

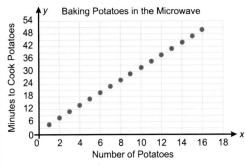

8. a) $C = \frac{5}{9}(F - 32)$

   b) The independent variable is degrees Fahrenheit; the dependent variable is degrees Celsius.

   c) $F = \frac{9}{5}C + 32$

   d) The independent variable is temperature in degrees Celsius; the dependent variable is temperature in degrees Fahrenheit.

   e) $C = \frac{5}{9}(70 - 32)$
   $C = \frac{5}{9}(38)$
   $C = \frac{190}{9}$
   $C = 21\frac{1}{9}$ or 21.1°

   $F = \frac{9}{5}(18) + 32$
   $F = \frac{162}{5} + 32$
   $F = 64\frac{2}{5}°$ or 64.4°

d) Yes, a value of 8 for *n* would make sense. It is possible that you would need to determine the baking time for 8 potatoes.

e) The relationship appears to be linear. There is a constant increase of 3 minutes for every increase of 1 potato.

n	m
1	5
2	8
3	11
4	14
5	17
6	20
7	23

Think Back

10. $\frac{8}{30} \cdot \frac{15}{28} =$

　A. $\frac{2}{7}$

　B. $10\frac{5}{21}$

　C. $\frac{23}{58}$

　D. $\frac{3}{21}$

11. **What went wrong?**

If cereal A is 55% sugar and cereal B is 70% sugar, how many ounces of sugar are in a bowl that contains 20 oz. of cereal A and 30 oz. of cereal B?

To answer this, Kerry added 0.55 + 0.70 = 1.25. She averaged this to get 0.625 or 62.5%. She then took 62.5% of 50 oz. of cereal (0.625 · 50) and got 31.25 oz. of sugar.

12. Find the pattern and fill in the blanks.

100, 98, 94, 88, 80, _____, _____, _____

What is the pattern?

13. Find the pattern and fill in the blanks.

−3, 9, −27, _____, _____

What is the pattern?

14. Solve for x: $3x + (2 − 5) = 7$

 **Think Beyond**

9.

a) $F = \frac{9}{5}C + 32$

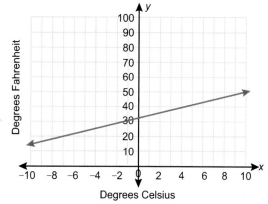

Degrees Fahrenheit

Degrees Celsius

$C = \frac{5}{9}(F − 32)$

b) They are similar in that both functions are linear and their graphs are rising lines from left to right.

They are different in that the function $F = \frac{9}{5}C + 32$ has a line that is steeper and crosses the y-axis at (0, 32). The function $C = \frac{5}{9}(F − 32)$ crosses the x-axis at (32, 0). (Notice the relationship of the x- and y-values for the x- and y-intercepts of these two functions.)

Think Back

10. **D.** $\frac{3}{21}$

11. Kerry needed to take the 0.55 • 20 oz. of cereal *A* and add that to 0.70 • 30 oz. of cereal *B* getting 11 oz. from *A* plus 21 oz. from *B* totaling 32 oz.

12. 100, 98, 94, 88, 80, <u>70, 58, 46</u>, the pattern is −2, −4, −6, −8, −10, etc. Subtract 2 more than the previous subtraction.

13. −3, 9, −27, <u>81</u>, <u>−243</u> The pattern is multiply the previous number by −3 to get the next number.

14. $x = 3.\overline{3}$

LESSON 1.5 Using a Graphing Calculator

Suggested Pacing: 2 Days

In this lesson students will learn to use the list and graph functions of the graphing calculator.

LESSON OBJECTIVES
- Students will use a graphing calculator to represent tables, graphs and equations.
- Students will apply their understanding of recursive and explicit rules to linear functions.
- Students will graph linear functions using a graphing calculator and be able to interpret them.

DAY 1	MATERIALS*	ESSENTIAL *ON YOUR OWN* QUESTIONS
Using a Graphing Calculator to Explore Linear Functions A Fast-Flapping Bird	**In Class** ▪ Graph paper ▪ Graphing calculators **On Your Own** ▪ Graph paper ▪ Graphing calculators	Question 3–6, 11, 12, 13

DAY 2	MATERIALS*	ESSENTIAL *ON YOUR OWN* QUESTIONS
Jogging Bonus		Question 1, 2, 7–10, 14, 15

* The Think Like a Mathematician Daily Record Sheet should be used daily

---

MATHEMATICALLY SPEAKING

▶ explicit rule ▶ recursive rule

LESSON 1.5 Using a Graphing Calculator

Start It Off

Let's Review A recursive rule is one that helps you find an output value from the previous output value. In the table below, you find each *y*, or output value, by adding 4 to the previous value of *y*. So the recursive rule for finding *y* is *New = Previous* + 4.

1.

x	1	2	3	4	5	6	7	8
y	4	8	12	16	20			

a) Fill in the table above using the recursive rule.

b) Find each recursive rule to complete the tables below.

x	1	2	3	4	5	6	7	8
y	8	16	24	32				

c)

x	1	2	3	4	5	6	7	8
y	25	24	23	22	21			

2. An explicit rule is one that directly relates an input variable with an output variable. In the table in 1a, the explicit rule is "multiply the input variable by 4 to find the output variable." As an equation, the rule is *y* = 4*x*. Write explicit rules in words and as equations to relate the input and output variables in 1b and 1c.

3. a) Explain the difference between a recursive rule and an explicit rule.

b) Which type of rule would be easier to use to find the 100ᵗʰ output value of a function? Why?

A graphing calculator is a great technology tool that helps you quickly form a visual picture of a function. We will be using graphing calculators throughout this unit to graph functions and make connections between equations, graphs and tables.

Start It Off

This is a review of the recursive and explicit rules from sixth and seventh grade. In this lesson, we will relate these rules to linear relationships.

1. a)

x	1	2	3	4	5	6	7	8
y	4	8	12	16	20	24	28	32

Recursive rule is *New = Previous* + 4

b)

x	1	2	3	4	5	6	7	8
y	3	5	7	9	11	13	15	17

Recursive rule is
New = Previous + 2

c)

x	1	2	3	4	5	6	7	8
y	−5	−4	−3	−2	−1	0	1	2

Recursive rule is
New = Previous + 1

2. The explicit rule for Part b is to multiply *x* by 2 and add, 1, or *y* = 2*x* + 1. The explicit rule for Part c is to subtract 6 from *x*, or *y* = *x* − 6.

3. When you use the recursive rule, you need to find a pattern in the output values and use the previous result to get the next value. When you use the explicit rule, you need to find the relationship between the input and the output values. The explicit rule would be the easiest to use to find the 100ᵗʰ output value since you would not have to find the 99 output values before it, to get the answer.

DAY 1 TEACHING THE LESSON

Using the Graphing Calculator to Explore Linear Functions

Begin this lesson by discussing with students the advantages of using a graphing calculator. Guide students through Steps 1–4. It is recommended that you model these steps together with students using an overhead projector, a document camera or an

LCD projector. Have students work in pairs; however, each student should have his or her own calculator.

 The directions in the student book are for the TI-84 calculator. If your students use a different calculator, consult the manual.

 Talk Moves Next, have students complete Questions 1–4 and compare their answers with a partner. As students work on these problems, circulate anad offer assistance if necessary. Have student pairs discuss any discrepancies as a class.

 Differentiation

Think Differently: You may wish to pair students with limited experience using a graphing calculator with more experienced ones to provide them with additional support.

Using the Graphing Calculator to Explore Linear Functions

Let's begin by graphing the mileage reimbursement function from Lesson 1.4.

Step 1. Enter the table values into the [LIST] function on your calculator. You will need to go to [STAT] and [EDIT] first to get to the list window shown below.

Step 2. Use the [STAT PLOT] function to graph the scatter plot.

Step 3. Enter Y = 0.4X into the equation editor by pressing the [Y=] button.

---

1. **a)** $40.00

   b) $52.00

   c) $80.00

   d) $70.00

2. **a)** 160 miles

   b) 105 miles

   c) 125 miles

3. There are infinite number of values in this table.

4. **a)** The recursive rule is add 0.40 to each reimbursement to get the next value, or *New = Previous* + 0.40.

   b) The explicit rule is the reimbursement cost, y, equals the number of miles, x, multiplied by 0.40, or $y = 0.40x$.

   c) The explicit rule is the equation of the function.

A Fast-Flapping Bird

5. **a)** The independent variable is the number of seconds.

   The dependent variable is the number of wing beats.

Step 4. Press the GRAPH button to display the graph of the function. How are the points on the scatter plot related to the graph of the line? Pressing TRACE will give you the x- and y-values at each point. (On the [FORMAT] menu be sure that [COORDINATES, AXIS], [LABELS], and [EXPRESSION] are turned ON.)

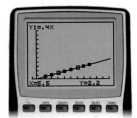 

For our mileage reimbursement function, the distance will generally be much greater than 10 miles. We can extend our graph by increasing the scales on the x-axis and y-axis to calculate reimbursements for greater distances such as 100, 130 or 200 miles. Use the window below to create a graph to use with Questions 1 and 2.

1. Use the graph to determine Ms. T's reimbursement if she drove:

   a) 100 miles

   b) 130 miles

   c) 200 miles

   d) 175 miles

2. Use the graph to determine Mr. B's travel distance if his reimbursement was:

   a) $64

   b) $42

   c) $50

6. a)

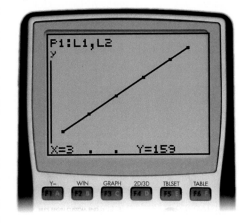

b) The explicit rule is $y = 53x$, where y is the number of wing beats and x is the number of seconds.

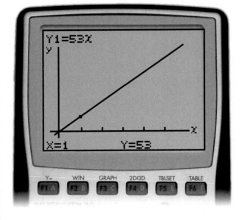

c) From the graph, the estimate for a minute should be around 3,200.

d) 3,180 beats per minute

7. a) one hour: $53 \cdot 60 \cdot 60 = 190{,}800$ beats per hour; one day: $53 \cdot 60 \cdot 60 \cdot 24 = 4{,}579{,}200$ beats per day; one week: $53 \cdot 60 \cdot 60 \cdot 24 \cdot 7 = 32{,}054{,}400$ beats per week

b) No, the hummingbird needs to rest so it is unlikely that it would be beating its wings constantly for an hour, a day or a week.

b)

Number of Seconds	Number of Wing Beats
1	53
2	106
3	159
4	212
5	265
6	318

c) The recursive rule is to add 53 to each number of wing beats to get the next value, or *New = Previous* + 53.

d) Yes, it will be linear. As x increases by 1 unit, y increases by 53 units, so the points will lie in a straight line.

3. On your calculator, you can also view a table of *x*- and *y*-values for a given function. Press the TABLE button. Scroll down on the table. How many values can you find on this table?

4. a) What is the recursive rule for this linear function?

   b) What is the explicit rule?

   c) How is the explicit rule related to the equation of the linear function?

A Fast-Flapping Bird!

A ruby-throated hummingbird beats its wings 53 times per second. We are interested in finding the total number of wing beats over a given period of time. Use this information to answer Questions 5, 6, and 7.

5. a) Identify the independent and dependent variables.

   b) Create a table of values for 1 through 6 seconds.

   c) Write the recursive rule for the increase in the total number of wing beats each additional second.

   d) Predict whether the graph of this relationship will be linear. Explain.

6. a) Graph this relationship using the table and your graphing calculator. Follow steps 1 and 2 above.

   b) Write an explicit rule for this function. Use this equation and follow steps 3 and 4 to graph the function.

   c) Use your graph to approximate the number of times a hummingbird beats its wings in one minute. (You may need to adjust your scales to do this.)

   d) From the table of values on your calculator, scroll down to find the exact number of wing beats in one minute.

Summarize Day 1

To summarize the day, ask students to consider how the recursive rule can help determine the explicit rule in the examples they have already used, and how it can help predict that the relationship is linear.

Students should recognize that the recursive rule shows a constant increase in the *y*-values for each 1 unit increase in the *x*-values. This indicates that the points will lie on a straight line when graphed. The number, or the value added each time, is the unit increase; it is also the coefficient of *x* in the explicit rule equation.

DAY 2 TEACHING THE LESSON

Jogging Bonus

Introduce students to the jogging trails scenario for Sports Mecca employees.

Have students work with a partner to complete Questions 19–26. Remind students that they must decide with their partner on an appropriate window for the graphing calculator for Question 20.

Differentiation

Think Differently: For students having difficulty deciding on an appropriate graphing calculator window for Question 11, ask:

- *What information will you need to consider to determine the minimum and the maximum values of the x- and the y-axes on the graphing calculator window?*

- *Which variable in this situation will be represented on the x-axis and which variable will be represented on the y-axis?*

7. **a)** Find the number of times a hummingbird beats its wings in an hour, a day and a week using the equation or function rule.

b) Is your answer to Part a realistic? Explain.

Jogging Bonus

Sports Mecca encourages its employees to exercise and, of course, to wear Sports Mecca sportswear while doing so. The conference center includes jogging trails. The welcome packet will include a chart that indicates the number of calories a participant can burn while jogging 30 minutes.

Jogger's Weight in Pounds	Calories Burned in 30 Minutes of Jogging
100	225
120	270
140	315
160	360
180	
200	
220	

Use the scenario and table above to answer Questions 8–16.

8. Describe in words how the number of calories burned is related to a jogger's weight.

9. What is the dependent variable in this situation? What is the independent variable?

10. Fill in the missing values on the chart.

11. Graph the relationship using your graphing calculator. Follow steps 1 and 2 above. Talk to your partner about appropriate scales for your *x*- and *y*-axes.

12. **a)** Write a recursive rule for the number of calories burned for each additional twenty pounds using your table.

b) Find the recursive rule for the number of calories burned for *every 1 pound*.

Hint
See page 155

10.

Weight in Pounds	Calories Burned in 30 Minutes of Jogging
100	225
120	270
140	315
160	360
180	405
200	450
220	495

11.

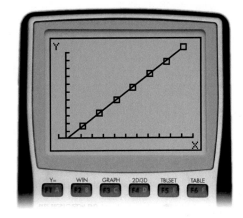

12. **a)** The rule is to add 45 calories burned for every 20 pounds increase in weight.

b) The recursive rule can be found by dividing 45 by 20. The recursive rule is to add 2.25 calories burned for every 1 pound increase in weight.

13. *y* = 2.25*x*, where *x* is the number of pounds a person weighs and *y* is the total number of calories burned.

14. **a)** Answers will vary. Students might indicate that they will use an [XMIN] of 100 and an [XMAX] of 220, and a [YMIN] of 225 and a [YMAX] of 495 (the actual [MAXES] and [MINS] from the table). An ⨯ and a ʏꜱᴄɪ of 20 would work.

Talk Moves Discuss student responses. Use talk moves, such as repeat/rephrase and adding on, to clarify student ideas and deepen their understanding.

8. As weight increases, the number of calories burned increases.

9. The dependent variable is the number of calories burned.

The independent variable is the weight in pounds.

b) Yes, the points on the scatter plot are also on the graph of the function using the equation. There are also additional points on the new graph that lie on the line.

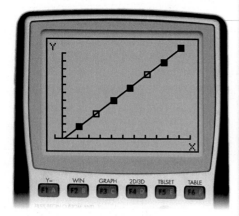

15. A person weighing 135 pounds will burn 303.75 calories.

A person weighing 190 pounds will burn 427.5 calories.

A person weighing 240 pounds will burn 540 calories.

---

13. Write the explicit rule or equation for the relationship between jogger's weight and calories burned.

 Hint
See page 155

14. Now graph this function on your graphing calculator using the explicit rule and the Y= button.

   a) Talk to your partner and decide on an appropriate window to use for this graph.

   b) Is this graph the same as the graph you created in Question 11? Explain why or why not.

15. Using your graphing calculator, find the number of calories burned by joggers who weigh 135 pounds, 190 pounds and 240 pounds.

Try This! There is an easier way to find *x*- and *y*-values than by scrolling down the table to these large numbers.

Go to [TBLSET]. Set the [TBLSTART] value at 100 and set increments for the table at 5. Go to [TABLE] and find the values.

W rap It Up

Talk to your partner and discuss the difference between recursive and explicit rules. Talk about how the explicit rule is related to the equation of the function.

MATHEMATICALLY SPEAKING

► explicit rule
► recursive rule

W rap It Up

Students should state that the recursive rule shows how to find the next output value from the previous one. In the examples that students have encountered, they have been adding a specific number to the prior value. The explicit rule is the equation of the function that relates the dependent and the independent variables. It can be used to find any output value, when given an input.

Reflect

Use these questions to help you reflect on the lesson and plan for future instruction.

- Are students able to represent linear functions in a table, as an equation, or on a graph?

- How comfortable are students interpreting linear functions using tables, graphs and equations?

- Do students understand the difference between the recursive and the explicit rule?

- Can students find the recursive and explicit rule of a function?

See corresponding assessments in Assessment Resources.

MATERIALS LIST
► Graph Paper
► Graphing Calculators

Write About It

1. Write several things you know about linear functions. Then add this term, and the new vocabulary terms you used to write about linear functions, to the concept map that your group created in Lesson 1.1.

2. How is a linear function related to a linear equation?

3. Find the recursive and explicit rules for each of the following functions.

a)
Number of Gallons of Gas Used	Number of Miles Driven
1	23.2
2	46.4
3	69.6
4	92.8
5	116.0

b)
Number of People at the Conference	Total Cost of Lunch in Dollars
25	250
26	260
27	270
30	300
35	350
40	400

Hint
See page 155

c)
Time in Hours	Distance in Miles Jogged
0	0
0.5	3
1	6
1.5	9
2	12

Hint
See page 155

Students may also state that linear functions have a constant rate of change. When represented in a table, the increase in the dependent (output) variable is constant for each unit increase in the independent (input) variable. This idea will be further developed in future lessons.

Possible addition to concept map for algebra:

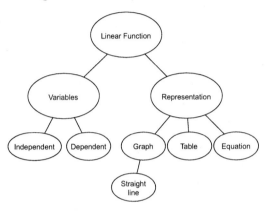

2. A linear function is a linear relationship between variables. A linear equation is the symbolic representation of a linear function. Note that the graph of a linear function, or its symbolic representation in the form of an equation, is a straight line.

3. a) recursive rule: *New = Previous + 23.2*; explicit rule: $y = 23.2x$, where y is the number of miles and x is the number of gallons of gas.

b) recursive rule: *New = Previous + 10*; explicit rule: $y = 10x$, where y is the cost of lunch and x is the number of people.

c) recursive rule: *New = Previous + 6*; explicit rule: $y = 6x$, where y is the distance jogged and x is the number of hours.

On Your Own

Write About It

1. Answers will vary. Student responses should include the following key ideas related to linear functions:

• Linear functions have independent and dependent variables.

• They are represented as a straight line on a graph.

• A linear function can be represented by a table, a graph or an equation.

We know that 1 in. = 2.54 cm. We can convert inches into centimeters using the equation $y = 2.54x$, where x is the number of inches and y is the corresponding number of centimeters. Use this relationship to answer Questions 4 through 6.

4. **a)** Is this a linear relationship?

   b) Enter this equation into your graphing calculator.

   c) Press GRAPH and compare the graph you get with the one below.

5. Describe what the window to the right means. Set a window that will give you more information about the relationship between centimeters and inches.

6. What values so you think are used for the display window shown? Explain the screen.

4.

This question is an important exercise for students to complete because it helps reinforce how to set the window on the graphing calculator. They will need to be able to do this throughout the year. If students do not have access to a graphing calculator at home, work through this problem in class.

a) Yes, it is a linear relationship.

b) Plot2   Plot3
\Y1 = 2.54X
\Y3 =
\Y4 =
\Y5 =
\Y6 =
\Y7=

c) Graphs will vary depending on the window setting of the graphing calculator.

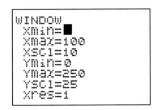

**Think
Beyond**

10. If this company's annual expenses are $2 million, would you invest in this company? Why or why not?

11. Mark keeps track of his math quiz scores in the table below.

Quiz Number	Score Based on 100 Points
1	61
2	61
3	64
4	68
5	72
6	73
7	75
8	80
9	82

Create two different graphs from this table:

a) One that accurately represents the Mark's math scores.

b) One that could be misleading. Explain why your graph is misleading.

Possible graph:

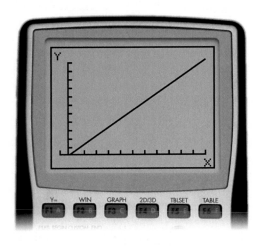

```
WINDOW
 Xmin=■
 Xmax=100
 XSCl=10
 Ymin=0
 Ymax=250
 YSCl=25
 Xres=1
```

Both graphs are straight lines, rising from left to right. The graph above has a line that appears to be less steep than the one given due to the scale that was set in the window.

10. **a)** Describe the situation when $t = 0$.

  b) What are the independent and dependent variables in this function? Explain your choices.

  c) How much money will they be able to donate if they sell 100 tickets?

  d) How many tickets must be sold to cover the cost of the band?

11. **a)** Create a table of values to find the amount of money collected for 50, 60, 70, 80, 90, and 100 tickets sold. Find the recursive rule for the amount of money collected. Predict whether the function is linear.

  b) Use your graphing calculator to graph the function using the equation. Does the function appear to linear?

 Think Back

12. A recipe requires 3 cups of oatmeal for every 48 cookies. How many cups of oatmeal would Miranda need to make 80 cookies?

13. Paul and Joanna own 15 shares of a stock. The value of each share increased by $3\frac{1}{2}$ dollars last year. How much more would they have gained if they had owned 35 shares of this stock?

14. Each side of a regular pentagon is 13.4 feet long. What is its perimeter?

15. Write an equation for the following question and solve.

  If the price of 1 dozen eggs is $3.06, what is the price of 1 egg?

16. Which of the following is NOT equivalent to the expression below:

$$|5 - 8|$$

  A. $|8 - 5|$

  B. $8 - 5$

  C. $-(5 - 8)$

  D. $(5 - 8)$

Optional Technology Lesson for this section available at
www.mymathinnovations.com

---

5. xmin $= -1$. The minimum value on the x-axis is -1.

  xmax $= 10$. The maximum value on the x-axis is 10.

  xscl $= 1$. The distance between tick marks on the x-axis is 1.

  ymin $= -1$. The minimum value on the y-axis is -1.

  ymax $= 10$. The maximum value on the y-axis is 10.

  yscl $= 1$. The distance between tick marks on the y-axis is 1.

 NOTE
Discussion of xres $= 1$ is optional. For your information, xres represents the value of the pixel resolution; 1 means that functions are evaluated and graphed at each pixel on the x-axis, whereas 8 means that functions are evaluate and graphed at every 8th pixel on the x-axis.

Windows students set will vary. Possible window:

```
WINDOW
 Xmin=10
 Xmax=200
 Xscl=20
 Ymin=-10
 Ymax=450
 Yscl=40
 Xres=■
```

6. Answers will vary. Possible response:
   ```
   Xmin = 0
   Xmax = 12
   XSCl = 1
   Ymin = 0
   Ymax = 50
   YSCl = 5
   Xres = 1
   ```

7. The screen is similar to an input/output table showing pairs of values. Each value in the Y1 column of the table increases by 2.54 cm for every 1-inch increase in the x column. Therefore, the value of Y1 when x is 11 inches will be 27.94 cm.

8. a) The length of the femur bone is the independent variable. Height is the dependent variable. If you know the length of the femur, then you can predict the height.

   b) i.) 6 feet

   c) 5 feet 8 inches

   d) No, it does not make sense to use 0 for T. While the femur bone may vary in size from person to person, it always has some length. Therefore, 0 would not be appropriate.

   e) No, it does not make sense to use a value of 40 for T. Using the rule, a femur bone of 40 inches would result in an overall height of almost 10 feet. Since there is no record of a human male being that tall, it would not make sense to use 40 for T.

9. This relationship is linear. The graph forms a straight line.

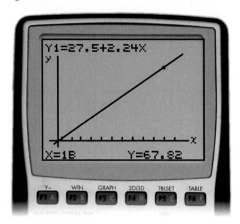

10. a) When $t = 0$, it represents that no tickets have been sold. Since the band charges $300 to perform, the students at Dodd Middle School have a negative cash flow of $300.

    b) The independent variable is the number of tickets sold. The dependent variable is the amount of money raised for the benefit, which depends linearly on the number of tickets sold.

    c) $300

    d) When they sell 50 tickets, the students will have made enough to cover the cost of the band, but not make any money for the benefit.

11. a)

Number of Tickets	Amount of Money
50	$0
60	$60
70	$120
80	$180
90	$240
100	$300

The pattern is to add $60 for every 10 tickets sold. So the recursive rule is to add $6 for every ticket sold. Because there is a constant increase, students should predict that the function is linear.

b) Yes, the relationship is linear. The graph is a straight line, rising from left to right.

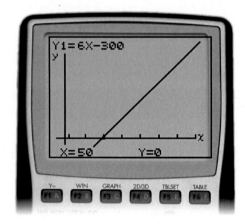

12. 5 cups

13. $70 more

14. 67 feet

15. $12e = 3.06$; $0.255 per egg

16. D.

Optional Technology Lesson for this section available at **www.mymathinnovations.com**

Sum It Up

In this section, you thought about the concepts of algebra and created a concept map to link concepts and terms. Then you learned about functions and the different ways to describe them, such as equations, verbal rules, tables and graphs. You connected these representations by looking at functions using all of these representations. You found recursive rules from tables and created explicit rules that defined these functions. You learned how to use a graphing calculator to create graphs of functions from both tables and equations.

The following are important mathematical ideas:

Interpreting Graphs

- Graphs provide a visual representation of how one variable is related to another variable.

- Line segments are sometimes used to connect points on a graph of discrete points in order to show a trend in the data.

- It is important to look at the scales on the x- and y-axes when interpreting graphs.

- Changing the scale on an axis can result in a misleading graph.

The Sum It Up summarizes the important mathematics students should have learned in this section. Encourage students to use this Sum It Up as they complete the Study Guide and prepare for quizzes and tests.

Functions

■ A function is a rule that describes how one variable relates to another variable. In a function, one variable depends on another and for every input value, there is only one output value.

■ A linear function is represented graphically by a line.

■ The independent variable, usually the *x*-coordinate of a point on a graph, is the variable upon which you perform operations.

■ The dependent variable, usually the *y*-coordinate of a point on the graph, is the output of a function. It depends on the value of the independent variable. It is the result of performing operations on the independent variable as part of the function rule.

Example: The relationship between the circumference of a circle and its diameter is that the circumference, *C*, is equal to the product of the length of the diameter, *d*, and the constant π.

■ The equation representing this function is $C = \pi d$.

■ The independent variable, or input variable, is length of the diameter, *d*. The dependent variable, or output variable, is the circumference, *C*. Circumference depends on the length of the diameter and will change as the length of the diameter changes.

MATHEMATICALLY SPEAKING

Do you know what these mathematical terms mean?

▶ compression bar	▶ linear function	▶ recursive rule
▶ dependent variable	▶ line graph	▶ scale
▶ explicit rule	▶ links	▶ variable
▶ function	▶ nodes	▶ x-axis
▶ independent variable	▶ output variable	▶ y-axis
▶ input variable		

Study Guide

Relationships on the Coordinate Plane

Part 1. What did you learn?

1. **a.** Revise your concept map from Lesson 1.1 to include new information you have learned about algebra in this section. Use the Mathematically Speaking vocabulary from the Sum It Up to help you.

   b. Use your concept map to explain what algebra is to someone who thinks it is just "using letters instead of numbers." Include all parts of your map.

2. The Sports Mecca conference planners will host an evening social event. They need to plan the dinner, dancing and raffle. Here is what they know about each of these:

   • The restaurant charges $27.50 per meal served at dinner.

   • The DJ charges $800 to play music for the entire evening.

   • There are 40 prizes that will be raffled off at random times throughout the evening. The raffle will continue until all prizes have been given away.

   a. Sketch a graph of each situation. Label the *x*- and *y*-axes of each graph with the variables of each situation.

   b. Is there a linear relationship between the variables in each situation? Why or why not?

3. Emma, Fran, Geri and Holley are pitchers on four different softball teams. They compared the number of walks and hits they had during their most recent game.

   • Fran gave up the same number of hits as Geri.

   • Emma gave up as many walks as Holley but fewer hits than Holley.

   • Geri gave up the most walks.

Study Guide

1. **a.** Student answers will vary.

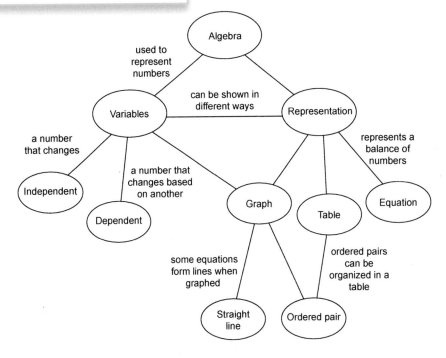

b. Student answers will vary. One possible answer: Algebra involves making generalizations and writing rules about patterns and relationships. It also involves working with writing, solving, and graphing equations.

2. a.

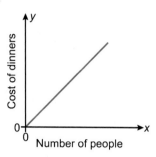

Cost of dinners / Number of people

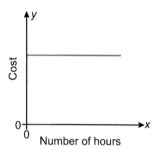

Cost / Number of hours

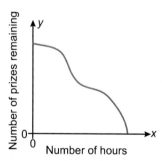

Number of prizes remaining / Number of hours

b. Student answers will vary. One possible answer: There is a linear relationship between the number of people and the total cost of the dinners because the total cost goes up by $27.50 for each additional meal served. There is a linear relationship between the number of hours the DJ plays and the total cost because the total cost is constant at $800. There is not necessarily a linear relationship between the number

The four pitchers graphed their data on the graph below.

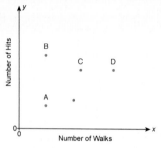

Number of Hits / Number of Walks

Match each point to the correct pitcher.

4. Jon's parents said that if he improved his math grade this term, they would buy him a new baseball glove. Jon's four quiz scores over the term were 75, 78, 80, and 82.

   a. Is each graph below an accurate representation of Jon's quiz grades?

   b. Which one of the graphs below would be more likely to convince Jon's parents to buy him a new baseball glove? Why?

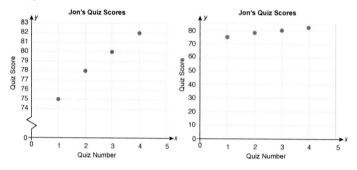

Jon's Quiz Scores

of hours and the number of raffle prizes remaining, since the prizes are distributed randomly throughout the evening.

3. Point A represents Emma, Point B represents Holley, Point C represents Fran and Point D represents Geri.

5. Match the table in column I to a graph in column II, a recursive rule in Column III, and an explicit rule in column IV.

Column I	Column II	Column III	Column IV
A. <table><tr><td>x</td><td>y</td></tr><tr><td>-2</td><td>-1</td></tr><tr><td>-1</td><td>-0.5</td></tr><tr><td>0</td><td>0</td></tr><tr><td>1</td><td>0.5</td></tr><tr><td>2</td><td>1</td></tr></table>	**a.**	**I.** New = Previous + $\frac{1}{2}$	**i.** $y = {}^{-}x$
B. <table><tr><td>x</td><td>y</td></tr><tr><td>-2</td><td>2</td></tr><tr><td>-1</td><td>1</td></tr><tr><td>0</td><td>0</td></tr><tr><td>1</td><td>-1</td></tr><tr><td>2</td><td>-2</td></tr></table>	**b.**	**II.** New = Previous + 2.5	**ii.** $y = 0.5x$
C. <table><tr><td>x</td><td>y</td></tr><tr><td>-2</td><td>-5</td></tr><tr><td>-1</td><td>-2.5</td></tr><tr><td>0</td><td>0</td></tr><tr><td>1</td><td>2.5</td></tr><tr><td>2</td><td>5</td></tr></table>	**c.**	**III.** New = Previous − 1	**iii.** $y = 2.5x$

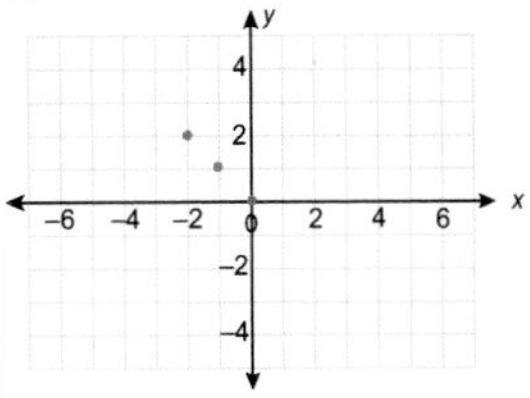

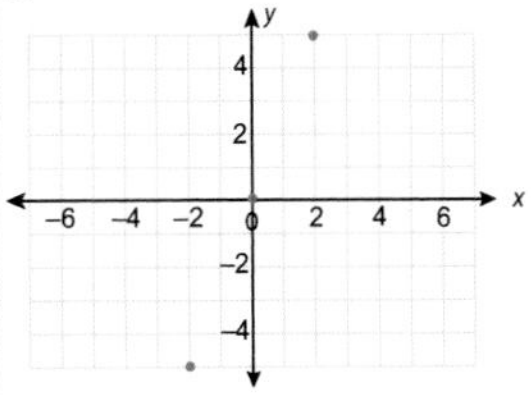

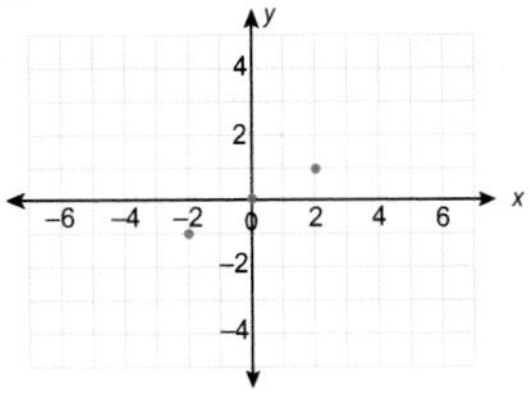

6. Identify the independent variable and the dependent variable in each of the following situations.

   a. In a dance-a-thon, an eighth grader at Silver Lake Middle School collects $5.00 for each hour he dances.

   b. The number of books in a packing box determines the weight of the box.

   c. The number of people at the ski resort is related to the number of inches of snow that fell the week before.

4. a. Yes, each graph is an accurate representation of the data since each data point corresponds to one of Jon's quiz scores.

   b. Student answers will vary. One possible answer: The graph on the left would most likely convince Jon's parents to buy him a new baseball glove since the steady and sharp increase in the points (due to the compression bar) makes it appear that Jon has improved his quiz scores quite dramatically.

5. a, f, g, k

   b, d, i, j

   c, e, h, l

7. The cost of using a telescope at a scenic look-out is $0.25 per minute.

   a. Create a table and find the cost for 1, 2, 3, 4, 5, 10 and 20 minutes.

   b. Write a function rule to show the relationship between the variables. State what the variables in your equation represent.

   c. Predict whether or not you think this is a linear function. Then graph the function. Remember *x* is the independent variable and *y* is the dependent variable.

   d. Is this a linear function? Why or why not?

Part 2. What went wrong?

8. Meena made a graph of the Sports Mecca mileage reimbursement. After she made her graph, she said, "The relationship used to determine travel allowance is not linear since the graph is not a straight line. It is a slanted line." What doesn't Meena understand about straight lines? What could you do or say to help her understand?

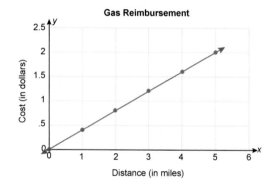

Gas Reimbursement

6. a. The number of hours danced is the independent variable. The total money collected is the dependent variable.

    b. The number of books is the independent variable. The weight of box is the dependent variable.

    c. The number of inches of snow is the independent variable. The number of people at a ski resort is the dependent variable.

7. a.

Number of Minutes	Total Cost
1	0.25
2	0.50
3	0.75
4	1.00
5	1.25
10	2.50
20	5.00

b. $0.25n = t$ where n is the number of minutes and t is the total cost.

c. This should be a linear function, since it is of the form $y = mx$.

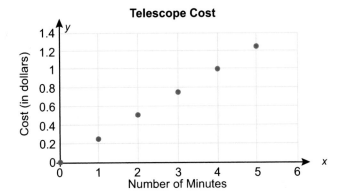

Telescope Cost

d. Yes, this is a linear function since the total cost increases by 25 cents every time the number of minutes increases by 1.

8. Student answers will vary. One possible answer: Meena seems to think that straight means horizontal or vertical, but this is not true. Horizontal and vertical are types of straight lines, but they are not the only types. Straight lines can be slanted as well. A line (or line segment) is straight if its steepness is constant.

Analyzing Change

Exploring Rate of Change

Suggested Pacing: 2 Days

In this lesson, students take a closer look at the relationship between independent and dependent variables. They use tables and graphs to analyze situations and determine if the relationship represents a constant rate of change.

LESSON OBJECTIVES

- Students will distinguish between varying rates of change and constant rates of change in given situations.

- Students will explore the relationship between the variables in a given situation by analyzing tables and graphs. They will determine whether the relationship represents a constant rate of change.

- Students will identify linear relationships as having a constant rate of change.

DAY 1	MATERIALS*	ESSENTIAL *ON YOUR OWN* QUESTIONS
Rate of Change	In Class ■ Graph paper ■ Rulers On Your Own ■ Graph paper	Questions 2, 3, 8, 10, 16–20

DAY 2	MATERIALS*	ESSENTIAL *ON YOUR OWN* QUESTIONS
Constant vs. Varying Rate of Change		Questions 1, 4–7, 9, 11–14

*The Think Like a Mathematician Daily Record Sheet should be used daily

---

MATHEMATICALLY SPEAKING

- discrete
- increasing function
- rate
- rate of change
- scatter plot
- unit rate

Analyzing Change

In this section, you will take a closer look at functions. You will study how a function's output changes when the input variable changes. You will also learn about the rate of change and a very important concept called slope.

LESSON 2.1 Exploring Rate of Change

➡ Start It Off

1. The 2006 winner of Nathan's Hot Dog Eating Contest was Takeru "The Tsunami" Kobayashi. He ate almost 60 hot dogs in 12 minutes. Write this rate as a ratio in fraction form. Then write the ratio so that the denominator is 1 minute.

2. Alvetina Ivanova from Russia won the seven-mile Annual Falmouth Road Race in August 2006. She finished with a time of about 35 minutes. Write this rate as a ratio in fraction form. Then write the ratio so that the denominator is 1 minute.

3. Ty Cobb is the all-time leader of batting averages. His average is .367. A batting average is the ratio of the number of hits to the number of times at bat. Explain what .367 means.

At the conference, Sports Mecca wants to have e-mail and Internet access for all participants. Three conference centers have submitted bids for the cost of this service for the 10-day conference. You must decide which company offers the best deal.

The Execustay Conference Center charges $10 a day for Internet use.

The Corporate Connection Conference Center increases the charge for Internet service each day of a conference because they find that use increases over the life of a conference. Each day, they charge $2 times the day number of the conference. So, on day 1, they charge $2 · 1, or $2; on day 2, they charge $2 · 2, or $4; on day 3, they charge $2 · 3, or $6; and so on.

Section 2: Analyzing Change • Lesson 2.1   **51**

 Talk Moves   Read with students about the different business centers' bids for Internet access. Working with a partner, have students complete Question 1. Discuss predictions as a class. Use talk moves, such as agree/disagree and why, to promote further justification and support for predictions made. Learn more about the "talk moves" in the Teaching and Learning Strategies on page T5.

Have students individually complete Questions 2–5 and then discuss responses as a class. When discussing Question 5, emphasize that a scatter plot is used when the data you are graphing represents numbers that are discrete, or distinct.

➡ Start It Off

Answers:

1. $\dfrac{60 \text{ hot dogs}}{12 \text{ minutes}} = \dfrac{5 \text{ hot dogs}}{1 \text{ minute}}$

2. $\dfrac{7 \text{ miles}}{35 \text{ minutes}} = \dfrac{0.2 \text{ mile}}{1 \text{ minute}}$

3. Ty averages 367 hits for every 1,000 times at bat.

Differentiation

Think Differently: To further help students distinguish discrete data from continuous data, ask "Can you think of situations in previous lessons where the input data you were graphing represented a discrete, or distinct, set of numbers?" ELL students will benefit from a physical tracing of the graph to determine whether or not it is continuous or discrete. Show that, for a continuous set, you can trace along the values of the set along a number line or graph without raising your pencil. For a discrete set, you must repeatedly lift your pencil to mark each point.

Offer these additional situations and ask students to determine whether the input data represents a discrete or continuous set of numbers.

- The number of people attending a county fair each day over a period of one week (discrete)

- The distance a runner travels over a 3-hour period (continuous)

- The number of cans of food a 5th grade class collects each day over a period of two weeks (discrete)

- The length of one's foot from birth to age 10 (continuous)

- A person's shoe size from birth to age 10 (discrete)

The Super Business Center charges $1 for the first day, and then double the amount of the previous day for each additional day. This means they charge $2 the second day, $4 the third day, $8 the fourth day, and so forth.

1. With a partner, make a prediction about which of the Internet providers will be the best choice for the 10-day conference. Explain your choice.

Let's look at the fees charged for Internet access by Corporate Connection Conference Center.

2. First consider the variables:

    a) What are the two variables involved?

    b) Which variable is the independent, or input, variable?

    c) Which variable is the dependent, or output, variable?

    d) Explain the relationship between the variables.

3. Now make a table and graph for this situation. Complete the table below to find the Corporate Connection Conference Center's Internet access fees.

Corporate Connection Fees	
Day Number	Daily Cost
1	$2
2	$4
3	$6
4	$8
5	
6	
7	
8	
9	
10	

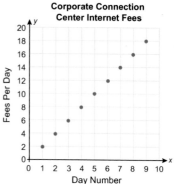

Corporate Connection Center Internet Fees

Let us assume that all three of the Internet access providers only charge by the whole day. So there is no reduced rate for accessing the Internet for only part of a day.

4. Should we connect the points on the graph for the Corporate Connection Conference Center? Why or why not?

Next have students individually complete Questions 6–8. When discussing responses, emphasize that the rate of change is the ratio of the change in the dependent (output) variable to the change in the independent (input) variable.

 Talk Moves Have students work with a partner to complete Questions 9–10. Discuss responses as a class. Use talk moves, such as repeat/rephrase and adding on, to clarify students' understanding. Guide the discussion to help students recognize the following:

- A situation where there is an increase in the dependent variable (*y*-variable) as the independent variable (*x*-variable) increases is represented graphically as points rising from left to right.

- A situation where there is an increase of 0 (no change) in the dependent variable (*y*-variable) as the independent variable (*x*-variable) increases is represented graphically as a horizontal line. This is also a constant rate of change of 0.

1. Predictions will vary. Look for justification and sound reasoning that appropriately support student predictions.

2. a) The variables are the day number and cost per day for Internet use.

b) The independent variable is the day number, which corresponds to the number of consecutive days that the center is rented.

c) The dependent variable is the cost per day for Internet use.

d) The cost of Internet use increases by $2 for each day the center is rented. The daily cost is two times the day number.

3. Corporate Connection Fees

Day Number	Cost
1	$2
2	$4
3	$6
4	$8
5	$10
6	$12
7	$14
8	$16
9	$18
10	$20

4. The data points are not connected by line segments because the set of numbers representing the independent variable (number of days) is discrete or distinct. In the above example, the center cannot be rented for $1\frac{1}{2}$ days, so there should not be a data point at $1\frac{1}{2}$ days.

5. Mathematicians call this graph a scatter plot because ordered pairs, which represent data from a situation, are plotted on a coordinate grid and are "scattered" across the coordinate grid. We do not connect points on a scatter plot.

Rate of Change

6. a) The dependent variable increases by $2.00 as the independent variable increases by 1 day.

b) $\frac{\$2.00}{1 \text{ day}}$. The rate of change is $2.00 per day.

c) Possible response:
You could find the rate of change in a table by looking at how the values of one variable change in relation to the other. The rate of change is the ratio of the change in the daily cost and the change in the day number.

7. Yes, the relationship is linear. The points on the graph lie on a straight line even though they are not actually connected by line segments. Also, the rate of change is constant ($2 increase for each 1-day increase).

8. The cost for Internet use increases by $2 each day, from the previous day's cost.

New = Previous + 2.

The explicit rule written as an equation is $y = 2x$, with x representing the day number and y representing the cost for the given day in dollars.

9.

Executstay		Super Business	
Day	Cost	Day	Cost
1	$10	1	$1
2	$10	2	$2
3	$10	3	$4
4	$10	4	$8
5	$10	5	$16
6	$10	6	$32
7	$10	7	$64
8	$10	8	$128
9	$10	9	$256
10	$10	10	$512

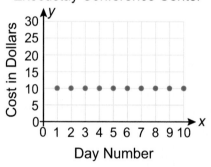

Executstay Conference Center

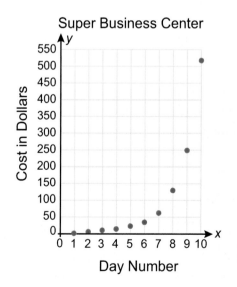

Super Business Center

MATHEMATICALLY SPEAKING

▶ scatter plot
▶ discrete

When a graph is made up of unconnected points, the graph is called a scatter plot, rather than a line graph. For a scatter plot, the input values are a distinct, or discrete, set of numbers. Since the conference runs for ten days, the values for x come from the discrete set, $\{1, 2, 3, 4, 5, 6, 7, 8, 9, 10\}$.

5. Why do you think mathematicians might use the term scatter plot for this type of graph?

Rate of Change

MATHEMATICALLY SPEAKING

▶ rate
▶ unit rate
▶ rate of change

  Let's Review

A rate is a ratio between two variables that have different units, such as miles and hours, or cents and pounds. For example, a rate can represent the number of miles traveled in a certain number of hours. If you travel 126 miles in 2 hours, your rate is $\frac{126 \text{ miles}}{2 \text{ hours}}$. You can write a rate with a denominator of 1, which is called a unit rate. The rate would become $\frac{63 \text{ miles}}{1 \text{ hour}}$, or 63 miles per hour (mph).

A rate of change is a ratio of the change in one variable, usually the dependent variable, to the change in another variable, usually the independent variable.

The rate of change is a very important concept in algebra and calculus. Let's take a look at a few examples and find the rate of change for each.

6. Look at the scatter plot above for Corporate Connection Center Internet Fees.

   a) Describe how the dependent variable changes as the number of days increases.

   b) Find the rate of change in the cost for Internet access as time increases.

   c) How can you find the rate of change using the table?

7. Is the relationship between days of Internet access and cost linear? How do you know?

8. Write a recursive rule that determines the output values for this function. Write the explicit rule for this function as an equation.

9. With a partner, make a table and graph for each of the other two options: the Executstay and Super Business Centers.

Summarize Day 1

Day 2 continues the discussion of different types of rate of change. This is an important concept and should not be rushed. We are developing the background for an intuitive understanding of slope with the discussion of rates of change and finding it using various representations. Questions 10b and c should provide a good summary discussion for the end of day 1.

10. a) The independent variable is the day number and the dependent variable is the Internet cost the given day.

   b) Execustay's fees remain the same each day. There is no change in the cost as the days increase. The points form a horizontal line. Super Business Center's fees do not change at a steady or constant rate. The fees increase more rapidly as the number of days increases. This forms a curve (exponential) rather than a straight line.

   c) The daily Internet fees for both centers increase as the number of days increases, but the rates of change are different.

Corporate Connection Conference Center's fee for Internet use increases at a constant rate of change, $2 per day. Super Business Center has a varying rate of change. For example, from day 1 to day 2, the increase is $1. From day 2 to day 3, the increase is $2.

   d) There is a constant rate of change for both the Execustay and Corporate Connection Conference Centers. The rate of change in fees per day for Execustay is $0 as the number of days increases by 1. The rate of change in fees per day for Corporate Connection Conference Center is an increase of $2 as the number of days increases by 1.

Constant vs. Varying Rate of Change

Begin by reviewing the three scenarios and their rates of change. As the class discusses Corporate Connection's fees, emphasize that linear relationships have a constant rate of change. This means that the *y*-value increases by a constant amount as the *x*-value increases by a constant amount. In this case, the *y*-value increases by 2 as the *x*-value increases by 1. This is shown on a graph by the points aligning to form a straight line.

Talk Moves Have students work with a partner to complete Questions 11–13. Share student responses as a class. Use talk moves, such as agree/disagree, why, and rephrasing to help clarify misconceptions and further student understanding.

---

10. **a)** State the independent and dependent variables for each Internet cost option.

    b) How do the fees change in each option as time increases? In other words, describe the rate of change for each situation.

    c) Look at the changes in fees for Corporate Connection Conference Center and the Super Business Center. What is different? What is similar?

    d) Look at the changes in fees for Execustay and Corporate Connection Conference Center? What is different? What is similar?

Constant vs. Varying Rate of Change

You can decide if there is a constant rate of change in two ways:

- by looking at the change in *x*-values and the change in the corresponding *y*-values on the table; or
- by looking at the points on the graph and seeing if they form a straight line.

Let's look at Corporate Connection Conference Center's fees to see if there is a constant rate of change.

Corporate Connection Fees	
Day Number	Cost
1	$2
2	$4
3	$6
4	$8
5	$10
6	$12
7	$14
8	$16
9	$18
10	$20

(+1 between each Day Number; +2 between each Cost)

- Each time *x* increases by 1 day, there is the same *y* increase of $2. This means that the rate of change is constant: $\frac{\$2}{1 \text{ day}} = \$2$ per day.

---

11. Super Business Center has a varying rate of change.

    a) Looking at the table, as the number of days increases from 1 to 2, the cost increases by $1. As the number of days increases from 9 to 10, the cost increases by $256. Therefore, there is not a constant rate of change.

    b) The points on the graph form a curve, not a straight line. Therefore, the fees at Super Business Center do not represent a linear function and do not have a constant rate of change.

12. Execustay Conference Center has a constant rate of change.

    a) Looking at the table, the cost ($10) stays the same as the day increases by 1 from 1 to 2 and from 5 to 6.

    b) The points on the graph form a straight line. This represents a constant rate of change and shows that the fees at the Execustay Conference Center represent a linear function.

    c) The rental cost for each day remains the same as the number of days increase. The rate of change is zero.

Now look at the graph for the Corporate Connection Conference Center.

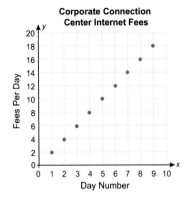

Corporate Connection Center Internet Fees

As *x* increases by 1, *y* always increases by 2. Note that all the points on the graph line up to form a straight line. Also notice that as the independent variable increases, the dependent variable increases. This is an **increasing function**. When the points on a graph line up to form a straight line, the relationship between the variables is linear. In linear relationships the rate of change will be a constant.

MATHEMATICALLY SPEAKING

▶ increasing function

Use the tables and graphs you created in Question 9 to find the following.

11. Find out if there is a constant rate of change for the fees charged by Super Business Center.

   a) Use the table to determine your answer. Explain.

   b) Use the graph to determine your answer. Explain.

12. Find out if there is a constant rate of change for the fees charged by Execustay Conference Center.

   a) Use the table to determine your answer. Explain.

   b) Use the graph to determine your answer. Explain.

   c) Describe the rate of change for this relationship.

13. If a set of points lie on the same horizontal line, what is the rate of change for the function?

14. Find the *total* cost of using the Internet for 10 days at each of the conference centers.

13. A horizontal line indicates that the *y*-values remain the same or have a constant rate of change of 0 as the *x*-values increase.

14. Corporate Connection Conference Center's total cost for 10 days is $110.

Execustay Conference Center's total cost for 10 days is $100.

Super Business Center's total cost for 10 days is $1,023.

15. a) There is a constant rate of change. For each increase of 1 in x, there is a corresponding increase of 1 in the y-values.

b) There is a varying rate of change. For the first three entries, as x increases by 5, y increases by 3. For the last three entries, as x increases by 5, y increases by 1.

c) There is a constant rate of change, 0. As x increases by 0.25, y stays the same.

d) There is a constant rate of change. As x increases by 2, y increases by 3. Note that students may think there is a varying rate because of the entry (5, 7.5). But in this instance, x increases by 1 and y increases by 1.5, which is the same rate of change. You can point out that these rates are equivalent ratios.
$$\frac{3}{2} = \frac{1.5}{1}$$

16. a) There is a constant rate of change, 0. Pooter's heart rate never changes over time.

b) There is a constant rate of change. The plant grows 0.5 inches per day.

c) There is a varying rate of change. The temperature of the soup drops more quickly in the beginning. As time increases, the temperature decreases at a slower rate.

d) There is a varying rate of change. As time increases, the ball quickly goes up, slows down as it reaches its highest point, picks up speed as it descends, and then hits the floor.

---

15. Use the tables below to see if there is a constant rate of change. If so, describe the rate of change.

a)

x	y
0	1.5
1	2.5
2	3.5
3	4.5
4	6.5
5	7.5

b)

x	y
20	3
25	6
30	9
35	10
40	11
45	12

c)

x	y
0.25	8
0.50	8
0.75	8
1.0	8
1.25	8
1.5	8

d)

x	y
2	3
4	6
5	7.5
6	9
8	12
10	15

16. Use the graphs below to determine if there is a constant rate of change. If so, describe the rate of change.

a) Pooter the Cat's Heart Rate While Asleep

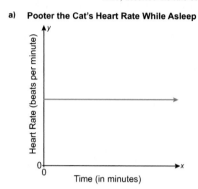

b) Plant Growth

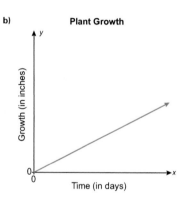

c) Hot Soup Cooling Off

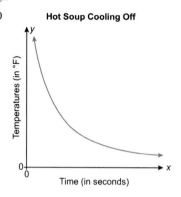

d) Sue Shoots a Free Throw in Basketball

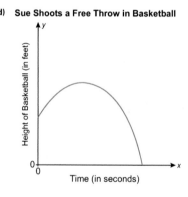

Wrap It Up

At the beginning of this lesson, Jesse predicted that Super Business Center had the best deal. Why do you think he chose this option? After finishing the lesson, he has changed his mind. Which conference center do you think he will now choose? Explain your answer.

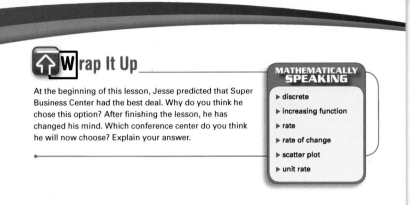

MATHEMATICALLY SPEAKING

▶ discrete

▶ increasing function

▶ rate

▶ rate of change

▶ scatter plot

▶ unit rate

Wrap It Up

Answers will vary. Encourage students to support their responses with sound reasoning.

- Super Business was the least expensive on Day 1 when compared to the other two options. This is why it was chosen as the best option initially. However, this situation has a varying rate of change, resulting in a rapid increase later on. (The equation for this curve is $y = 2^{x-1}$.) Ultimately, this was the most expensive option at Day 10.

- On Day 1, Execustay Conference Center appeared to be the most expensive at $10. However, since the cost remained the same each day and Execustay Conference Center fees had a constant rate of change of 0, it was ultimately the least expensive option.

To further the discussion, ask:

- *How can you use rate of change to help make better predictions in the future?*

Reflect

Use these questions to help you reflect on the lesson and plan for future instruction.

- How successful are students in analyzing tables and graphs to determine whether the relationship between variables represents a constant rate of change?

- Are students able to accurately describe the rate of change between variables in given situations?

Write About It

a) A graph that represents a change of zero in the dependent variable as the independent variable increase has points that align to form a horizontal line.

Graphs will vary. Possible response:

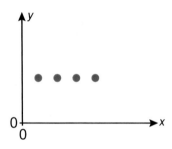

b) A graph that represents a constant rate of change that is not zero has points that are aligned to form a straight line that is not horizontal or vertical. An increasing function rises at a steady rate from left to right.

Possible graph:

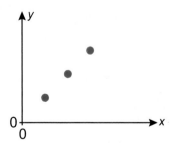

c) A graph that represents a varying rate of change between variables does not consist of every point aligning in a straight line. The graph could be a curved line. Another option is a graph that might have some points (or a segment between points) rising from left to right, and then some points (or a segment between points) falling. It may also include some points that align in a horizontal segment between points. In the example below, each segment between points has a constant rate of change, but the overall graph does not.

Possible graph:

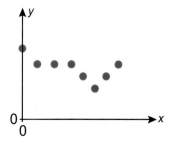

Write About It

1. Describe what each of the following graphs might look like. Draw a possible graph for each situation:

   a) A graph that represents a rate of change of zero.

   b) A graph that represents a constant rate of change for an increasing function.

   c) A graph that represents a varying rate of change.

2. **a)** Is the following graph of the NBA Stars from Lesson 1.2 a scatterplot? Why or why not?

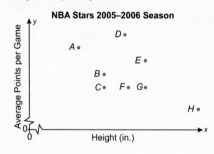

   b) Would it be appropriate to connect the points on this graph? Explain.

3. **a)** Create a situation where it would be better to use a scatter plot than a line graph.

   b) Create another situation in which it would be better to use a line graph than a scatter plot.

4. Write up a report for the president of Sports Mecca with your choice of conference center to use. Explain your choice with tables and graphs.

Answer the following questions for each of the graphs in Questions 5, 6, and 7.

 a) Identify the two variables. Determine which is the independent variable and which is the dependent variable.

 b) Is this a constant or a varying rate of change over the entire graph? How do you know?

 c) Write a description for the situation.

 d) For each labeled point, give a description of what the coordinates mean.

 e) Is the relationship linear? Why or why not?

5.

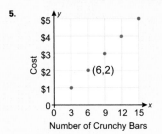

Number of Crunchy Bars

6.

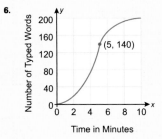

Time in Minutes

 NOTE Students may choose to connect points on graphs with line segments to make rate of change more prominent. If the data is discrete, instruct students to draw a lightweight line between data points. If the data is continuous, instruct students to draw a line equal to the weight of the points.

2. a) The NBA graph in Lesson 1.1 is a scatter plot because the variable on the *x*-axis (players' heights) represents data that is discrete.

 b) The NBA plot does not have a pattern and the points are discrete points so it would not make sense to connect the points.

3. a) Answers will vary. Possible response:

 Joe's Video Rentals charges $3.50 for every DVD movie rented. The number of DVD movies rented is discrete, or distinct. You cannot rent $1\frac{1}{2}$ DVDs.

 b) Answers will vary. Possible response:

 Bedford Farms Dairy sells ice cream cones for 30¢ an ounce. The number of ounces in an ice cream cone is continuous.

4. Answers will vary: Possible response:

 I would recommend the Execustay Conference Center. Although its per-day rental cost is more than the other two facilities initially, the rental fee of $10 per day remains constant for ten days. At the end of ten days, the total rental cost for Execustay is the least expensive. Execustay's rental fee for 10 days is $100, while Super Business Center's fee is $1,023, and Corporate Connection Conference Center's fee is $110. Corporate Connection Conference Center's fees are initially lower per day than Execustay, but increase at a steady rate. After day 5, Corporate Connection Conference Center's rental fee becomes more expensive than Execustay Conference Center. Super Business Center's fees also are lower per day initially; however, the per-day fee increases rapidly and the company's fees become more expensive after day 4 compared to Execustay Conference Center's rental fee.

7.

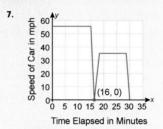

8. For the graphs in Questions 6 and 7 explain why all of the points on the graphs are connected.

9. For Question 7, describe what each horizontal line segment means.

10. Why aren't the points on the graph in Question 5 connected?

11. For Questions 5 and 7:

  a) Make a table using the values of x that are marked on the x-axis.

  b) How can you tell from each table whether the rate of change for the function is constant or varying?

  c) If the rate of change is constant, find it using the table.

12. Match each of the following situations with the corresponding graph and table.

Situation 1: The cost per night of a hotel room is the same over a specific number of nights.

Situation 2: For every 20 minutes of metered parking in West Hartford center, you pay one quarter. The meter will only accept quarters.

Situation 3: The Caroling Card Company offers a special deal to retailers. For every 20 packages of cards retailers purchase, the cost is $30.

Situation 4: Their electric company charges Super Business Center $0.16 for every kilowatt-hour of electricity they use.

5. a) The number of Crunchy Bars, x, is the independent variable and total cost, y, is the dependent variable. The total cost depends on the number of Crunchy Bars purchased.

  b) There is a constant rate of change. As the x-value increases, the y-value increases at a constant rate. For each increase of 3 Crunchy Bars, the y-value increases by $1. The points on the graph are aligned in a straight line.

  c) Crunchy Bars come in 3-bar packages. Each package costs $1.

  d) (6, 2); 6 Crunchy Bars cost $2.

  e) Yes, the relationship is linear. There is a constant rate of change between the dependent and independent variables. The points on the graph are aligned in a straight line.

6. a) Time in minutes, x, is the independent variable and number of typed words, y, is the dependent variable.

  b) There is no constant rate of change over the entire graph. The y-values do not increase or decrease at a constant rate as the x-values increase. Rather, the change in y-values varies. For example, as the x-value changes from 0–2 minutes, the y-value changes from 0–20. This means that the person typed a total of 20 words at the end of 2 minutes. However, from 4 to 5 minutes the words typed went from 60 words to 140 words, typing at a rate of 80 words per minute. This is almost 4 times the rate for the first two minutes. The graph is not a straight line.

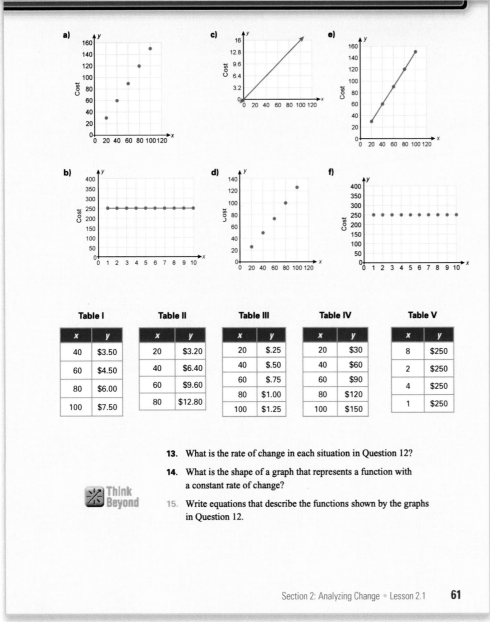

13. What is the rate of change in each situation in Question 12?

14. What is the shape of a graph that represents a function with a constant rate of change?

Think Beyond

15. Write equations that describe the functions shown by the graphs in Question 12.

c) Getting used to the keyboard on her new computer, Clara started typing very slowly in the first 2 minutes, completing about 10 words per minute. She then began to warm up and typed at a faster rate, about 20 words per minute for each of the next 2 minutes. At the end of 4 minutes, Clara typed a total of approximately 60 words. For the next minute, Clara sped up, typing 80 additional words. However, from 5 to 6 minutes, Clara's typing speed slowed down, perhaps due to her hand feeling cramped. During this minute, she only typed an additional 30 words. This rate is less than half her rate from the previous minute. Clara's typing rate continued to decline.

From 6 to 8 minutes, she typed an additional 20 words, averaging a rate of 10 words per minute. For the last two minutes, Clara only typed 5 additional words, averaging 2.5 words per minute.

d) (5,140); At the end of 5 minutes, the person had typed 140 words.

e) The relationship is not linear. The graph is curved and not a straight line.

7. a) Time in minutes is the independent variable and speed of the car in miles per hour is the dependent variable.

b) There is no constant rate of change in this situation. As the x-values increase, the y-values do not increase or decrease at a constant rate. Rather, the rate of change varies. For example, between 0 and 15 minutes, the speed of the car was 55 mph. Between 15 and 16 minutes, the speed of the car decreases to 0 mph. Also, the graph is not a straight line.

c) For the first 15 minutes of this particular part of the trip, the car was traveling on the highway at 55 mph. Between 15 and 16 minutes, the car exited the highway and the speed decreased; eventually the car came to a stop at the end of the exit ramp. After stopping at the stop sign, the car's speed began to increase as it proceeded onto another road. From 18 to 29 minutes, the car traveled steadily on a secondary road at 35 mph. Then the car began to slow down as it approached its final destination and turned into a driveway. At 30 minutes, the car reached the final destination and came to a complete stop.

d) (16, 0); At 16 minutes into this part of the trip, the car had come to a complete stop. The rate of speed was 0 mph.

e) No, the relationship is not linear.

 While there are sections of the graph that depict a constant rate of change, the entire relationship between the two variables does not have a constant rate of change. As a result, this function has a varying rate of change overall.

8. The graphs are continuous curves since the set of numbers that represent the independent variable, x, and the dependent variable, y, on both graphs are continuous rather than discrete.

 Think Back

Mr. Kirwalsky is a very unusual teacher. He has a Grislaw beast as a classroom pet. The beast, contrary to its name, is very friendly. All the students love to take care of him. But Mr. Kirwalsky has a strict rule. A student must have a 80% average (or higher) on their 7 math quizzes at the end of each grading period. Otherwise, they cannot play with the beast for the entire next grading period.

16. John has 6 quiz scores so far: 88, 83, 79, 80, 70, and 68. What is John's current average?

17. What is the lowest grade John can get on the final quiz so that he will be allowed to take care of the beast?

Grislaw beasts are claustrophobic. It is very important that a Grislaw's cage has a height of at least two and a half times the Grislaw's height. Its cage must have a floor area in square units with the number os square meters equal to twelve times the number of meters of the Grislaw's height.

18. If Mr. Kirwalsky has a Grislaw that is three meters tall, what are the minimum dimensions of the cage? Assume that the floor of the cage is square.

Mr. Kirwalsky cannot find a room to fit the Grislaw's cage. The closest room has a floor that is six meters by five meters in size.

19. What is the area of the floor of this room?

20. Mr. Kirwalsky makes a cage with the same floor area as the room, How high will he have to make the cage to keep the total volume of the cage the same as the cage with the minimum dimensions in Question 18? How high will he have to make the cage to keep the total volume of the cage the same as the cage with the minimum dimensions in Question 18? How tall is the cage?

9. In Graph 7, the horizontal line segment between 0 and 15 minutes means that as time increased, the speed of the car remained the same at 55 mph. The horizontal line segment between 18 and 29 minutes means that as time increased, the speed of the car remained the same, approximately 35 mph.

10. The points on Graph 5 are not connected since the independent variable, x, represents a discrete or discontinuous set of numbers. Stores do not sell $1\frac{1}{2}$ Crunchy Bars. Since the data is not continuous, a scatter plot is appropriate.

11. a) Crunchy Bars

Number of Crunchy Bars	Cost
3	$1
6	$2
9	$3
12	$4
15	$5

Speed of a Car During a Trip

Time Elapsed in Minutes	Speed of Car in mph
0	55
5	55
10	55
15	55
20	35
25	35
30	0

b) If for all equal-sized intervals in the x-values, the amount of change in the y-values remains the same, there is a steady or constant rate of change. If not, the rate is varying.

c) The rate of change for the Crunchy Bars is constant, while the rate for the speed of the car is varying. From the Crunchy Bar table, the difference in the y-values ($1) is the same for each change of 3 units in the x-axis. Therefore, the rate of change is constant and equal to $\frac{\$1}{3 \text{ bars}}$ or $\$\frac{1}{3}$ per bar.

12. Situation 1 – Graph F – Table V

Situation 2 – Graph D – Table III

Situation 3 – Graph A – Table IV

Situation 4 – Graph C – Table II

13. Situation 1: There is no increase in the y-value (dollars) for each unit increase in the x-value (a one night stay in a hotel room). This relationship represents a constant rate of change of zero.

Situation 2: There is a 25-unit increase in the y-value (cents) for each 20-unit increase in x-value (minutes). The rate is charged in full 20-minute intervals. This relationship represents a constant rate of change of $\frac{\$0.25}{20 \text{ minutes}}$.

Situation 3: There is an increase of 30 units in the y-value (dollars) for each 20-unit increase in x-value (packages of cards). The rate is charged for full packages of cards. This relationship represents a constant rate of change of $\frac{\$30}{20 \text{ cards}}$, or $\frac{\$1.50}{1 \text{ card}}$.

Situation 4: There is an increase of 0.16 unit in the y-value (dollars) for each unit increase in x-value (kilowatt-hours used). The rate is continuously charged as electricity is used. This relationship represents a constant rate of change of $\frac{\$0.16}{1 \text{ kilowatt hour}}$.

14. The shape of a graph that represents a constant rate of change is a straight line.

15. **Think Beyond**

Graph A: $y = 1.5x$ where $x = \{20, 40, 60, 80, 100\}$

Graph B: $y = 250$ where $1 \leq x \leq 10$

Graph C: $y = 0.16x$, where x is any real number.

Graph D: $y = 1.25x$; $x = \{20, 40, 60, 80, 100\}$

Graph E: $y = 1.5x$; $20 \leq x \leq 100$

Graph F: $y = 250$; $x = \{1, 2, 3, 4,..., 10\}$

Think Back

16. John's current average is 78.

17. John must get at least a 92 on the final test to be able to play with the Grislaw during the next grading period.

18. The cage must be 7.5 meters tall, 6 meters long, and 6 meters wide.

19. 30 square meters

20. The cage must be 9 meters tall.

LESSON 2.2 Exploring Slope

Suggested Pacing: 2 Days

In this lesson, students first explore slope conceptually as related to the steepness of a line. Then they investigate slope in more depth as a constant rate of change between two variables in a given situation. To compare changes in the dependent variable (*y*-values) to changes in the independent variable (*x*-values), students work with tables, graphs and equations to identify and interpret slope as it relates to a real-world conference.

LESSON OBJECTIVES

- Students will explore the relationship between the slope and the steepness of a line, and discover that as the slope increases, the steepness of the line increases.
- Students will investigate slope as a ratio of the change in the dependent variable (*y*-value) to the change in the independent variable (*x*-value), and apply this in different situations.
- Students will identify slope using tables and equations.

DAY 1	MATERIALS*	ESSENTIAL *ON YOUR OWN* QUESTIONS
Slope and Steepness of a Line Graphing Situations	**In Class** - Graph paper - Rulers - Colored pencils or markers (optional to make multiple lines on the same graph) - Graphing calculators **On Your Own** - Graph paper - Graphing calculators (optional)	Questions 2, 3, 6, 9–13
DAY 2	**MATERIALS***	**ESSENTIAL *ON YOUR OWN* QUESTIONS**
Slope and Rate of Change		Questions 1, 4, 5, 7, 8, 14, 15

*The Think Like a Mathematician Daily Record Sheet should be used daily

---

MATHEMATICALLY SPEAKING

▶ numerical coefficient   ▶ slope

LESSON 2.2 Exploring Slope

➡️ Start It Off

Mark and Katrina train for a marathon on the trails at the conference center. Mark jogged for 1.5 hours and ran 15 miles. Katrina jogged for a half-hour and covered 5 miles. Mark claims he ran at a faster rate than Katrina. Katrina thinks they both ran at the same rate.

1. Who is correct? Explain your answer.

2. Write Mark's rate in miles per hour as a ratio.

3. Write Katrina's rate in miles per hour as a ratio.

4. Kristen runs at the same rate as Katrina. She jogged for 1.25 hours. How many miles did she run?

Slope and Steepness of a Line

What do skiing and algebra have in common?

The answer to this question is *slope*. Think about the slope of the mountain that you ski down. What does slope mean in this situation?

It means how steep the mountain is. The bunny hill, where young children learn to ski, is not very steep. The black diamond trail, which is for experts, is very steep. So the slope of the bunny hill is smaller than the slope of the black diamond trail.

In algebra, the slope of a line means the same thing—how steep the line is.

➡️ Start It Off

1. Katrina is right. They both ran at the same rate.

2. $\dfrac{15 \text{ miles}}{1.5 \text{ hour}} = 10$ miles per hour

3. $\dfrac{5 \text{ miles}}{0.5 \text{ hour}} = 10$ miles per hour.

4. $\dfrac{10 \text{ miles}}{1 \text{ hour}} \times 1.25$ hours = 12.5 miles.

DAY 1 TEACHING THE LESSON

Slope and Steepness of a Line

Introduce the term *slope* to students. Guide students to recognize conceptually that in algebra, slope refers the steepness of a line.

Discuss each of the given conference situations. Have students work in pairs to complete Question 1. Remind students that for Question 1c, they will graph all four situations on the same coordinate grid. This is to provide consistency with the scale of their graphs. For example, two lines that have the same slope may appear to have different levels of steepness on the graphs depending on the scales used. Putting the graphs of all four situations on the same coordinate grid avoids this confusion. Encourage students to carefully consider an appropriate scale, as they will need to show costs for up to 100 people. As an option, you may wish to distribute an overhead transparency with a coordinate grid to each pair. This may be used instead of regular grid paper so students' work can be readily shared when making presentations to the class.

When students check their graphs using the graphing calculator, explain to them that they will not be able to label graphs on the screen. Therefore, they should input the graphs one at a time to check them.

Discuss student responses as a class when they have finished. Have student pairs compare the graphs for the four situations. Ask:

- *What is the same about the graphs for the four situations?*

- *What is different about the graphs?*

Graphing Situations

You are going to make a presentation about projected conference costs to the executives at Sports Mecca. You need to include costs that change based on the number of people at the conference.

Consider these situations:

Situation 1: You need to have bottled water available during the morning meetings. To provide this, the conference center will charge $1 per person per day.

Situation 2: You need to provide lunch each day. The cost is $10 per person per day.

Situation 3: You need to provide snacks at each afternoon session. The snacks cost $5 per person per day.

Situation 4: You need to provide name tags for each attendee. The cost is $0.50 per person per day.

To make your presentation, you decide to use graphs for each situation. You want to graph them on the same coordinate plane so that you can compare the costs.

1. Work in pairs to design your presentation.

    a) Find the independent and dependent variables for each situation.

    b) Create a table of values that goes up to 100 people for each situation. It would take a long time to list every number between 1 and 100. Decide on appropriate intervals to use in your tables. Use the same intervals for each table.

    c) Graph all the situations on the *same* coordinate grid. Make sure to:

    - Decide on scales for the *x*- and *y*-axes that will make your graph easy to read.

    - Label each axis with the scale.

    - Connect the points on the graph of each situation. This creates a line graph. Remember, a line graph is used to make a graph more effective by showing the pattern more clearly.

    - Label each line to indicate the situation it represents.

---

1. a) The independent variable for all four situations is the number of people attending the conference. The dependent variable is the total cost in dollars.

b) Possible tables:

Situation 1 Water Bottle Cost		Situation 2 Lunch Cost		Situation 3 Afternoon Snacks Cost		Situation 4 Name Tags Cost	
Number of Bottles	Cost	Number of Lunches	Cost	Number of Snacks	Cost	Number of Name Tags	Cost
0	$0	0	$0	0	$0	0	$0
5	$5	5	$50	5	$25	5	$2.50
10	$10	10	$100	10	$50	10	$5.00
15	$15	15	$150	15	$75	15	$7.50
20	$20	20	$200	20	$100	20	$10.00
25	$25	25	$250	25	$125	25	$12.50
30	$30	30	$300	30	$150	30	$15.00
35	$35	35	$350	35	$175	35	$17.50
40	$40	40	$400	40	$200	40	$20.00
45	$45	45	$450	45	$225	45	$22.50
50	$50	50	$500	50	$250	50	$25.00
55	$55	55	$550	55	$275	55	$27.50
60	$60	60	$600	60	$300	60	$30.00
65	$65	65	$650	65	$325	65	$32.50
70	$70	70	$700	70	$350	70	$35.00
75	$75	75	$750	75	$375	75	$37.50
80	$80	80	$800	80	$400	80	$40.00
85	$85	85	$850	85	$425	85	$42.50
90	$90	90	$900	90	$450	90	$45.00
95	$95	95	$950	95	$475	95	$47.50
100	$100	100	$1,000	100	$500	100	$50.00

c)

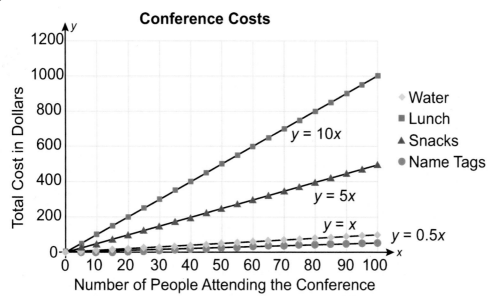

Notice that, although we are using a line graph to more clearly show the linear relationship and the constant rate of change, the set of numbers representing the independent variable (x) is discrete. It is a distinct, countable set of numbers. It doesn't make sense to have a value that is between two whole numbers, such as 1 and 2, since you cannot have $1\frac{1}{2}$ people attending the conference.

2. **Water Bottles:** The cost is equal to the number of people attending.
$y = 1x$ or $y = x$

   Lunches: The cost is ten times the number of people attending. $y = 10x$

   Snacks: The cost is five times the number of people attending. $y = 5x$

   Name tags: The cost is half the number of people attending. $y = 0.5x$

 3. Cost for 25 people attending:

Water: $25.00
Lunch: $250.00
Snacks: $125.00
Name tags: $12.50

Total Cost: $412.50

Cost for 60 people attending:
Water: $60.00
Lunch: $600.00
Snacks: $300.00
Name tags: $30.00

Total Cost: $990.00

Cost for 75 people attending:
Water: $75.00
Lunch: $750.00
Snacks: $375.00
Name tags: $37.50

Total Cost: $1,237.50

In all cases y is the cost in dollars and x is the number of people attending the conference. Yes, the amounts found on the graph match those found using the equations.

4. **a)** 120 people

   b) 83

5. **a)** The graphs should all show the lines as increasing linear functions as shown in the answer to Question 1c above. They all go through the point (0, 0), meaning if no people show up, the cost is zero. However, their slopes are all different. Students may have used different scales for the x-axis and so the graphs of the lines may appear to have different steepness. However, on a particular coordinate grid the relationship among the steepness of the lines should remain the same.

   b) Yes. The coordinates of the points are the same on all the graphs.

Have students complete Question 6 independently and share their responses in a class discussion. Guide students to recognize that as the value of the coefficient of x increases in the equations, the steepness of the line increases, and so the value of the slope increases.

6. **a)** Name tags: $y = 0.5x$
      Water Bottles: $y = 1x$
      Snacks: $y = 5x$
      Lunches: $y = 10x$

   b) As the steepness, or slope, of the lines increase, the value of the coefficient of x increases.

7. Students will probably make the conjecture that the coefficient of x tells how steep the line is.

After ordering the equations in Question 8, discuss this further with students and make sure they recognize that each equation is in the form of $y = mx$. The slope of the line is the coefficient of x only when the equation is in this particular format.

8. In order from least to most steep, the equations are $y = \frac{1}{4}x$, $y = 0.36x$, $y = 4x$, $y = 5.3x$, and $y = \frac{16}{3}x$

2. Write an explicit rule that describes how the two variables are related for each of the four situations. Write each rule as an equation that begins "$y =$". Write each equation next to its graph.

 Use your graphing calculator to check your work. Set your window so you can see the entire graph.

3. For each situation, use the graph to find the total cost per day for 25, 60 and 75 people. See if these amounts match the results you get by using the equations.

4. a) If you have budgeted $1,200 per day for lunch, how many people could be served?

   b) If you budgeted $41.50 per day for name tags, how many name tags would you be able to provide each day?

5. a) Make your presentation to the class. Compare graphs from each group. How are the graphs alike? How are they different?

   b) Compare your answers to Questions 3 and 4 with your classmates. Should you all get the same answer from your graphs? Why or why not?

6. a) Examine your graphs. Write the equations you graphed in order from the equation corresponding to the least steep graph to the equation corresponding to the steepest graph.

   b) What do you notice about the equations of the lines as they increase in steepness?

7. Make a conjecture about the relationship between the steepness of a line and a number in the equation of the line. Discuss with your partner and then with the class.

8. Order the graphs of these equations from least steep to steepest.

   a) $y = 4x$ d) $y = \frac{16}{3}x$

   b) $y = \frac{1}{4}x$ e) $y = 5.3x$

   c) $y = 0.36x$

 Check with your graphing calculator

9. a) $\frac{1}{4}$

   b) 0.36

   c) 4

   d) $\frac{16}{3}$

   e) 5.3

Summarize Day 1

As a wrap up question for day 1, ask students to describe what the graphs of $y = 2x$ and $y = 3x$ on the same coordinate plane would look like, without actually graphing them.

They should be able to say that both graphs would be lines that rise up and to the right. They both meet at the origin and the graph of $y = 3x$ would be steeper than $y = 2x$ since it has a greater coefficient of x.

Slope and Rate of Change

Help students relate the rate of change in the given situations to the cost of the item per person. Write this relationship as a ratio. Emphasize that the change in y (the dependent variable) is written in the numerator and the change in x (the independent variable) is written in the denominator. This shows the rate of change as a ratio of the changes in each variable. Discuss the independent and dependent variables in the rate miles per hour. To further students' understanding, have them identify the independent and dependent variables in the rate cents per pound. It is important students are able to make this connection.

 Differentiation

Think Differently: For those students who are unsure about what the independent and dependent variables are in the given rates, offer some additional practice with the following:

- miles per gallon of gas
- dollars per DVD
- dollars per square yard of carpet
- weight of bag in lbs per number of books

10. Both are right. If students are having difficulty seeing this, encourage them to write $\frac{10}{1} = \frac{50}{5}$.

11. **a)** For every fifty additional people, the cost increases by $25.00.

    b) For every 100 additional people, the cost increases by $50.00.

    c) For each additional person, the cost increases by $0.50. (If students have trouble finding the cost per additional person, remind them that this is the cost of a single name tag.)

12. Yes, the situation has a constant rate of change. For each increase of 1 person, the cost increases by 0.5.

13. **Situation 1 (Water):** The value of y (cost in dollars) increases by 1 as the value of x (number of people) increases by 1.

    Situation 2 (Snack): The value of y (cost in dollars) increases by 5 as the value of x (number of people) increases by 1.

MATHEMATICALLY SPEAKING

▸ numerical coefficient

The steepness of a line is given by the coefficient of x. The numerical coefficient of a variable is the number it is multiplied by. If equations are in the form, $y = mx$, then the slope of the line is m. Note that, as a rule, mathematicians use the letter m for slope in linear equations.

9. State the slope of the line for the graph of each equation in problem 8.

Slope and Rate of Change

Hannah looked at the table for the cost of the lunches. She said the cost of the lunches increased by $10 for each additional person. Kobe said there was an increase of $50 for every 5 people.

10. Talk to your partner and decide who is correct. Be ready to explain your reasoning to the class.

For each additional person, the cost of lunches increased by $10.

I think there is an increase of $50 for every 5 people.

11. Below is the table for the cost of the name tags. For every 10 people, the cost goes up by $5. How does the cost change for

a) every 50 additional people?

b) every 100 additional people?

c) each additional person?

Number of People	Cost
0	$0
5	$2.50
10	$5.00
15	$7.50
20	$10.00
25	$12.50
30	$15.00
35	$17.50
40	$20.00
45	$22.50
50	$25.00
55	$27.50
60	$30.00
65	$32.50
70	$35.00
75	$37.50
80	$40.00
85	$42.50
90	$45.00
95	$47.50
100	$50.00

(Left side: + 10 between successive pairs; Right side: + 5 between successive pairs)

In the situations we have been studying, the rate of change is the ratio of the change in the cost of an item to the change in the number of people receiving that item.

• The cost of lunches changes from $100 to $250 when the number of people receiving lunches changes from 10 to 25 persons. The rate of change is $\frac{250 - 100}{25 - 10} = \frac{\$150}{15 \text{ persons}}$.

• The unit rate is the average cost of the item per person. For example, the unit rate of the lunches is 10 dollars per 1 person, or $10 per person.

• The change in y, the dependent variable, is written in the numerator of the ratio. The change in x, the independent variable, is written in the denominator.

14. The relationship between the variables in each of the four situations is given by a constant rate of change. Relationships that are linear have constant rates of change. There is a constant increase in the y-value for every unit increase in the x-value. The rates of change are:

Situation 1 (water): $\frac{\$1}{1 \text{ person}}$

Situation 2 (lunch): $\frac{\$10}{1 \text{ person}}$

Situation 3 (snack): $\frac{\$5}{1 \text{ person}}$

Situation 4 (name tags): $\frac{\$0.50}{1 \text{ person}}$

15. This question will give students practice in finding the rate of change and slope from tables.

a) slope $= \frac{1}{2}$

b) slope $= 2$

c) slope $= \frac{2}{3}$

 **Wrap It Up**

Students should discuss the fact that slope is a numerical value that represents the steepness of the line. It is the coefficient of x in an equation of the form $y = mx$. A larger slope corresponds to a steeper line. Slope is also the rate of change of a function, represented by the change in the y-values of two points divided by the change in the corresponding x-values of the same two points. This is a constant rate of change which means that it does not matter which two points you choose, the slope is always the same.

 NOTE These concepts will be reinforced further in the next lesson when the rate of change is examined graphically. Students may still only have a tentative understanding at this point.

12. Does the cost of the name tags have a constant rate of change? Explain.

13. Describe the rate of change in words for the cost of the water bottles and the cost of afternoon snacks. Make sure to use the given tables.

14. Find the rate of change using a ratio for each situation. Is there a constant rate of change in each situation? Explain.

Mathematicians define slope as the ratio of the change in y (the dependent variable) to the corresponding change in x (the independent variable). The slope of a line is represented by the steepness of the line. So the ratios you found for the rate of change in these situations are the slopes of the corresponding lines!

Earlier you saw that with an equation of the form $y = ax$ is a. You can use the idea of rate of change to show where this number comes from.

 NOTE Mathematicians use the Greek letter Δ (delta) to indicate "change in." We can write this slope as $\frac{\Delta y}{\Delta x} = \frac{10}{1}$ or 10.

Example

For example, $y = 10x$.
Choose any two points.
Let $x = 0$ and $x = 10$.
When $x = 0$, $y = 0$.
When $x = 10$, $y = 100$.
The slope of the line $y = 10x$ is $\frac{\text{change in } y}{\text{change in } x} = \frac{100 - 0}{10 - 0} = \frac{100}{10} = \frac{10}{1}$ or 10.

15. Using two points, find the slope of the functions in the tables below. Check your answer by finding the slope with two other points.

a)

x	y
−4	−2
−2	−1
0	0
4	2

b)

x	y
−4	10
−3	12
−2	14
−1	16

c)

x	y
9	10
12	12
15	14
18	16

 **Wrap It Up**

How is the slope of a line related to its graph? How is the slope of a line related to the rate of change of a function? Is this a constant or varying rate of change? Explain.

Reflect

Use these questions to help you reflect on the lesson and plan for future instruction.

- Do students understand the connection between slope and the steepness of a line?

- Do students understand the connection between slope and a constant rate of change?

- How readily are students able to identify the slope of a linear function from tables and equations?

Write
About It

1. Define the slope of a line. How would you find it from a table of values or from the equation of a line?

2. Describe a situation where the slope of a physical object is important. Explain what a change in the slope would do in this situation.

3. Madelyn thinks it is mathematically incorrect to connect the points with lines for the four situations at the conference.

   a) Is she correct?

   b) Explain why we asked you to connect them.

4. The table below represents a linear function. Without graphing, answer the questions.

x	y
−1	−1.5
0	0
1	1.5
2	3

   a) How does the x-value change? How does the y-value change?

   b) Find the rate of change when the x-variable increases by 1. Is this a constant rate of change? Explain.

   c) What do you know about this rate of change between any two points?

   d) Find the value of y if $x = \frac{1}{2}$.

   e) Write the explicit rule in words that describes the relationship between the variables. Now write the rule as an equation.

   f) What is the slope of the line through the points in the table?

On Your Own

Write
About It   Students should discuss slope in terms of the graphical representation of the steepness of a line and the numerical representation as the rate of change of the linear function. They should explain how slope can be found using a table by looking at the change in y for every unit increase in x. They should also explain how slope can be found using an equation by looking at the coefficient of x in an equation of the form $y = mx$.

2. Answers will vary. Possible responses where slope is important may include: Designing skateboard ramps; racing Cub Scout Pinewood Derby cars; building ramps for handicapped people; designing ski resort trails.

3. a) Yes, she is correct.

   b) The authors asked for students to connect the points in order to show more clearly that the relationship was linear and that there was a constant rate of change in the function.

4. a) The x-values increase by 1 in the table and the y-values increase by 1.5 in the table.

   b) The y-values increase by 1.5 for each 1-unit increase in x-values. The rate of change is $\frac{1.5}{1}$, or 1.5. Yes, the rate of change between the variables is constant.

   c) The rate of change will remain constant between any two points of the function.

   d) 0.75

   e) Each y-values is one and a half times the corresponding x-value; $y = 1.5x$.

   f) The slope of the line is the coefficient of the variable x in the equation above: $\frac{1.5}{1}$ or 1.5.

5. Below are tables for two linear functions.

   a) Find the slopes of the lines through the points.

   b) Which function will have the steeper line?

   c) Graph the functions to check.

Table 1	
x	y
0.25	1
1.25	5
2.25	9
3.25	13

Table 2	
x	y
0	0
1	0.75
2	1.5
3	2.25

6. Write the following equations in the order of the steepness of their lines, from least to most steep.

   a) $y = \frac{5}{8}x$

   b) $y = x$

   c) $y = \frac{3}{4}x$

   d) $y = 0.6x$

   e) $y = \frac{8}{5}x$

7. Find the slope of each of the lines for Question 6, Parts a–e.

8. Jonas thinks the slope of the line for the linear function whose points are given in the table below is $\frac{1}{2}$.

   a) Figure out what he did wrong.

   b) What is the correct slope?

x	y
26	52
30	60
34	68
38	76
42	84

5. a) For Table 1, the slope is 4; For Table 2, the slope is 0.75;

   b) The function in Table 1 will have the steeper line.

   c)

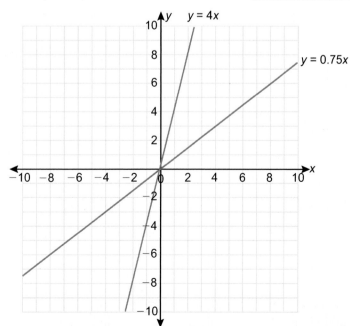

6. The order of steepness is $y = 0.6x$, $y = \frac{5}{8}x$, $y = \frac{3}{4}x$, $y = x$, $y = \frac{8}{5}x$.

7. a) $\frac{5}{8}$

   b) 1

   c) $\frac{3}{4}$

   d) 0.6

   e) $\frac{8}{5}$

9. In planning the conference, there are a few more items to price.

Situation 1: A tip for porter service is $1.50 for each piece of luggage.

Situation 2: The cost of a phone call is $0.75 per call.

Situation 3: The cost of photocopying is $0.25 per copy.

For each situation:

a) Name the independent and dependent variables.

b) Predict which graph will have the steepest line.

c) Write the equation.

d) Draw the graphs of the equations on the same coordinate grid. Connect the points to form a straight line. Was your prediction correct?

10. Use the situations in Question 9 to answer the following questions.

a) What is the tip for a porter who moves 20 pieces of luggage?

b) If the phone bill at the hotel was $13.50, how many phone calls had been made?

c) What is the cost of 100 photocopies? 250 copies? 500 copies?

d) If the cost of photocopying was $29.75, how many copies were made?

11. Dave thought that the slope of the line with the equation $2y = 2x$ is 2. He graphed the line and $y = 1.5x$ on the same graph. He found that the new line is steeper than the line of $2y = 2x$. He is confused and thinks: "If the slope were 2, the line should be steeper than the new line." Explain to Dave why the slope for the line represented by $2y = 2x$ is not 2.

Think Beyond

12. Sierra thinks that for any number she picks, she can find a line whose slope is equal to that number. Carolina asks, "What if you pick one thousand?" Sierra says that is not a problem.

a) Create a table of values for a linear function that would have a slope of one thousand.

b) What would the graph of this line look like?

Situation 2
(Cost of Phone Calls): The independent variable is the number of calls and dependent variable is the total cost in dollars for the calls.

Situation 3
(Photocopying Costs): The independent variable is the number of photocopies made and the dependent variable is the total cost in dollars for the copies.

b) Predictions will vary. Situation 1 (Tip for a Porter) will have the steepest slope.

c) **Situation 1** (Tip for a Porter): $y = 1.50x$. (*x* represents the number of bags and *y* represents the total tip amount.)

Situation 2 (Cost for Phone Calls): $y = 0.75x$. (*x* represents the number of calls made and *y* represents the total cost.)

Situation 3 (Photocopying Costs): $y = 0.25x$. (*x* represents the number of copies made and *y* represents the total cost.)

---

8. a) Jonas probably inverted the ratio. Using the first two points (26, 52) and (30, 60), instead of looking at the change in *y* over the change in *x*, he calculated the change in *x* (4) over the change in *y* (8), and found $\frac{4}{8} = \frac{1}{2}$

b) He should look at the change in *y* (8) over the change in *x* (4), and determine the slope to be $\frac{8}{4} = 2$.

9. a) **Situation 1** (Tip for a Porter): The independent variable is the number of bags, and the dependent variable is the tip amount in dollars.

d)

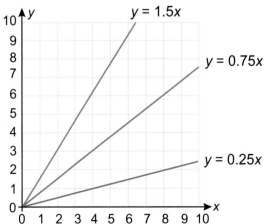

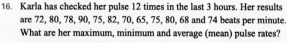

Think Back

13. The cost of 7 gallons of paint is $140.00. What do 4 gallons cost? Write an equation to find the cost of x gallons of paint.

14. Given $y = 15 - 4x$, solve for y if $x = -3$.

15. Match the expressions that are equal.

a) $\frac{1}{6} + \frac{1}{6} + \frac{1}{6}$ i. $\frac{13}{24}$

b) $\frac{1}{6} + \frac{2}{6} + \frac{1}{24}$ ii. $\left(2 \cdot \frac{1}{6}\right) + \frac{1}{4}$

c) $\frac{5}{6} + \frac{5}{24} + \frac{2}{48}$ iii. $3 \cdot \frac{1}{6}$

d) $\frac{1}{6} + \frac{1}{6} + \frac{1}{4}$ iv. $\frac{20}{24} + \frac{5}{24} + \frac{1}{24}$

16. Karla has checked her pulse 12 times in the last 3 hours. Her results are 72, 80, 78, 90, 75, 82, 70, 65, 75, 80, 68 and 74 beats per minute. What are her maximum, minimum and average (mean) pulse rates?

17. Which equation matches the following situation: A sunflower grows 1.5 centimeters per day, where h = height of sunflower and d = number of days.

A. $d = 1.5h$

B. $h = 1.5d$

C. $\frac{h}{d} = \frac{0.5}{1}$

D. $\frac{h}{d} = \frac{1}{0.5}$

10. **a)** 20 pieces of luggage will cost $30.

    b) 18 calls were made.

    c) 100 photocopies will cost $25; 250 photocopies will cost $62.50; and 500 copies will cost $125.

    d) 119 copies were made.

11. The equation is not in the form $y = mx$, since the coefficient of y is 2 rather than 1. Thus, the slope of the line is not 2. (In fact, the slope of the line is 1. To get the equation in the right form, you need to divide both sides of the equation by 2. This gives you an equivalent equation of $y = x$. At this point, students should know the slope is not 2 because the equation was not in the correct format. We are not going to discuss how to transform this equation in this unit. We will be using slope-intercept form throughout.)

12. **Think Beyond**

a) Answers will vary. One possibility is the following.

x	y
1	0
2	1000
3	2000
4	3000
5	4000
6	5000
7	6000

b) The graph would be a very steep line very close to the y-axis.

Think Back

13. $80; $y = 20x$ where y is the cost in dollars for x gallons of paint.

14. 27

15. a) iii

   b) i

   c) iv

   d) ii

16. maximum = 90; minimum = 65; mean = 75.75

17. B.

LESSON 2.3 Slope as the Ratio $\frac{rise}{run}$

Suggested Pacing: 2 Days

In this lesson, students graph the given lines, and then they discover the ratio $\frac{rise}{run}$.

LESSON OBJECTIVES

■ Students will explore slope graphically, moving vertically and horizontally from one point on the line to another. They create "slope triangles" in this manner.

■ Students will find slope on the graph of the line as the ratio $\frac{rise}{run}$.

■ Students will discover that the slope of a horizontal line is 0.

■ Students will identify slope using tables, graphs and equations.

DAY 1	MATERIALS*	ESSENTIAL *ON YOUR OWN* QUESTIONS
A New Situation Creating Slope Triangles	**In Class** ■ Graph paper ■ Rulers ■ Colored pencils or markers ■ Graphing calculators ■ Lesson Guide 2.3A *Execustay's Conference Center* (optional) ■ Lesson Guide 2.3 *A New Situation* ■ Lesson Guide 2.3 *Creating Slope Triangles*	Questions 4 ,5, 7a, 7b, 11–14;
DAY 2	MATERIALS*	ESSENTIAL *ON YOUR OWN* QUESTIONS
A New Look at Drawing Slope Triangles Staying the Same		Questions 1, 2, 3, 6, 7c, 8, 9, 15

* The Think Like a Mathematician Daily Record Sheet should be used daily

---

MATHEMATICALLY SPEAKING

▶ $\frac{rise}{run}$

LESSON 2.3 Slope as the Ratio $\frac{\text{rise}}{\text{run}}$

➡ Start It Off

Simplify the following:

1. $\frac{120}{40}$

2. $\frac{1.5}{3}$

3. $\frac{6}{0}$

4. $\frac{0}{4}$

5. $\frac{4}{0.25}$

6. $\frac{0.5}{0.2}$

7. $\frac{-16}{-3200}$

8. $\frac{-32}{-4}$

Let's take a look at $y = 1x$. We can also write this as $y = x$, since $1 \times x = x$. This function represents the situation where a bottle of water costs $1 per person.

This means that y, the cost, will increase by $1 as x increases by 1 person.

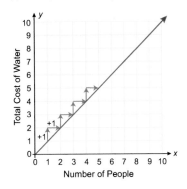

To show this change on the graph, first we move UP 1 unit. This shows the increase in y, the cost. Then move OVER 1. This shows the increase in x, the number of people. We call the triangles we have drawn "slope triangles." These will be useful in later problems in which we find the slope of a line.

MATHEMATICALLY SPEAKING
▶ rise run

Many times mathematicians talk about the slope of a line in terms of the ratio, $\frac{\text{rise}}{\text{run}}$. This is read as "rise over run."

The rise is the amount of vertical change (the change in the y-value).

The run is the amount of horizontal change (the change in the x-value).

---

1. 3

2. $\frac{1}{2}$

3. undefined

4. 0

5. 16

6. $\frac{5}{2}$

7. $\frac{1}{200}$

8. 8

DAY 1

TEACHING THE LESSON

As students graph the given lines, they discover the phrase "rise over run" written as the ratio $\frac{\text{rise}}{\text{run}}$. They will also see that they can use any two points on a line to determine its slope. Please note in this unit we are purposely NOT introducing the traditional formula for slope, $\frac{(y_2 - y_1)}{(x_2 - x_1)}$. This formula often confuses students as they don't understand subscripts or why they are subtracting values. Rather we focus on the change in y and the change in x in a table and as a visual interpretation of $\frac{\text{rise}}{\text{run}}$ on the graph. This strengthens students' understanding of slope and will help them make sense of the formula when it is introduced later in an algebra course.

We also want students to understand that the slope of a line represents a constant rate of change. Ask them to find the slope of a given line using different slope triangles. Don't think of this as redundant. It is necessary, at least for some students, to do this to reinforce the idea that a line has a constant rate of change and that it does not matter which points they choose.

➡ Start It Off

This initial exercise will help students recall how to simplify ratios, which is necessary in finding the slope of a line. They will see ratios with a numerator or denominator of 0. You should discuss why it is impossible to divide by 0, yet if the numerator is 0, then the fraction is 0. Students also need to recall that if the numerator and denominator are both negative, the result is a positive number. This will come up in finding the slope using slope triangles.

Begin the lesson by reading together and discussing as a class how the relationship between the variables can be illustrated on a graph using slope triangles.

Discuss with students that the rate of change associated with slope is referred to as "rise over run," written $\frac{\text{rise}}{\text{run}}$. To help students remember that run represents a change in x-values, you might connect run to the fact that humans run horizontally. To help students remember that rise represents a vertical change, you can discuss how a building rises as it is being built. The y-axis goes up and down, and so rise is associated with changes in the y-values.

1. a) When the total cost of the water changes from 2 to 3, the number of people also increases from 2 to 3. The ratio of the change in the y-value compared to change in the x-value is $\frac{1}{1}$, so the slope is 1.

   b) When the total cost of the water changes from 4 to 5, the number of people also increases from 4 to 5. The ratio of the change in the y-value compared to change in the x-value is $\frac{1}{1}$, so the slope is 1.

   c) When the total cost of the water changes from 9 to 10, the number of people also increases from 9 to 10. The ratio of the change in the y-value compared to change in the x-value is $\frac{1}{1}$, therefore the slope is 1.

   d) In terms of "rise over run," for each rise of $1 (move vertically 1 unit), there is a run of 1 person (move horizontally one unit), so the slope is $\frac{\text{rise}}{\text{run}} = \frac{1}{1} = 1$.

As we trace the line from left to right, we move up 1 unit every time we move over 1 unit.

For the function $y = x$ its slope is given by:

$$\text{Slope} = \frac{\text{Change in the } y\text{-variable}}{\text{Change in the } x\text{-variable}} = \frac{\text{rise}}{\text{run}} = \frac{\$1 \text{ increase}}{1 \text{ person increase}} = 1$$

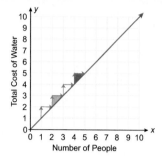

1. Use the slope triangles 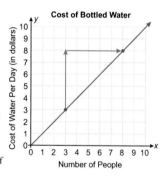 in the graph above.

   a) Find the slope of the line $y = x$ using the blue slope triangle between the points $(2, 2)$ and $(3, 3)$.

   b) Find the slope of the line $y = x$ using the red slope triangle between the points $(4, 4)$ and $(5, 5)$.

   c) Find the slope of the line $y = x$ when x changes from 9 to 10 people. Write the slope in fraction form.

   d) Describe the slope in terms of $\frac{\text{rise}}{\text{run}}$.

2. a) What happens to the cost of bottled water when the number of people increases from 3 to 8?

   b) Find the slope of the line $y = x$ when the number of people increases from 3 to 8. Use the slope triangle at the right and write the slope as a ratio.

   c) Describe the slope as "rise over run" when the number of people changes from 3 to 8.

You can find the slope of a line by looking at ANY two points on the graph.

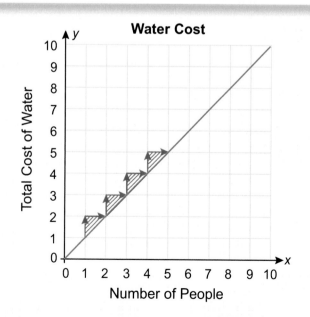

The slope of the line $y = x$ is 1 between any two points we choose.

3. Why is the slope of a linear function always the same no matter which points we use?

Hint
See page 155

A New Situation

If we change the relationship between the variables, the slope will change. For example, suppose the cost of the water is now $2 for every 1 person. This new relationship is represented by the red line below. But notice that the new red line (*b*) is steeper than the original green line (*a*).

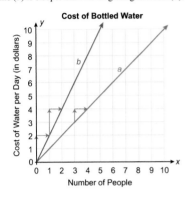

Cost of Bottled Water

Use the graph above to answer items 4–6.

4. Find the slope of line *b* using two different pairs of points. How does this compare to the slope of line *a*?

5. Draw the slope triangle between the points (4, 8) and (5, 10) on the red line *b*. Use this triangle to find the slope.

6. a) Describe the slope of line *b* in terms of $\frac{\text{rise}}{\text{run}}$.

   b) What is the real-world meaning of the point (4, 8)?

   c) What is the real-world meaning of the slope of line *b*?

   d) Write the equation for this function. How can you find the slope by looking at the equation?

3. All linear functions have a constant rate of change. The slope of a line is the same as its rate of change because the slope is a ratio of the change in the dependent variable to the change in the independent variable. Therefore, no matter what points we use to determine the slope of a particular line, the slope will always be the same.

A New Situation

Have students use Lesson Guide 2.3 *New Situation* to create triangles and answer the questions, which are repeated on the lesson guide. Be sure to discuss the special format for linear equations, $y = mx$, where *m* is a numerical value that represents the slope of a line and is the coefficient of *x*.

4. The set of points students will use may vary. With water bottles now costing $2 each, the slope is $\frac{2}{1}$ or 2.

This line is twice as steep as the line with a slope of 1.

5. The slope of the line is 2.

2. a) The cost of bottled water increases by $5.

b) The slope is $\frac{5}{5} = \frac{1}{1} = 1$.

c) When the number of people increases from 3 to 8, the run (horizontal move to the right) is 5 units while the cost of water—the rise—increases by 5 dollars (a vertical move upwards of 5 units). Therefore, the $\frac{\text{rise}}{\text{run}}$ ratio is $\frac{5}{5}$.

6. a) As the number of people increases by 1 (a horizontal run of 1 on the graph), the cost of the water increases by $2 (a vertical rise of 2 on the graph). So $\frac{\text{rise}}{\text{run}} = \frac{2}{1}$.

b) If 4 people are at the conference, bottled water will cost $8.

c) For every increase of 1 person, there will be a $2 increase in the cost of bottled water.

d) The equation is $y = 2x$ where y is the cost for bottled water in dollars for x people at the conference. In an equation written in this form, the slope is the numerical coefficient of x. So, in this case, the slope is 2.

Creating Slope Triangles

Next pass out Lesson Guide 2.3 *Creating Slope Triangles* for students to create slope triangles for the graphs in Question 7a. Circulate and observe students as they are working. Use the Student Snapshot observation tool to take notes and assess student understanding of the key ideas presented in this lesson.

 **Talk Moves** Discuss student responses as a class when finished. Use talk moves, such as adding on and agree/disagree and why, to clarify misconceptions and deepen understanding.

7. a) Students will use different slope triangles. Slope for the line of Graph A is 4, slope for the line of Graph B is $\frac{5}{2}$, slope for line of Graph C is $\frac{1}{4}$. Have students share the way they determined the slope using the

---

Creating Slope Triangles

7. Create two slope triangles on each line and calculate the slope of the line. For graphs A and C, locate one slope triangle in the third quadrant.

Graph A

Graph B

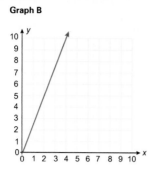

Graph C

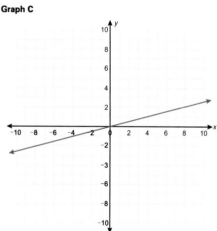

---

triangles they created in the third quadrants. These involve negative coordinates.

b) Table 1 matches Graph C. Table 2 matches Graph A. Table 3 matches Graph B.

c) The slope of Table 1 is $\frac{1}{4}$. The slope of Table 2 is 4. The slope of Table 3 is $\frac{5}{2}$. These slopes match those found by the slope triangles.

d) For Table 1, the recursive rule is *New = Previous + 0.25*. For Table 2, the recursive rule is *New = Previous + 4*. For Table 3, the recursive rule is *New = Previous + 2.5*.

b) Match the table of values with the graphs of the lines on the previous page.

Table 1	
x	**y**
0	0
4	1
5	1.25
6	1.5

Table 2	
x	**y**
0	0
1	4
1.25	5
1.5	6

Table 3	
x	**y**
0	0
1	2.5
2	5
4	10

c) Use the tables to calculate the slope of each function by finding the rate of change. Does this match the slope found by using slope triangles?

Many ideas that you study in linear relationships connect to one another.

d) State the recursive rule for each function.

e) How is the recursive rule for each function connected to the slope of the line?

f) Match the equations with their graphs. Find the slope of each line by using just the equation. Does this match the slope found using the slope triangles and the tables?

Equation 1 $y = 2.5x$

Equation 2 $y = 0.25x$

Equation 3 $y = 4x$

g) How is each equation connected to the slope of the line?

e) The number added to the previous number to get the new value is the slope of the line.

f) Equation 1 matches Graph B. Equation 2 matches Graph C. Equation 3 matches Graph A.

g) The coefficient of x is the slope of the line when the equation is written in the form $y = mx$. (Actually this is true for equations written in the form $y = mx + b$. In all equations students have been exposed to in this unit to date, $b = 0$.) They will work with equations of the form $y = mx + b$ in the next section, where the y-intercept is introduced.

Differentiation

Think Differently: For students who need further practice before completing the *On Your Own* questions, Lesson Guide 2.3A offers additional problem-solving exercises.

Summarize Day 1

As a wrap up for Day 1, ask students to talk with their partners about how they can identify the slope from the recursive rule and the equation of the line.

DAY

2 TEACHING THE LESSON

A New Look at Drawing Slope Triangles

8. a) Kalina found the slope ratio of $\frac{\text{rise}}{\text{run}}$ by drawing a slope triangle below or underneath the graph of the line. The $\frac{\text{rise}}{\text{run}}$ ratio is $\frac{-3}{-1}$, which is equal to 3.

Yes, this is a valid way to find slope.

Pass out another copy of Lesson Guide 2.3 *Creating Slope Triangles*. Have students compete it using Kalina's method and compare this to the original slope triangles they made the first time.

b) and c) Students should find the ratio of $\frac{\text{rise}}{\text{run}}$ to be the same. They will calculate a negative run value and a negative rise value which when divided will be a positive slope.

d) The slope of a line can be found by selecting any two points on the line, drawing a right triangle between the two points, with the hypotenuse along the line, and determining the ratio comparing the rise (the change in *y*-values) to the run (the change in *x*-values).

Staying the Same

9. a) $y = 250$ where *y* is the cost to rent the audiovisual equipment.

b)

Days of Rental	Total Cost
1	250
2	250
6	250
10	250

c) The rate of change is 0.

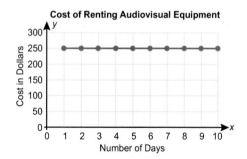

Cost of Renting Audiovisual Equipment

d) Graph above. The graph is a horizontal line where every *y* value is 250.

e) *y* changes by 0 as *x* increases by 1.

f) Using any two consecutive on the graph points students will find $\frac{\text{rise}}{\text{run}} = \frac{0}{1} = 0$. So the slope is 0.

A New Look at Drawing Slope Triangles

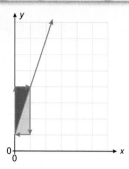

Kody and Kalina were asked to find the slope of the line above. Kody drew the red triangle ( ), starting at $x = 0$ and $y = 1$. He found that, as the *y*-value increased by 3 units, the *x*-value increased by 1 unit. He found the $\frac{\text{rise}}{\text{run}} = \frac{3}{1}$. He said the slope is 3.

Kalina drew the pink triangle ( ), starting at $x = 1$ and $y = 4$. She found that, as the *y*-value decreased by 3 units, the *x*-value decreased by 1 unit. She said the $\frac{\text{rise}}{\text{run}}$ was $\frac{-3}{-1}$. The rise is actually a fall! The value is negative. The run goes "backwards" on the graph from right to left so that is also a negative value. But you still get 3 because a negative number divided by a negative number gives a positive value. She also said the slope is 3.

8. a) Is Kalina's method a correct way to find the slope of a line? Think about the definition of slope.

b) Use Kalina's method to find the slope of the lines in Question 7.

c) Compare these slopes to the ones you found earlier.

d) Make a generalization about finding the slope of the line using triangles.

g) The cost of renting the projector remains the same as the number of days increases. There is no change in the total rental cost over any rental period.

h) This is a constant rate of change.

10. The slope of any horizontal line is 0. When comparing the change in *y*-values of a horizontal line (a rise of 0) to the change in *x*-values, the ratio is $\frac{0}{\text{change in } x}$, making the slope of the horizontal line 0.

 This is a constant rate of change, the constant 0.

9. The cost of renting an LCD projector is $250. This is a one-time charge for the entire conference. It does not depend on the length of the conference.

   a) Let x be the number of days the conference runs and y be cost. Write an equation for this situation.

   Hint
   See page 155

   b) Create a table of values for renting the projector for 1, 2, 6, and 10 days.

   c) Find the rate of change.

   d) Graph the points from the table and connect them. Describe the graph.

   e) As x changes, what is the change in y?

   f) Find the slope of the line.

   g) What is the real-world meaning of the slope in this situation?

   h) Is this a constant or varying rate of change?

10. What is the slope of any horizontal line? Why?

How are slope and the rate of change connected in a given situation? How can you find the slope of a linear function using its graph? How can you find slope of a linear function using its equation? How can you find the slope of a linear function using its table of values?

MATHEMATICALLY
SPEAKING
▸ $\frac{\text{rise}}{\text{run}}$

- Slope is the numerical value m (the coefficient of x) in the equation $y = mx$.

- Using a table of values, slope can be found by finding the ratio of the change in the y-values compared to the change in the x-values over intervals of equal size.

Reflect

Use these questions to help you reflect on the lesson and plan for future instruction.

- How readily are students able to identify slope using tables, graphs and equations?

- Do students understand the connection between slope and a constant rate of change?

- What are some misconceptions related to slope that need to be addressed in future instruction to solidify student understanding?

Student responses will vary. Guide the discussion to include the following key ideas:

- Slope is a ratio between the variables in a given situation in which the change in the dependent variable (y-values) is compared to the change in the independent variable (x-values).

- Slope can be found on the graph by selecting two points on a line, creating slope triangles and determining the rise (change in y-values) compared to the run (change in x-values) and expressed this as the ratio $\frac{rise}{run}$.

1. **Write About It** Answers will vary. Student responses should include the following key ideas:

- The rate of change in a function is the ratio of the change in the *y*-variable to the corresponding change in the *x*-variable.

- A linear function has a constant rate of change.

- The slope of a line is a physical representation of the change in the *y*-variable as the *x*-variable changes. It indicates the steepness of the line.

- The slope is the ratio that represents the rate of change. Slope is the comparison in the change in the dependent variable (*y*-values) to the change in the independent variable (*x*-values) over a specific interval.

- The slope is
$$\frac{\text{change in vertical distance}}{\text{change in horizontal distance}} = \frac{\text{rise}}{\text{run}}.$$

2. Answers will vary.

   a) The coefficient of *x* must be greater than $1\frac{1}{3}$.

   b) The coefficient of *x* must be less than $1\frac{1}{3}$.

3. **a)** The recursive rule is *New = Previous + 2.*

   b) The number added (2) is the slope of the line.

Write About It

1. Explain to a friend the meaning of slope. Use the words $\frac{rise}{run}$, *ratio*, *change in x*, *change in y*, *linear relationship*, *function* and *rate* in your explanation.

2. Use your graphing calculator to check your answers.

   a) Write an equation of a line whose graph is steeper than the graph of $y = 1\frac{1}{3}x$.

   b) Write an equation of a line whose graph is less steep than the graph of $y = 1\frac{1}{3}x$.

3. **a)** State the recursive rule for the cost of the bottled water if it costs $2 per person.

   b) How is the recursive rule connected to the slope?

   c) State the explicit rule as an equation for this situation.

   d) How is the equation connected to the slope?

4. **True or False.** The slope of a line always represents a constant rate of change. Explain your answer.

5. **Geometry Connection.**

   a) Slope triangles on the same line are always:

      i) congruent

      ii) similar

      iii) equilateral

      iv) none of these

   b) Explain your answer.

6. Describe a new situation that can be represented by a graph that is a horizontal line. Write an equation for the situation, and tell what *x* and *y* represent. Then graph your equation.

---

   c) $y = 2x$ where *y* is the cost in dollars for bottled water for *x* persons.

   d) The coefficient of *x* is the slope of the line.

4. True. Slope represents the ratio of the change in *y*-values to the change in the corresponding *x*-values between any two points on the line. When there is a constant rate of change, the points on the graph are aligned in a straight line; therefore the rate of change of a line is always constant and equal to the slope.

7. Remember these situations from Lesson 2.2 *On Your Own* Question 9, p. 71.

Situation 1: A tip for porter service is $1.50 for each piece of luggage.

Situation 2: The cost of a phone call is $0.75 per call.

Situation 3: The cost of copying a page of paper is $0.25.

Look back at your graphs of each situation.

    a) Find the slope of each line using two different slope triangles. How does this compare to the coefficient of x in each equation?

    b) Explain what the slope of the line means in each situation.

    c) Use Kalina's method on page 78 to find the slope of each line. Compare these slopes to the ones you found in Part a.

8. Match each graph or table to its slope or equation.

a)

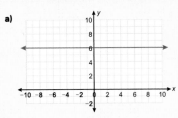

  i) slope $= \frac{3}{4}$

  ii) slope $= 5$

  iii) $y = 6$

  iv) $y = 3.5x$

b)

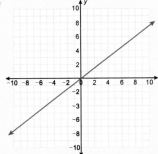

NOTE ↓↑ Some slope triangles are also congruent. It is important that students recognize that these congruent triangles are also similar.

6. Answers may vary. Example: There were 24 cars on sale at an auto dealership. The dealership was open for 8 hours. However, due to a severe snowstorm, no one came by to purchase a car.

The equation is $y = 24$.

The independent variable (x-values) is the time in hours that the dealership was open and the dependent variable (y-values) is the number of cars for sale at the auto dealership.

5. **a)** ii) similar

  b) All slope triangles are similar because they have corresponding angles that are congruent and the lengths of corresponding sides are proportional. The ratio of the vertical leg length to the horizontal leg length in each slope triangle is actually the slope of the line and is a constant. Thus, corresponding sides are always in proportion.

7. **a)** Situation 1:

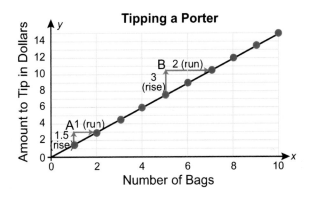

Situation 2:

Cost of Phone Calls

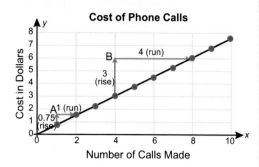

Situation 3:

Cost of Photocopying

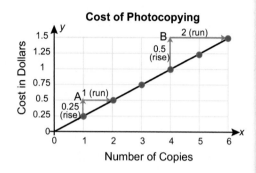

Situation 1 (Tip for a Porter):

A. $\frac{\text{rise}}{\text{run}} = \frac{1.5}{1} = 1.5$

B. $\frac{\text{rise}}{\text{run}} = \frac{3}{2} = 1.5$

The slopes from the graph and the coefficient of x are the same: 1.5.

Situation 2 (Phone Cost):

A. $\frac{\text{rise}}{\text{run}} = \frac{0.75}{1} = 0.75$

B. $\frac{\text{rise}}{\text{run}} = \frac{3}{4} = 0.75$

The slope from the graph and the coefficient of x are the same: 0.75.

Situation 3 (Photocopying Cost):

A. $\frac{\text{rise}}{\text{run}} = \frac{0.25}{1} = 0.25$

B. $\frac{\text{rise}}{\text{run}} = \frac{0.50}{2} = 0.25$

The slope of the graph and the coefficient of x are the same: 0.25.

c)

x	y
1	0
3	10
5	20
7	30

d)

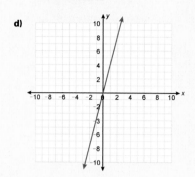

9. **a)** Graph the line $x = 4$.

   b) Can you find the slope of this line? Explain.

   ? **Hint** See page 155

   c) What will be the slope of any vertical line? Why?

 Think Beyond

10. On a coordinate plane, for a–e, draw a line through (0, 0) with:

   a) slope $= \frac{1}{2}$ **d)** slope $= \frac{1}{3}$

   b) slope $= 1$ **e)** slope $= 3$

   c) slope $= 0$

   Label each line with its slope. Compare the lines that you have drawn.

   Here is the first one to help you out.

   f) Using words, describe the rate of change of the linear function on the graph.

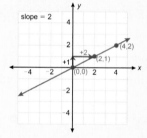

NOTE It is important that students make the connection that the slopes of 1.5 and $\frac{3}{2}$, of 0.75 and $\frac{3}{4}$, and of 0.25 and $\frac{1}{4}$ are the same. Be sure to discuss this idea of equivalence.

b) Situation 1: As the number of pieces of luggage increase by 1, the tip increases by $1.50.

Situation 2. As the number of phone calls increases by 1, the total cost increases by $0.75.

Situation 3: As the number of pages copied increases by 1, the total cost increases by $0.25.

c)

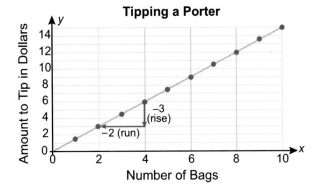

Tipping a Porter

$\dfrac{\text{rise}}{\text{run}} = \dfrac{-3}{-2}$,

Slope is $\dfrac{3}{2}$ or 1.5.

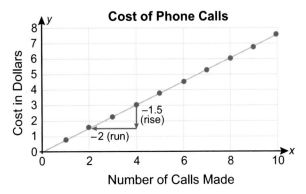

Cost of Phone Calls

$\dfrac{\text{rise}}{\text{run}} = \dfrac{-1.5}{-2}$,

Slope is $\dfrac{3}{4}$ or 0.75.

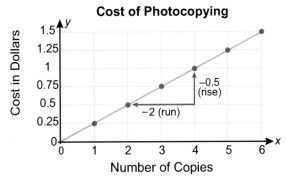

Cost of Photocopying

$\dfrac{\text{rise}}{\text{run}} = \dfrac{-0.5}{-2}$ Slope is $\dfrac{1}{4}$, or 0.25.

The slopes are the same as those found in Part a.

8. a) iii

  b) i

  c) ii

  d) iv

9. a)

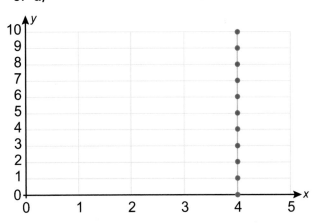

b) You cannot find the slope of this line. Possible response: Slope is defined as the ratio of the change in y-values compared to the corresponding change in x-values. Using the following two points on the given line, (4, 1) and (4, 2), the change in y-values (rise) is 1 and the change in x-values (run) is 0.

$\dfrac{\text{rise}}{\text{run}} = \dfrac{1}{0}$

Since you cannot divide by 0, the slope of the line cannot be determined and is undefined.

c) The slope of any vertical line will always be undefined. Since the change in x-values is 0, and we cannot divide by 0, the slope will always be undefined.

Think Beyond

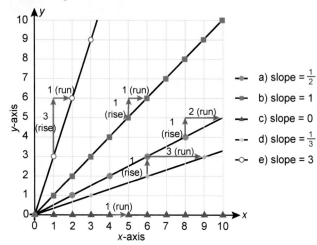

a) slope = $\frac{1}{2}$

b) slope = 1

c) slope = 0

d) slope = $\frac{1}{3}$

e) slope = 3

a) The rate of change is a constant $\frac{1}{2}$. The change in y (rise) is 1 while the change in x (run) is 2, so the slope is $\frac{1}{2}$.

b) The rate of change is a constant $\frac{1}{1}$. The change in y (rise) is 1 and the change in x (run) is 1. This represents a slope of $\frac{1}{1}$, or 1. This line has the second steepest slope since it has the second greatest slope value.

c) The rate of change is 0. The change in y (rise) is 0 for any change in x. This represents a slope of $\frac{0}{1}$ or 0. Since this line has a slope of 0, it is a horizontal line and has the lowest slope.

d) The rate of change is $\frac{1}{3}$. The change in y (rise) is 1 when the change in x (run) is 3. This represents a slope of $\frac{1}{3}$. Since this line has a slope of $\frac{1}{3}$, its slope is not as steep as the line that has a slope of $\frac{1}{2}$ or 1.

e) The rate of change is 3. The change in y (rise) is 3 when the change in x (run) is 1. This represents a slope of $\frac{3}{1}$, or 3. Since this line has a slope of 3, its slope is the steepest of all the lines, since the slope value is the greatest.

Think Back

11. In the formula $d = r \times t$, d is the distance traveled, r is the rate of travel, and t is the time traveled. If $d = 24$ and $r = 3$, then $t =$

   A. $\frac{1}{8}$ **B.** 8   **C.** 21   **D.** 72

12. Eighteen is twelve less than five times 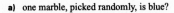.

13. Evaluate the following.

   a) $16 - 25$

   b) $16 - (-25)$

   c) $-16 + (-25)$

   d) $-16 - (-25)$

14. Timothy has five marbles in a bag. Three are blue and two are red. What is the probability that:

   a) one marble, picked randomly, is blue?

   b) two marbles, picked randomly without replacing the first one, are blue?

   c) three marbles, picked randomly without replacement, are blue?

   d) four marbles, picked randomly without replacement, are blue?

15. Jeff is to find the area of circle with a radius of 6 cm. He knows that the formula is $A = \pi r^2$. Using 3.14 for π, he found 3.14×6. Then he squared the answer and got 354.9456 sq cm. He said that seemed too large. Do you agree with Jeff? Why or why not? If you agree with Jeff, find the actual area of the circle.

 Think Back

11. b) 8

12. six

13. a) -9

   b) 41

   c) -41

   d) 9

14. a) $\frac{3}{5}$

   b) $\frac{3}{10} = \left(\frac{3}{5} \cdot \frac{1}{2}\right)$ $\frac{3}{5} \cdot \frac{1}{2} \cdot \frac{1}{3}$

   c) $\frac{1}{10} = \left(\frac{3}{5} \cdot \frac{1}{2} \cdot \frac{1}{3}\right)$

   d) 0

15. Jeff should have squared the 6 before multiplying by 3.14, getting $36 \cdot 3.14$ or 113.04 sq cm.

Let's revisit Execustay's fees. Previously we looked at the cost per day.
Now let's make a table for the total cost as the number of days increases.

1. Complete the table below to find the total cost of Internet access
for the first 10 days if Execustay were hosting the conference.

Total Cost for Execustay's Conference Fees	
Number of Days	**Total Cost for Center's Fees**
1	$10
2	$20
3	$30
4	
5	
6	
7	
8	
9	
10	

a) Make a graph of the table above. Make three different slope triangles
connecting points on the line. Find the $\frac{\text{rise}}{\text{run}}$ for each of these triangles.

b) What is the slope of the line?

c) What is the real-world meaning of the slope of this function?

d) Write the rule or equation for this situation.

e) How can you find the slope of the line by using the explicit rule?

f) Write the recursive rule for this situation.

g) How can you find the slope by using the recursive rule?

Lesson Guide 2.3A *Execustay Conference Center* (Answer Key)

Let's revisit Execustay's fees. Previously we looked at the cost per day.
Now let's make a table for the total cost as the number of days increases.

1. Complete the table below to find the total cost of Internet access
for the first 10 days if Execustay were hosting the conference.

Total Cost for Execustay's Conference Fees	
Number of Days	**Total Cost for Center's Fees**
1	$10
2	$20
3	$30
4	$40
5	$50
6	$60
7	$70
8	$80
9	$90
10	$100

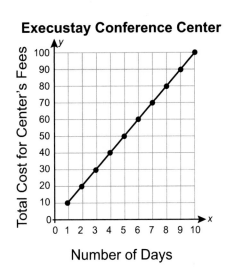

Execustay Conference Center

Total Cost for Center's Fees (y-axis: 0, 10, 20, 30, 40, 50, 60, 70, 80, 90, 100)

Number of Days (x-axis: 0 1 2 3 4 5 6 7 8 9 10)

a) Make a graph of the table above. Make three different slope triangles
connecting points on the line. Find the $\frac{\text{rise}}{\text{run}}$ for each of these triangles.

Triangles will vary. All $\frac{\text{rise}}{\text{run}}$ ratios should be 10.

b) What is the slope of the line? $\frac{10}{1}$ **or 10**

c) What is the real-world meaning of the slope of this function?
**The total cost to have Internet access at the conference center
increases $10 per day.**

d) Write the rule or equation for this situation. $y = 10x$

e) How can you find the slope of the line by using the explicit rule?
The slope is the coefficient of x.

f) Write the recursive rule for this situation. *New = Previous + 10.*

g) How can you find the slope by using the recursive rule? **You can use
the recursive rule to find slope by comparing the change in the
y-values (10) to the change in x-values (1), creating a ratio.**

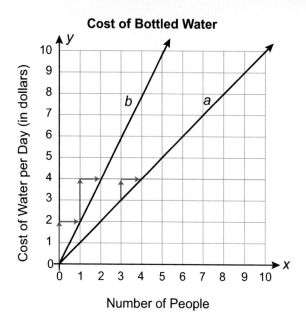

Cost of Bottled Water

Cost of Water per Day (in dollars)

Number of People

4. Find the slope of line *b* using two different pairs of points.
   How does this compare to the slope of line *a*?

5. Draw the slope triangle between the points (4, 8) and (5, 10) on the red line *b*.
   Use this triangle to find the slope.

6. **a)** Describe the slope of Line B in terms of $\frac{\text{rise}}{\text{run}}$.

   b) What is the real-world meaning of the point (4, 8)?

   c) What is the real-world meaning of the slope of line *b*?

   d) Write the equation for this function.
   How can you find the slope by looking at the equation?

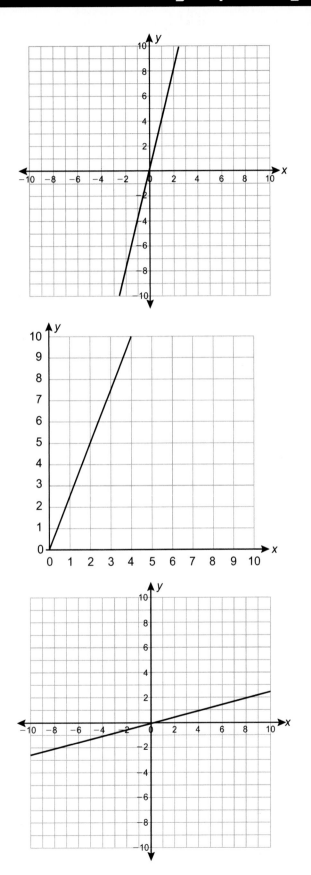

LESSON 2.4 Increasing and Decreasing Functions

Suggested Pacing: 1 Day

Students will continue to explore the slope, using equations, tables and graphs. They will discover that the rate of change in some situation is negative. Students will explore real-world situations where the change in the y-values is negative while the change in x-values is positive. This results in a negative slope. Students will investigate and compare how positive and negative slopes are represented on a graph.

LESSON OBJECTIVES

- Students will explore positive and negative slopes and identify what they represent in a given situation.

DAY 1	MATERIALS*	ESSENTIAL *ON YOUR OWN* QUESTIONS
Going Up, Coming Down Comparing Increasing and Decreasing Functions Tiger Woods Comes to the Conference Making Generalizations About Slope	**In Class** ■ Graph paper ■ Graphing calculators ■ Lesson Guide 2.4A: *Scottsdale Conference* (optional) **On Your Own** ■ Graph paper ■ Graphing calculators	Questions 1, 2, 5, 7–9, 11–15

*The Think Like a Mathematician Daily Record Sheet should be used daily

---

MATHEMATICALLY SPEAKING

▶ decreasing function

 **Start It Off**

Answers:

1. $\dfrac{100}{67} \approx \dfrac{1.5}{1}$

2. $\dfrac{5{,}280}{1.5} = 3{,}520$ strides to walk a mile

3. Answers will vary. He would probably slow down a bit over the course of the mile, either shortening his stride or just taking fewer steps per minute.

4. Student answers may vary. Since it is highly unlikely that he walked at a consistent pace, there is no constant rate of change. Therefore, the graph would not look like a straight line because it does not represent a linear function.

5. He chose a longer length to get a more accurate average. Measuring over a few strides might give a misleading average.

6. Answers will vary.

DAY 1 · TEACHING THE LESSON

Going Up, Coming Down

Remind students about the previous conference planning situations in which the cost always increased as the number of participants increased. Guide students to recognize that the slopes representing these rates of change were positive. Caution students that this is not always the case. Ask:

- *Can you think of a real-world situation where the dependent variable is decreasing as the independent variable is increasing?*

Discuss the effect of an increase in the temperature on the number of people attending the conference in Scottsdale, Arizona. Have students complete Question 1 and share their responses in a class discussion.

 Differentiation

Think Differently: For those students experiencing difficulty in completing the table, offer Lesson Guide 2.4A to nudge student thinking forward. This accommodation guide includes a partially completed table to scaffold students' learning. This graphic organizer can be particularly helpful to ELL learners.

Discuss the $\dfrac{\text{rise}}{\text{run}}$ ratio for the Scottsdale situation. Draw students' attention to the fact that the slope is negative. Have students complete Question 2 independently and then share their responses with a partner before discussing them as a class. Emphasize that the graphs slant in different directions—a graph with a positive slope rises from left to right; a graph with a negative slope falls from left to right. Also, help students recognize that the steepness of the line is related to the absolute value of the slope. The greater the absolute value of the slope is, the steeper the line. A graph with a slope of $-\dfrac{1}{2}$ is not as steep as a graph with a slope of 2, since $\dfrac{1}{2}$ is less than 2. Similarly, a graph with a slope of -3 is steeper than a graph with a slope of 1.

1. a) The independent variable is the temperature in degrees Fahrenheit, and the dependent variable is the number of people attending the conference.

b) Scottsdale Conference

Temperatures in Degrees	Number of People Attending Conference
90	175
92	174
94	173
96	172
98	171
100	170
102	169
104	168

c) Predictions will vary. This function is linear.

d)

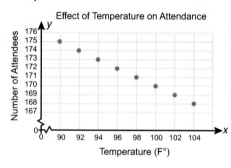

Effect of Temperature on Attendance

You should not connect the points. The set of numbers that represents the number of attendees is discrete so it does not make sense to connect the points.

e) The y-value decreases by 1 unit as the x-value increases by 2 units. The rate of change is -1 person per two-degree increase in temperature. The rates of change we looked at in previous lessons were different in that the y-values always increased as the x-values increased.

→ Start It Off

Tyrone checked the length of his stride. He found that it took him 67 strides to cross 100 ft.

1. Write Tyrone's stride length as a ratio of distance in feet to number of strides.
2. How many strides would it take him to walk a mile?
3. Do you think he could be consistent in his stride length for a mile?
4. If you graph the points (strides, total distance in feet) over the course of a mile, do you think they would represent a linear function? Explain.
5. Why do you think Tyrone crossed such a long distance to count his number of strides rather than just taking a few steps?
6. Find the length of your stride. Explain how you did it.

In Lesson 2.2, we looked at the Sports Mecca Conference situations about the cost of bottled water, lunch, and snack per person. These costs always increased as the number of people increased. So for every INCREASE in x (people), there was an INCREASE in y (cost), and the slope, which represents the ratio of the change in y to the change in x, was always positive.

Functions with positive slope are called increasing functions. However, not all functions are increasing. For example, when you walk up a hill, your speed usually decreases as your distance traveled up the hill increases.

Going Up, Coming Down

You are planning a conference in Scottsdale, Arizona to introduce a new line of golf clubs. Conference participants will be playing golf to test out the clubs. Scottsdale can get very hot, and, from past conferences, you have found out that something interesting generally happens.

Above 90° F, for every predicted *increase* in temperature of two degrees, there is an anticipated *decrease* of one person planning to come to the conference due to the outdoor heat. Suppose that you were originally anticipating 175 people at the conference.

Comparing Increasing and Decreasing Functions

Next, students have an opportunity to compare two functions that have slopes with the same absolute value, but whose graphs are lines that slant in different directions. It is important that students create these graphs by hand to see how the table of values affects the direction of the line.

1. a) Identify the independent and dependent variables in the situation.

   b) Make a table of values to show the decrease in the number of people based on the increase in temperature of up to 14 degrees above 90.

   c) Predict whether this relationship will be a linear function.

   d) Should you connect the points on the graph? Why or why not?

   e) What is the rate of change for this function? How does it compare to previous rates of change that we have looked at?

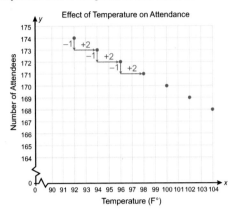

Effect of Temperature on Attendance

As x "runs," or increases by 2 (shown by the horizontal arrow), what happens to the y-values?

Writing this relationship as a ratio in the form $\frac{\text{rise}}{\text{run}}$, the "rise" is actually a negative value representing a decrease in the y-values. $\frac{\text{rise}}{\text{run}} = \frac{-1}{+2}$. Simplifying this ratio, we find that the slope is $-\frac{1}{2}$.

This function is a **decreasing function**; a decreasing linear function has a negative slope.

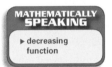

MATHEMATICALLY SPEAKING

▸ decreasing function

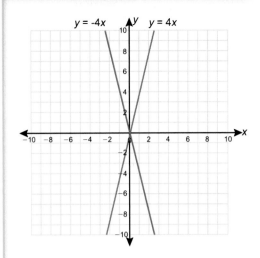

$y = -4x$ $y = 4x$

The similarity among the graphs is that they both represent a constant rate of change.

The difference between the graphs is that the lines are slanting in different directions.

   b) Both lines have the same steepness.

   c) The graph of $y = -4x$ has a negative slope. The line falls from left to right. The graph of $y = 4x$ has a positive slope. The line rises from left to right.

   d) The slope of the line $y = -4x$ is -4. The slope of $y = 4x$ is $+4$.

2. a) Tables might look like the following:

$y = 4x$

x	y
-2	-8
-1	-4
0	0
1	4
2	8

$y = -4x$

x	y
-2	8
-1	4
0	0
1	-4
2	-8

Tiger Woods Comes to the Conference

Discuss the effect on admission prices for the Tiger Woods speaking engagement at the conference.

Ask:

• **Does this situation represent a rate of change where both variables are increasing? Why or why not?**

Talk Moves Have students work with a partner to complete Question 3. Encourage students to share their responses as a class when finished. Encourage students to use talk moves, such as repeat/rephrase and adding on, to clarify their ideas and extend the discussion.

3. **a)** The independent variable is the admission charge and the dependent variable is the number of people attending the event.

b)

Effect of an Increase in Admission Price for the Event	
Admission Charge in Dollars	Number of People Attending the Event
0	150
10	147
20	144
30	141
40	138
50	135
60	132
70	129
80	126
90	123
100	120

c) Predictions may vary. This is a linear function that is decreasing. As the value of the independent variable (admission charge) increases, the value of the dependent variable (number of people attending the event) decreases.

Comparing Increasing and Decreasing Functions

2. **a)** Make a table of values for $y = 4x$ and $y = -4x$ and graph the lines on the same grid.

Compare these two functions as you look across their graphs from left to right. Discuss with your partner how the two lines are similar and how they are different.

b) Compare the steepness of the two lines.

c) Compare the direction of the two lines.

d) Compare the slope of the two lines.

Tiger Woods Comes to the Conference

© Dept. of Defense

You are planning to bring Tiger Woods as a guest speaker for the conference. You must charge admission for this special event. You have determined that for every ten-dollar increase in the price of admission, there will be three fewer people who will come to hear Tiger Woods speak. You anticipate that 150 people will come if there is no charge.

3. **a)** Identify the independent and dependent variables in the situation.

b) Create a table of values to show the relationship between the number of people attending the event and the cost of admission (up to $100).

c) Predict whether the function is linear and whether it will be increasing or decreasing.

d) Graph the function on a grid paper. Was your prediction correct?

e) What is the rate of change in the number of attendees per unit increase in the cost of admission?

f) Find the slope of the graph of the function.

g) How can you determine the slope from the table of values created in Part b?

h) What does the rate of change mean in terms of the real-world situation?

d)

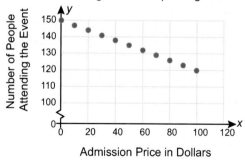

Effect of an Increase in Admission Price for the Tiger Woods Speaking Event

e) There is a 3-person decrease in attendance for every $10 increase in the admission price.

f)

Effect of an Increase in Admission Price
for the Tiger Woods Speaking Event

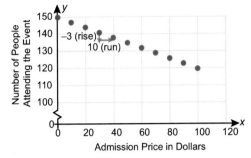

$$\frac{\text{rise}}{\text{run}} = \frac{-3}{10} \quad \text{The slope is } -\frac{3}{10}.$$

g) Select two data points on the table. Find the change in the *y*-values of two points and the change in the corresponding *x*-values. The slope is the ratio that represents the change in *y*-values (numerator) compared to the change in *x*-values (denominator).

For example, an admission charge of 10 dollars results in an attendance of 147 people and an admission charge of 20 dollars will result in an attendance of 144 people. The change in attendance is −3 and the change in the admission cost is +10. Therefore, the slope of the line is $-\frac{3}{10}$.

h) There is a 3-person drop in attendance for every $10 increase in admission price.

Making Generalizations About Slope

Have students work independently on Questions 4–6 and then have them share their responses with the class. Do not rush a discussion. It is important that students are able to generalize and make connections between the direction and the steepness of lines and their slopes.

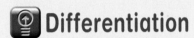 **Differentiation**

Think Differently: For students ready for further challenges, assign Think Beyond Question 7.

4. a) Predictions may vary. Possible response:

 The graph of $y = \frac{1}{2}x$ will appear as a line rising from left to right. The graph of $y = -\frac{1}{2}x$ will appear as a line falling from left to right. The lines slant in opposite directions, but have the same steepness.

The slope of $y = \frac{1}{2}x$ is $\frac{1}{2}$ and the slope of $y = -\frac{1}{2}x$ is $-\frac{1}{2}$.

The rate of change for $y = \frac{1}{2}x$ is a 1-unit increase in the y-value for every 2-unit increase in the x-value. The rate of change for $y = -\frac{1}{2}x$ is a 1-unit decrease in the y-value for every 2-unit increase in the x-value.

b) $y = \frac{1}{2}x$ $y = -\frac{1}{2}x$

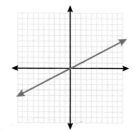 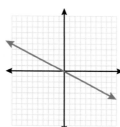

The graphs match the predictions listed above for Part a. The function $y = \frac{1}{2}x$ is an increasing function because the coefficient for x is positive. The function $y = -\frac{1}{2}x$ is a decreasing function because the coefficient for x is negative.

5. a) Equations will vary. The slopes should be opposites, or additive inverses, of each other.

Possible response: $y = 3x$ and $y = -3x$

b) The graph of $y = 3x$ is a line with a slope of 3, and will rise from left to right.

The graph of $y = -3x$ is a line with a slope of -3, and will have the same steepness as the graph of $y = 3x$. However, it will slant in the opposite direction, falling from left to right.

c)

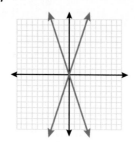

6. Possible response: $y = x$ and $y = -\frac{3}{4}x$

7.  **Think Beyond** Answers will vary depending on equations listed. Possible response:

for $y = 3x$: The local movie theater charges $3 for each person attending the movie.

for $y = -3x$: Bill had 3 minutes of his computer time taken away every time he forgot to pick up his clothes off the floor.

Wrap It Up

Answers will vary. Student discussion should include the following key ideas:

- A slope of $-\frac{1}{2}$ in the Scottsdale conference situation means that there is a decrease of 1 person for every 2° Fahrenheit increase in temperature.

- The graph of a line with a positive slope will appear to rise from left to right. The positive slope indicates that there is an increase in both variables.

- The graph of a line with a negative slope will appear to fall from left to right. The negative slope indicates that one variable is increasing while the other is decreasing.

Making Generalizations About Slope

4. **a)** Predict how the graphs, the slopes and the steepness of the lines for the functions $y = \frac{1}{2}x$ and $y = -\frac{1}{2}x$ will compare.

   b) Use a graphing calculator and graph both functions. Which function is increasing? Which function is decreasing? How can you tell that by looking at their equations?

5. **a)** Write two linear equations whose lines will have the same steepness when graphed on the same coordinate grid, but will slant in opposite directions.

   b) Find the slope of each line and describe the direction of the corresponding graph.

   c) Graph the equations on your calculator to check your work.

6. Write equations for two linear functions. One should have a slope that is $\frac{3}{4}$ of the slope of the other. The lines should slant in opposite directions.

 Think Beyond

7. Create real-world situations for each equation from Questions 5.

 **rap It Up**

Discuss with a partner.

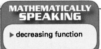
MATHEMATICALLY SPEAKING
▶ decreasing function

• What does slope mean in a specific situation? Give an example.

• How are positive and negative slopes related to increasing and decreasing functions?

Reflect

Use these questions to help you reflect on the lesson and plan for future instruction.

• To what extent can students predict and describe the slope of a linear function when the rate of change is positive or negative?

• What strategies do students use to identify the slope of a linear function from a graph?

See corresponding assessments in Assessment Resources.

The exercises in On Your Own can help students make sense of what they have learned about the slope in Lessons 2.2, 2.3, and 2.4. They are very important to discuss.

1. **Write About It** I agree with Crystal. Explanations will vary. Student explanations should include the following key ideas:

- Lines that fall from left to right have negative slopes. The rate of change is negative, since the *y*-values are decreasing as the *x*-values are increasing.

- Lines that rise from left to right have positive slopes. The rate of change is positive, since the *y*-values are increasing as the *x*-values are increasing.

2. When the equation of the line is written in the form $y = mx$, *m* is the coefficient of the variable *x*, which represents the slope of the line. When the numerical value of *m* (the coefficient) is positive, the slope is positive. When the numerical value of *m* is negative, the slope is negative.

3. **a)** The line is falling from left to right on the graph.

   b) As the *x*-values increase by 1, the *y*-values decrease by 2.

   c) A line with a slope of 2 is a line rising from left to right. As the *x*-values increase by 1, the *y*-values increase by 2.

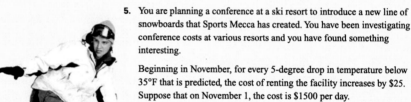

Write About It

1. Crystal states that she can tell whether a line has a positive or a negative slope just by looking at it. Do you agree or disagree with her? Explain your answer. Use the term "rate of change" in your explanation.

2. How can you tell if a line has a positive or negative slope by looking at its equation?

3. Gina drew a line with a slope of −2.

   a) Describe what the line looks like as you move across the graph from left to right.

   b) Describe the rate of change of the variables.

   c) How would this line compare to a line with a slope of 2?

4. Give an example of a real-world situation involving a linear function whose graph has a slope of:

   a) 6

   b) $-\frac{1}{3}$

   c) 0

5. You are planning a conference at a ski resort to introduce a new line of snowboards that Sports Mecca has created. You have been investigating conference costs at various resorts and you have found something interesting.

   Beginning in November, for every 5-degree drop in temperature below 35°F that is predicted, the cost of renting the facility increases by $25. Suppose that on November 1, the cost is $1500 per day.

   a) Describe this situation in terms of the variables and the rate of change.

   b) Predict whether or not the relationship is linear and whether it will be increasing or decreasing as you move along the graph from left to right.

   c) Graph the function and find the slope of the line.

   d) Name two points on the graph and describe what they represent in terms of the given situation.

---

4. Answers will vary. Possible response:

   a) Tickets to the basketball game cost $6 per person.

   b) For every 1° drop in temperature, three more logs are added to the fire.

   c) The cost of renting a hall for a party is $50 regardless of the number of people attending.

5. **a)** The independent variable is the temperature and the dependent variable is the cost of renting the facility. The cost of renting the facility increases by $25 as the temperature decreases by 5°.

6. Find the slope of each line graphed below.

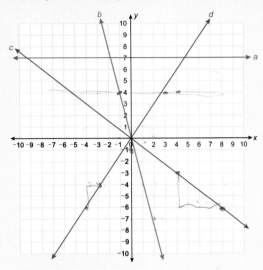

7. Plot each set of points and draw a line through them. Find the slope of each line using two different slope triangles.

a) (3, −3), (4, −4), (6, −6)   c) (−1, 4), (3, 4), (4, 4)

b) (2, 1), (4, 2), (6, 3)   d) (0,−1), (1, −4), (2, −7)

8. Make up real-world situations that would match the function described in Questions 7b and 7d. Describe the relationship between the variables in each situation.

b) The relationship is described by a decreasing linear function.

c)

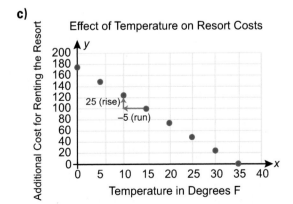

$\dfrac{\text{rise}}{\text{run}} = \dfrac{25}{(-5)}$. The slope is $-\dfrac{25}{5}$, or −5.

d) Answers will vary. Possible points from the graph above:

The two points are (10, 125) and (15, 100).

The point (10, 125) means that there will be an additional charge of $125 to rent the resort if the temperature reaches 10°.

The point (15, 100) means that there will be an additional charge of $100 to rent the resort if the temperature reaches 15°.

6. a) The slope is 0.

b) The slope is −4.

c) The slope is −$\frac{3}{4}$.

d) The slope is $\frac{3}{2}$.

7. a) The triangles students may use will vary. The slope is −1.

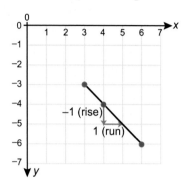

b) The triangles students may use will vary. The slope is $\frac{1}{2}$.

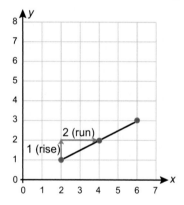

c) The slope is 0.

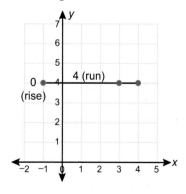

d) The triangles students may use will vary. The slope is −3.

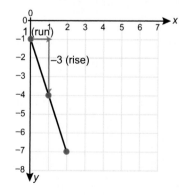

9. Remember Ms. Tootyourhorn's sales from Lesson 1.3? The graph and the table of values for this situation are shown below. The graph represents a "piecewise linear function," where each piece of the graph is linear but the entire graph is not.

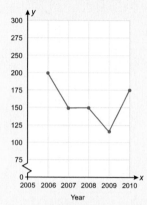

2006	
2007	
2008	150
2009	120
2010	175

We can analyze each piece of the graph separately.

a) Find the slope of each of the individual line segments on the graph.

b) Discuss how the slope of each segment of the graph relates to Ms. Tootyourhorn's performance.

c) Which segment has the greatest slope? What does that mean in the real-world context? How might Ms. Tootyourhorn use this information to her advantage in a presentation?

d) In which segments is the graph increasing? Decreasing? Constant?

Think Beyond

10. Create a table of values and graph the equations $y = \frac{1}{3}x$ and $y = \frac{1}{3}x + 2$ on the same coordinate grid. How are they alike? How are they different? Make a connection between the graphs of the functions and the equations that they represent.

11. Which is greater, the area of a square with a side of length 2 units or the area of a circle with a diameter of 2 units? Explain your answer.

12. $4 = 4\frac{4}{5} \cdot x$. Find the value of x and show your work.

13. **What went wrong?** Help Maya find her mistake.

$$\frac{1}{5} \div \frac{2}{5} =$$

$$\frac{5}{1} \cdot \frac{2}{5} =$$

$$\frac{10}{5} =$$

$$2$$

14. Provide the missing numbers in the sequence:
1, –2, _____, –8, –11, _____,
What is the recursive rule?

15. $-1 - (-1.5) =$

A. -2.5

B. $+2.5$

C. -0.5

D. $+0.5$

Optional Technology Lesson for this section available at **www.mymathinnovations.com**

8. Answers will vary. Possible response:

For 7b: Mangoes are on sale. The cost is $1 for every two mangoes purchased.

d) At the start of the second round of a quiz game, you have a loss of $1. You continue to answer questions incorrectly and lose $3 for each incorrect answer.

9. a) The line segment from 2001 to 2002 has a slope of −50.

   The line segment from 2002 to 2003 has a slope of 0.

   The line segment from 2003 to 2004 has a slope of −30.

   The line segment from 2004 to 2005 has a slope of 55.

   b) Answers will vary. Possible response:

   The slopes relate to the rate of change in unit sales for the one-year period. For example, from year 2001 to 2002, unit sales declined by 50. This segment has a slope of −50.

   c) The line segment for the year 2004 to 2005 has the greatest slope. This represents the greatest rate of change in unit sales, an increase of 55 units. Ms. Tootyourhorn might suggest that this was her best year, since her sales had the greatest overall increase, even though her unit sales ended a little lower than what they started in 2001.

   d) The line segment for 2004 to 2005 represents an increasing function. Line segments for 2001 to 2002 and for 2003 to 2004 represent decreasing functions. The line segment from 2002 to 2003 represents a constant function.

Think Beyond

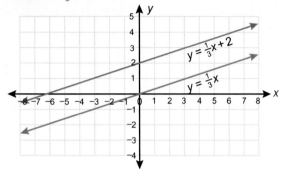

On the graph above, the lines are parallel. This means that they have the same slope. Both lines rise from left to right, so they both have the same positive slope. Looking at the equations, they have the same value for m, that is $\left(\frac{1}{3}\right)$ which is the coefficient of x. This means that there is a 1-unit increase in y for each 3-unit increase in x.

On the graph, the point where the y-intercept crosses the x-axis, i.e. the y-intercept, is different. The line for the equation $y = \frac{1}{3}x$ has a y-intercept of (0, 0) and the line for the equation $y = \frac{1}{3}x + 2$ has a y-intercept of (0, 2).

Think Back

11. The area of the square is 2 • 2, or 4 units. The area of the circle is $1^2 • \pi$, which is approximately equal to 3.14 units. So the area of the square is greater.

12. $\frac{5}{6}$

13. Maya inverted the first fraction rather than the second when she replaced division by multiplication.

14. 1, ⁻2, <u>⁻5</u>, ⁻8, ⁻11, <u>⁻14</u>

    New = Previous ⁻ 3 or

    New = Previous + (⁻3).

15. **d)** ⁺0.5

Optional Technology Lesson for this section available at **www.mymathinnovations.com**

Effect of Temperature on Attendance	
Temperatures in Degrees	**Number of People Attending Conference**
90	175
92	174

The Sum It Up summarizes the important mathematics students should have learned in this section. Encourage students to use this Sum It Up as they complete the Study Guide and prepare for quizzes and tests.

Sum It Up

In this section you have studied the rate of change of linear functions. A function is a special relationship between two variables where there is only one output value for each input value. The graph of a linear function is a straight line. The key ideas associated with analyzing change in linear functions are listed below.

Analyzing Change in Functions

■ The **rate of change** of a linear function is the amount of change in the y-variable compared to the amount of change in the x-variable. This rate, like all rates, is a ratio.

For example, if the cost of reams of paper is a function of the number of reams purchased, the rate of change would be the change in the cost of paper for each additional ream purchased.

■ The **slope** of a line is the geometric representation of the rate of change; it is the ratio of the change in the y-variable relative to the change in the x-variable. The slope indicates the steepness of the line.

■ The slope is the ratio represented by:

$$\frac{\text{change in the vertical distance}}{\text{change in the horizontal distance}} = \frac{\text{rise}}{\text{run}} = \frac{\text{increase or decrease in } y\text{-values}}{\text{increase or decrease in } x\text{-values}}$$

■ You can find the slope of a line by drawing slope triangles as shown below.

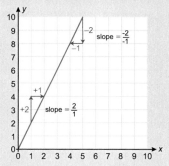

- The rate of change of a linear function is constant. Therefore, the slope you calculate will be the same no matter which slope triangle you use. For the line above, both slope triangles represent the same slope of 2.

- The slope of the line through the point (0, 0) is the value of m, when written in the form $y = mx$.

Graphs of Functions

When graphing functions, you need to determine whether or not to connect the points related to the table of values.

If the x-variable is discrete and represents distinct numbers, you should not connect the points. You use a **scatter plot** to graph discrete points.

The scatter plot at the right, and the linear relationship it represents, consists of 5 discrete points.

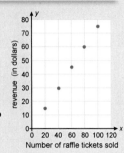

A **line graph** represents a continuous set of points as opposed to a discrete set. Every point on the line represents a valid value for the x- and y-variables. This includes all real values, including fractions and decimals.

The line graph to the right is continuous, and the linear relationship it represents consists of an infinite number of points.

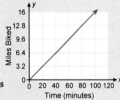

- Throughout this unit, we have been connecting the points of discrete sets to represent **trends in data.** This enhances the visual presentation of a situation and is often done in the business world and in newspaper graphs to clearly show the pattern. However, mathematically, when a line is drawn, it means that every point of the function represented by that line (such as points whose x- and y-values are fractions and decimals) is included.

Characteristics of Linear Functions

■ An increase in the value of the dependent variable, y, as the value of the independent variable, x, increases results in the graph of a line that rises from left to right. Since the function is increasing, it is called an **increasing function**. A decrease in the value of the dependent variable as the independent variable increases results in the graph of a line that falls from left to right. Since the function is decreasing, it is called a **decreasing function**.

■ No change in the dependent variable as the independent variable changes corresponds to the graph of a horizontal line. This function has the constant rate of change of zero.

■ A line with a positive slope increases from left to right (represented by the red line below, which has a slope of 2). A line with a negative slope decreases from left to right (represented by the blue line below, which has a slope of -2).

■ A horizontal line has a slope of 0 and is parallel to the x-axis. This is because there is no change in y as x varies. (The green line to the right has a slope of 0.)

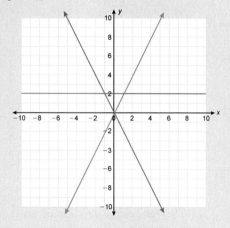

MATHEMATICALLY SPEAKING

Do you know what these mathematical terms mean?

▶ decreasing function	▶ rate	▶ scatter plot
▶ discrete	▶ rate of change	▶ slope
▶ increasing function	▶ $\frac{\text{rise}}{\text{run}}$	▶ unit rate

Part 1. What did you learn?

1. Add the words listed under *Mathematically Speaking* at the end of Section 2 to your concept map.

2. Examine the graph below.

   a. Is the slope of the line positive, negative or zero?

   b. Find the slope of the line. Write the slope as a ratio.

   c. Describe the slope in words as a rate of change.

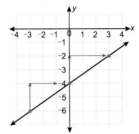

3. Examine the graph below.

   a. Is the slope positive, negative or zero?

   b. Use slope triangles to find the slope of the line.

   c. Write the slope as a ratio.

   d. Describe the slope in words as a rate of change.

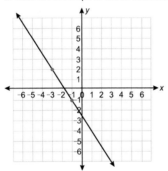

Study Guide

1. Student maps will vary. One possible concept map is given on the right:

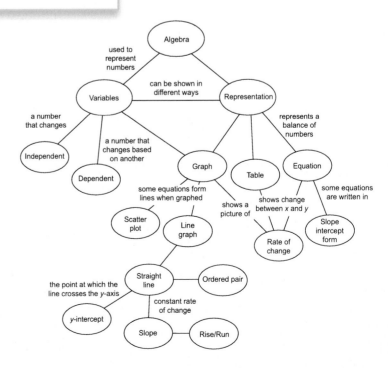

2. **a.** positive

   b. $\frac{2}{3}$

   c. y increases by 2 every time x increases by 3 (or equivalent).

3. **a.** negative

   b. $-\frac{3}{2}$

   c. y decreases by 3 every time x increases by 2 (or equivalent).

4. **a.** Temperature is the independent variable. Number of hot beverages sold is the dependent variable.

   b. Student answers will vary. One possible answer.

x	y
70	20
75	16
80	12
85	8

   c. Yes, this is a linear function. It is decreasing.

   d. $-\frac{4}{5}$

   e. $-\frac{4}{5}$

   f. y decreases by 4 every time x increases by 5 (or equivalent).

   g. The number of hot beverage sold decreases by 4 for each 5 degree increase in the temperature.

4. Erica runs the snack shop at her town pool. She noticed that she sells 4 fewer hot beverages every time the temperature increases by 5 degrees Fahrenheit.

   a. Identify the independent and dependent variables in this situation.

   b. Create a table of values to show this relationship between the number of hot beverages sold and the corresponding temperature.

   c. Is the relationship between temperature and number of hot beverages sold a linear function? If so, is it increasing or decreasing?

   d. What is the rate of change between the two variables in this situation?

   e. Find the slope of this function.

   f. How can you determine the slope from the table of values?

   g. What does this rate of change mean in terms of the real-world situation?

5. Match each situation in the first column with the slope of its line in the second column, an equation in the third column and independent and dependent variables in the last column.

Situation	Slope of Line	Equation	Independent and Dependent Variables
a. The cost of hiring a personal trainer who charges $20 for each hour.	**e.** 20	**i.** $y = 150x$	**m.** x = number of miles y = money raised (in dollars)
b. The speed, in meters per minute, of a person who walks at a steady pace of 50 meters every 20 seconds.	**f.** $\frac{1}{2}$	**j.** $y = 70x$	**n.** x = number of minutes y = number of meters
c. The amount in dollars raised by a participant in a walkathon who earns 50 cents for each mile walked.	**g.** 70	**k.** $y = 20x$	**o.** x = number of cases y = number of bottles
d. The total number of water bottles in a certain number of cases if each case holds 70 bottles.	**h.** 150	**l.** $y = 0.5x$	**p.** x = number of hours y = total charge (in dollars)

5. a, e, k, p
   b, h, i, n

 NOTE Students may have difficulty if they don't read carefully and notice that time is given in seconds but answer is requested in minutes.

   c, f, l, m
   d, g, j, o

6. Situation d would be graphed using a scatter plot because the x-values are discrete. Situations a, b, and c would be graphed using a line graph since the x-values are continuous.

6. Which situations in Question 5 would be graphed using a scatter plot? Which would be graphed using a line graph? Justify your choices.

7. Plot each set of points on a separate coordinate grid. Draw a line connecting them.

   • Line 1: (−3, 2) (0, 4) (3, 6)

   • Line 2: (−8, −1) (0, 1) (4, 2)

   • Line 3: (−3, 4) (0, −5) (1, −8)

   a. Find the slope of each line using two different triangles.

   b. Write the slope of each line as a ratio. Does each line have one slope or two different slopes? Explain.

   c. Describe, in words, the rate at which y changes with respect to x.

   d. What do you notice about your answers to Parts b and c?

8. Examine each table below.

   a. Which table(s) shows data from functions with a constant rate of change?

I.		II.		III.		IV.		V.	
x	y	x	y	x	y	x	y	x	y
−3	−12	−3	−9	−18	−3	−3	9	−10	20
−2	−8	−2	−3	−12	−2	2	4	−5	10
−1	−4	−1	−1	−6	−1	−1	1	0	0
0	0	0	0	0	0	0	0	5	−10
1	4	1	1	6	1	1	1	10	−20
2	8	2	2	12	2	2	4	15	−30
3	12	3	3	18	3	3	9	20	−40

   b. For each table you chose in Part a, write the rate of change as a ratio.

   c. For each table you chose in Part a, find the slope of the graph of the function.

   d. What do you notice about your answers to Parts b and c?

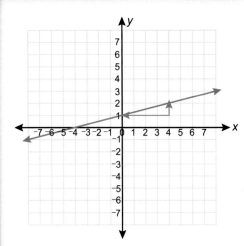

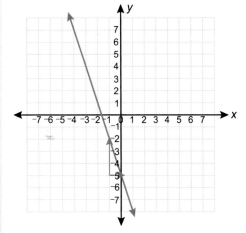

b. Line 1: $\frac{2}{3}$ or $\frac{4}{6}$ or equivalent

   Line 2: $\frac{1}{4}$ or $\frac{2}{8}$ or equivalent

   Line 3: $-\frac{3}{1}$ or $-\frac{6}{2}$ or equivalent

Each line has one slope. For the same line, any slope triangles create equivalent ratios. Since the points fall on a line, the rate of change is constant, so the slope is the same no matter which slope triangle we use.

c. Student answers will vary. One possible answer:

   Line 1: y increases by 2 every time x increases by 3

   Line 2: y increases by 1 every time x increase by 4

   Line 3: y decreases by 3 every time x increases by 1

7. a.

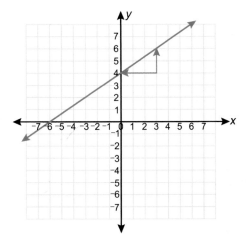

d. Student answers will vary. One possible answer: The slope of the line is the same as the rate at which y changes with respect to x.

8. a. Tables I, III, and V show a constant rate of change.

b. Table I: $\frac{4}{1}$ (or equivalent)

Table III: $\frac{1}{6}$ (or equivalent)

Table V: $-\frac{10}{5}$ or $-\frac{2}{1}$ or equivalent

c. Table I: $\frac{4}{1}$ (or equivalent)

Table III: $\frac{1}{6}$ (or equivalent)

Table V: $-\frac{10}{5}$ or $-\frac{2}{1}$ or equivalent

d. They are equivalent.

9. Student explanations will vary. One possible explanation: Jamal is right. If the graph of the function is a straight line or is a set of points that falls in the straight line, then the function is a linear function.

10. a. Slope is $\frac{1}{3}$

b. Slope is $\frac{5}{1}$

c. Slope is $\frac{1}{5}$

d. Slope is $\frac{3}{1}$

e. Slope is 0

From least to greatest: line e, line c, line a, line d, line b

---

9. Jamal says that he can look at a graph of a function and tell right away if it is a linear function. Shirley disagrees. She said, "In order to tell whether the function is linear, you have to make a table of (x, y) values and see if there is a constant rate of change." Who do you agree with? Why?

10. Each of the equations below represents a linear function. Find the slope of each line. Order the lines by slope from least to greatest.

Line a	$y = \frac{1}{3}x$
Line b	$y = 5x$
Line c	$y = \frac{1}{5}x$
Line d	$y = 3x$
Line e	$y = 3$

11. Graph each of the following functions:

a. A linear function with a positive rate of change.

b. A linear function with a negative rate of change.

12. Match each function with the correct description.

Description		Function
a. The function is a linear function with a positive rate of change.		**e.** $y = 2$
b. The function is not a linear function.		**f.** $y = 2x$
c. The function is a linear function with a slope of zero.		**g.** $y = x^2$
d. The function is a linear function with a negative rate of change.		**h.** $y = -2x$

---

11. Student graphs will vary. One possible answer:

a.

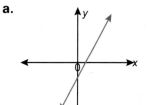

b.

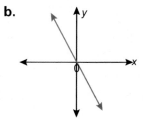

12. a, f

b, g

c, e

d, h

Part 2. What went wrong?

13. Gina is confused about the different ways people describe slope. Her teacher posted the graph below and asked for the slope. One student said, "three over two." Another said, "three down, two left." A third student said, "up three, over two." Yet another student said, "the slope is 1.5." Gina waited for the teacher to tell which one was right, but then her teacher said that they were all correct. How can you help Gina make sense of the different ways to describe the slope of this line?

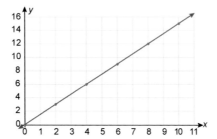

14. Dion thinks that the functions $y = \frac{1}{5}x$ and $y = 5x$ have the same slope because, "They both show a change of 5 compared to a change of 1." What is wrong with Dion's reasoning? What could you say or do to help Dion learn more about slope?

15. Tatiana wrote that the slope of the line below was $\frac{1}{3}$ since "the ratio of rise to run is 1 to 3." Her answer was marked wrong. Why? What is the slope of the line?

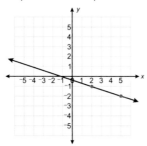

13. Student answers will vary. One possible answer:

The same slope can be described in many different ways. The first student who says, "three over two" is giving the ratio of the vertical change to the horizontal change. His answer is probably written in fraction form as $\frac{3}{2}$. The second student is describing the movement from one point to another point on the line. She is saying that in order to move from one point to another, you need to move down three units, and then left two units. This is another way of describing the ratio of the vertical change to horizontal change, $\frac{3}{2}$. The third student is saying that in order to move from one point to another, you need to move up three units, and then over (left) two units. This is another way of describing the ratio of the vertical change to horizontal change, $\frac{3}{2}$. The fourth student has taken this ratio, $\frac{3}{2}$, and simplified it to 1.5, or $\frac{1.5}{1}$. This means that if you started at one point on the line and moved down 1.5 units and across 1 unit, you would end up at another point on the line.

14. Student answers will vary. One possible answer: The function $y = \frac{1}{5}x$ has a slope of $\frac{1}{5}$, which means that y increases by 1 every time x increases by 5. The function $y = 5x$ has a slope of 5 or $\frac{5}{1}$, which means that y increases by 5 every time x increases by 1. So, these slopes are different. Dion needs to remember that slope means rise/run and that these two measures cannot be switched. Dion could see that these two functions have different slopes if he graphed each one, or if he made a table of (x, y) values for each one.

15. Student answers will vary. One possible answer: The slope of the line is $-\frac{1}{3}$ since the line is moving down from left to right.

> See corresponding assessments in Assessment Resources.

SECTION 3

Analyzing Linear Functions

LESSON 3.1 More About Slope

Suggested Pacing: 2 Days

In this lesson students will connect what they have already learned about direct variation and the constant of proportionality, k, to the concept of slope. Students will recognize the role of the y-intercept in linear equations and will learn the slope-intercept form, $y = mx + b$.

LESSON OBJECTIVES

- Students will recognize linear functions in the form $y = mx$ as direct variations with m as the constant of proportionality.
- Students will determine slopes of linear functions and discover that lines with the same slope are parallel.
- Students will identify the y-intercept of a linear function and describe the y-intercept as it relates to a given real-world situation.
- Students will find equations of lines and graph linear functions using the slope-intercept form.

DAY 1	MATERIALS*	ESSENTIAL *ON YOUR OWN* QUESTIONS
Another Slant on Slope: Direct Variation Snack Break at the Conference	**In Class** ■ Graphing calculators ■ Lesson Guide 3.1A, The *y*-intercept (optional) **On Your Own** ■ Graph paper ■ Graphing calculators	Questions 2–5, 15, 17, 18–21
DAY 2	**MATERIALS***	**ESSENTIAL *ON YOUR OWN* QUESTIONS**
The *y*-Intercept		Questions 1, 6–4

* The Think Like a Mathematician Daily Record Sheet should be used daily

---

MATHEMATICALLY SPEAKING

▶ constant of proportionality	▶ direct variation	▶ parallel
▶ slope-intercept form	▶ *y*-intercept	

Analyzing Linear Functions

In this section, you will learn how the slope and the *y*-intercept of a linear function affect the shape of the graph. You will also learn how to analyze a system of two linear equations and how this can be useful in everyday situations.

 More about Slope

 **Start It Off**

Hayden and Stephanie needed to prepare registration packets for the conference. Hayden can make 4 packets in 10 minutes. Stephanie found out that it took her 15 minutes to make 5 packets.

1. How many packets could Hayden make in 15 minutes?

2. How many packets could Hayden and Stephanie make together in one hour?

3. If they have to make 110 packets as quickly as possible, how much time must they spend if they work together the entire time? Justify your answer.

All the linear equations you have studied so far can be written in the form $y = mx$. As you have learned, m is a numerical value that represents the slope of the line.

 **Start It Off**

1. Hayden could make 6 packets in 15 minutes (4 : 10 = 6 : 15).

2. In an hour, Hayden could make 6 • 4, or 24 packets, and Stephanie could make 5 • 4, or 20 packets. Together they could make 44 packets in one hour.

3. If they have to make 110 packets, then dividing 110 by 44 results 2.5 hours.

OR

4 : 10 = 6 : 15 for Hayden, so together they could make (6 + 5 packets) in 15 minutes.

11 : 15 = 110 : n, so n = 150 minutes = 2.5 hours.

Another Slant on Slope: Direct Variation

The first part of this lesson is designed to connect what students have learned about direct variation and the constant of proportionality, k, in Grade 7 to the concept of slope. Discuss the given situation regarding the certified nurse assistant's hourly pay and then have students work with a partner to complete Question 1.

1. a) The independent variable is the number of hours worked. The dependent variable is the amount earned.

b) $y = \$18.50x$, where x is the number of hours worked and y is the amount earned.

c) The constant of proportionality is the amount of money earned per hour (the hourly rate of $18.50). The amount of money earned increases by $18.50 as the number of hours worked increases by 1.

d) The slope of the line would be 18.5.

e) Graphed values will vary depending on the table of values created by the students.

Another Slant on Slope: Direct Variation

MATHEMATICALLY SPEAKING
- ▸ direct variation
- ▸ constant of proportionality

 Let's Review The equation $y = mx$ should remind you of the equation $y = kx$, which you studied previously. You learned that the second equation is called a direct variation. A direct variation is a situation in which two quantities, such as distance and time, both increase or decrease at the same rate. So, if for example one quantity doubles, the other quantity would double too. The ratio between the quantities is the constant k, which is always positive.

A real-life example would be the earnings of a certified nurse assistant (CNA), who is paid hourly. Her pay varies directly with the number of hours she works, and, as her hours increase, so does her pay.

In a direct variation, the ratio of the variable y to the variable x is always the same. We can write this as $y/x = k$, where k represents a constant known as the constant of proportionality. This equation can be written in the standard form $y = kx$. We say that "y varies directly with x."

1. Let's consider a situation. Near the conference center, there is a clinic where guests can receive medical treatment. A certified nurse assistant in the clinic is paid $18.50 per hour and receives her paycheck weekly.

   a) What are the two variables in this situation? State which is the independent variable and which is the dependent variable.

   b) Write an equation in the form of $y = kx$ to represent the total amount a certified nurse assistant will earn each week based on the number of hours she works.

   c) What is the constant of proportionality? Discuss how one variable varies directly with the other.

   d) If we graph this linear function, what is the slope of the resulting line?

   e) Graph this function using grid paper and find the slope using two points on the line. Compare your answer with Part d above.

   f) How is the slope of the line related to the constant of proportionality?

   g) Does this function have a constant or a varying rate of change? How can you tell?

   h) Is a linear function in the form $y = mx$ always a direct variation? Explain.

Not every situation is a direct variation. Let's examine some other relationships.

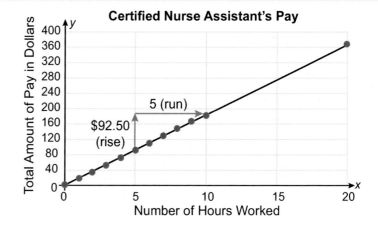

Certified Nurse Assistant's Pay

The two points are (5, 92.5) and (10, 185).

The rise is 92.5 and the run is 5.

Slope $= \dfrac{\text{rise}}{\text{run}} = \dfrac{92.5}{5} = 18.5$. The slope is the same as in Question 1d.

Snack Break at the Conference

Remember that we have used the equation $y = 5x$ to represent how much afternoon snacks will cost for each participant.

Now, you have some options.

Option 1 If you would like one server to distribute the snacks, add an additional one-time charge of $30.

Option 2 If you would like two servers, add an additional one-time charge of $60.

Option 3 If you would like three servers, add an additional one-time charge of $90.

2. a) Complete the table below for the cost of the snack break with one server. Use the given x-values, starting with $x = 10$ people.

Cost of Afternoon Snack	
Number of People (x)	Cost of the Snack Break (y) With One Server
10	5 (10) + 30 = 80
11	
12	
13	
15	
17	
25	
x	

b) Use the table to determine whether or not the relationship is linear. Explain.

c) Create a scatter plot on grid paper and check your answer to Part b.

d) Write the equation that shows the relationship between x and y.

 e) Using a graphing calculator, graph the equation and draw a trendline. Make sure you use the appropriate scales for x and y.

f) What is the slope of this line?

In the second part of this lesson, students investigate the meaning of the y-intercept beyond the idea of a point on the graph where a line crosses the y-axis. Students further explore the idea of the y-value of the y-intercept as a constant that is added to or subtracted from a function. Also, students discover the slope-intercept form, $y = mx + b$, and explore how the slope and the y-intercept can be used to graph a linear equation or write a linear equation from a graph. These activities lead to the discovery that lines with the same slope are parallel.

Snack Break at the Conference

Introduce the scenario of an additional charge of $30 for having one server distribute snacks during an afternoon break at the conference. Have students complete Questions 2 and 3 with a partner.

---

f) The slope of the line and the constant of proportionality are the same. The slope is the constant of proportionality, k, in a direct variation equation, $y = kx$.

g) This function has a constant rate of change. There is a steady increase of $18.50 in pay (the y-value) for every 1-hour increase (the x-value), resulting in a graph that forms a straight line.

h) Yes, a linear function of the form $y = mx$ is an example of direct variation where m is the constant of proportionality. There is a steady ratio (rate of change) between the x- and y-variables.

 NOTE A trendline is being used in Question 2e and Question 3 to highlight the slope, even though the set of points is discrete. Also, remind students to use the same scale when using a graphing calculator to compare the graphs for different number of servers. This ensures that the graphs do not get distorted when making comparisons.

Talk Moves Discuss students' responses as a class. Guide the discussion to focus on similarities and differences between graphs and between equations. Emphasize that the lines are parallel and have the same slope. Use talk moves, such as adding on and agree/disagree and why, to enhance their understanding. Learn more about the "talk moves" in the Teaching and Learning Strategies on page T5.

Next, have students complete Questions 4–9 independently and compare their responses with a partner before having a class discussion.

 Differentiation

Think Differently: For students who have difficulty finding the slope of a line, suggest they use grid paper to graph the lines and draw slope triangles to determine the $\frac{rise}{run}$ ratios.

Do not rush the discussion for Question 9. This is a key idea and it is important for students to understand that lines with the same slope are parallel to each other.

 2. a) Snack Cost with One Server

Number of People (x)	Cost of the Snack Break (y)
10	$80
11	$85
12	$90
13	$95
15	$105
17	$115
25	$155
x	$5x + 30$

b) Yes, it is a linear relationship. There is a constant rate of change of $5 increase in y (the cost) for every 1-unit increase in x (the number of people).

c) When connected, the points of the scatter plot form a line.

---

3. Using your calculator, graph the equation for the cost of the snacks with no servers in the same window as the equation for one server from Question 2. Discuss the following with your partner:

   a) How does this graph compare to the graph that includes the cost of one server? How are the two graphs alike? How are they different?

   b) Compare the equations of the graphs in Part a. Discuss their similarities and differences.

   c) What is the rate of change (that is, the change in cost per unit increase in the number of people) for each function?

   d) Compare the slopes of the two graphs.

4. Now consider adding two servers.

   a) Predict how the graph of this function will compare to the graph of the function for only one server.

   b) Write an equation for this new situation. Using your graphing calculator, graph it in the same window as the first two functions. Were you correct?

   c) What is the rate of change for the function with two servers?

   d) What is the slope?

   e) How are the three equations similar? How are the three graphs similar?

   f) How are the three equations different? How are the three graphs different?

5. Next consider the situation where three servers will be added. Predict what the graph will look like.

   a) Where will it cross the y-axis?

   b) How will it be placed relative to the function describing the addition of only one server? What about two servers?

6. a) Write an equation that describes the cost of adding three servers. Graph it in the same calculator window as the other functions.

   b) What is the rate of change for the function describing the cost of adding three servers?

   c) What is the slope of the corresponding line?

   d) How is this equation similar to the other equations? How is the graph similar to the other graphs?

   e) How is this equation different from the other equations? How is the graph different from the other graphs?

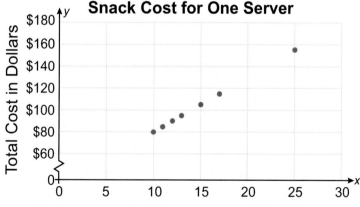

Snack Cost for One Server

d) $y = 5x + 30$, where x is the number of people and y is the total cost of the snack service.

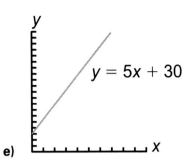

e)

f) The slope of the line is 5.

3. Graphs may vary slightly depending on scale set on the graphing calculator.

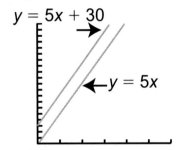

a) The lines on both graphs rise from left to right. The lines have the same steepness, which means they have the same slope (5). The lines appear parallel to each other.

The graph representing the cost for one server is higher up on the y-axis (30 units) compared to the graph representing the cost with no server. The graph with one server crosses the y-axis at 30. The graph with no server crosses the y-axis at 0.

b) Both equations have the same coefficient for x, which is 5.

They differ in that one equation has an added value of 30.

c) For the function y (cost in dollars) $= 5x$, there is an increase of 5 units in y for each increase of 1 unit in x (the number of people), so the rate of change is 5 dollars per additional person.

For the function y (cost in dollars) $= 5x + 30$, there is also an increase of 5 units in y for each unit increase in x (the number of people), so the rate of change is 5 dollars per additional person.

d) The slope of each function is 5. Students can verify this by identifying the coefficient of x in the equation of each linear function or by selecting two points on the table and comparing the change in the y-values to the change in x-values.

4. a) Predictions will vary. The graph will begin at (0, 60), and it will be a line that is 30 units higher than the graph representing the cost of snacks with one server. The line will have the same slope, or steepness, rising from left to right. The line will be parallel to the line representing the cost of snacks with one server and to the line representing the cost of snacks with no server.

b) $y = 5x + 60$, where x is the number of people attending the conference and y is the total cost of the snack service.

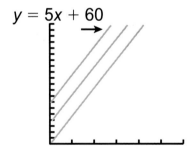

Predictions stated in Question 3a were correct.

c) For the function $y = 5x + 60$, there is an increase of 5 units (cost in dollars) in y for each unit increase in x (the number of people), so the rate of change is 5 dollars per additional person.

d) The slope of the line is 5.

e) The coefficient of x is the same in all three equations and therefore the slope, or steepness, of the lines is the same, so they are parallel. All lines rise from left to right.

f) The constant that is added to each equation is different. With no servers, the amount added is 0. With one server, the amount added is 30. With two servers, the amount added is 60.

The graphs intersect the y-axis at different points. The graph with no servers intersects the y-axis at the origin, the graph with one server at $(0, 30)$, and the graph with two servers at $(0, 60)$.

5. a) The line will cross the y-axis at $(0, 90)$.

b) The line will be placed 60 units higher on the y-axis than the graph of the line describing the cost of snacks with one server. It will be placed 30 units higher on the y-axis than the graph of the line describing the cost of snacks with two servers.

6. a) $y = 5x + 90$, where x is the number of people attending and y is the total cost of the snack service in dollars.

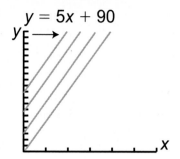

$y = 5x + 90$

b) There is a 5-unit (dollar) increase in y for each unit increase in x (the number of people), so the rate of change is 5 dollars per additional person.

c) The slope of the line is 5.

d) The coefficient of x is the same in each equation and therefore the slope, or steepness, of the lines is the same. All lines are parallel to one another.

e) The difference is in the constant being added to the function (90). As a result, the graph crosses the y-axis at $(0, 90)$. This function is located higher along the y-axis than the others.

7. The graphs of lines written in the form of $y = mx + b$ that have the same values of m and different values for b have the same slope and will be parallel to each other, but they will have different y-intercepts.

8. Graphs may vary depending on the window scale set on the graphing calculator.

a)

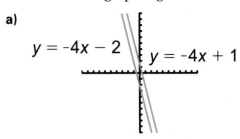

$y = -4x - 2$ $y = -4x + 1$

b)

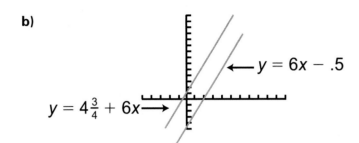

$y = 4\frac{3}{4} + 6x \longrightarrow$ $\longleftarrow y = 6x - .5$

c)

$y = \frac{1}{2}x$

$y = -1\frac{1}{2} + x$

9. Based on the observations from the examples above, lines with the same slope are parallel to each other regardless of the constant that is being added to or subtracted from the function.

Summarize Day 1

Use Question 9 as a Wrap Up for this first day. Students should make a generalization based on their observations from working with lines that have the same slope and different y-intercepts.

TEACHING THE LESSON

The *y*-Intercept

This part of the lesson leads students to recognize the role of the *y*-intercept in linear equations and introduces students to the slope-intercept form, $y = mx + b$. Although the y-intercept is sometimes referred to as the *y*-value of the point, in this text the *y*-intercept is defined as the point as which the line crosses the *y*-axis (0,*b*) and *b* is the *y*-value of the intercept.

 **Talk Moves** Have students complete Questions 10–17 and compare their responses to those of a partner. Encourage students to share the conjectures they made in answering Question 14 about the graphs of linear functions that have the same coefficient of *x* but differing constant value added to or subtracted from them. Use talk moves, such as agree/disagree and why, to clarify misconceptions and reinforce student understanding of key ideas such as the *y*-intercept and the relationship of linear functions that have the same slope. For Question 15, it is important for students to recognize that some linear functions, such as $y = 5x$, do not have a constant term. The constant being added here is 0, so the line will cross the *y*-axis at the origin.

Next, have students work independently on Questions 16 and 17. Discuss students' responses as a class. With regard to Question 16, it is important that students are exposed to different forms of the equation $y = mx + b$. Sometimes the constant appears first in the equation. However, this term still represents the *y*-intercept and not the slope of the line. Be sure to draw students' attention to this key idea. Question 17 allows students to work in the opposite direction; that is, they are given the graph of a function and they must determine its slope and *y*-intercept. They should make slope triangles to help them find the slope.

Differentiation

Think Differently: For students having difficulty with Question 13 in predicting where the equation $y = 5x - 10$ will be located on the graph, offer Lesson Guide 2.4A as an aid. This accommodation guide offers a table of values that students can complete to help them make more accurate predictions. This is helpful for ELL students as well as students who need support in organizing their thinking.

10. Student responses should include the following key ideas:

   - The *y*-intercepts will be located at different points along the *y*-axis. The equation with the greatest constant, $y = 5x + 90$, will have a *y*-intercept located above the others.

   - Moving up the *y*-axis, the *y*-intercept of $y = 5x + 30$ will be first, or on the bottom, the *y*-intercept of $y = 5x + 60$ will be second, or in the middle, and $y = 5x + 90$ will be third, or on the top. These three lines have graphs that are parallel to each other.

   - The position of the *y*-intercept coincides with the value of the constant being added to the functions.

   - The constant value helps identify the point where the graph crosses the *y*-axis.

11 a) Conjectures may vary. Possible response:

   The graph will be a line with the same steepness as the other lines for 1, 2, and 3 servers, and will rise from left to right. This graph will intersect the *y*-axis 30 units above the graph describing three servers. It will cross the *y*-axis at (0, 120). The slope of the line is 5, so it will be parallel to the previous graphs.

   b) The equation for 4 servers is $y = 5x + 120$.

7. Make some predictions about the graphs of lines with equations similar to the ones above.

8. Predict how the graphs of the equations in each pair will compare. Check your prediction by graphing the pair of equations in the same window of your graphing calculator.

   a) $y = -4x + 1$ and $y = -4x - 2$

   b) $y = 6x - 5$ and $y = 4\frac{3}{4} + 6x$

   c) $y = -1 + \left(\frac{1}{2}\right)x$ and $y = \left(\frac{1}{2}\right)x$

9. Make a generalization about the graphs of lines with the same slope.

The *y*-Intercept

Now, let's concentrate on what is *different* about the four functions describing the snack service options.

10. Examine the three equations you wrote to describe the addition of one, two and three servers.

    What can you tell about the graphs of these functions by looking at the differences in their equations?

11. **a)** Talk to your partner and make a prediction about the graph of a function that describes adding four servers.

    b) Now write the equation. Enter it into your calculator and graph it.

    c) Were you correct?

12. Write an equation of a line that crosses the *y*-axis at 15 and is parallel to the lines you have graphed already. Enter the equation in your calculator, graph it, and see if you were correct.

13. The conference center decided to give you a one-time discount of $10 for not using any servers. Predict where the line for $y = 5x - 10$ will be on the graph. Graph the equation to check your prediction.

14. Talk to your partner and make a generalization about linear functions with equations that have the same coefficient of *x* but a different constant value that is added or subtracted. In other words, equations of the form $y = mx + b$ where *m* stays the same and *b* varies.

    What do these graphs look like? Discuss the rate of change of these functions, the slope of the functions and the point where they cross the *y*-axis.

15. Are equations in the form $y = mx + b$ direct variations? Explain.

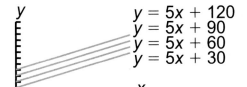

$y = 5x + 120$
$y = 5x + 90$
$y = 5x + 60$
$y = 5x + 30$

c) Yes, the conjecture listed in Question 11a is correct.

12. One possible answer might be $y = 5x + 15$

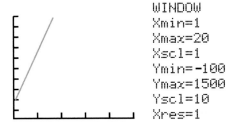

```
WINDOW
Xmin=1
Xmax=20
Xscl=1
Ymin=-100
Ymax=1500
Yscl=10
Xres=1
```

13. The graph will be a line with the same steepness as the other lines shown in Question 11b, so it will be parallel to them. It will cross the *y*-axis at (0, −10), and will be located below the other lines.

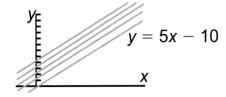

$y = 5x - 10$

14. Students should include the following key ideas in their generalizations:

    • The graphs of linear functions, written in the form $y = mx + b$, that have the same coefficient of *x*, will be parallel lines, since the lines have the same steepness, or slope.

    • Since the lines have the same rate of change, they have the same slope.

    • The lines will cross the *y*-axis at the point on the graph where the *x*-value is 0 and the *y*-value is the same as the constant value in their equation.

    • When no constant is given, the *y*-intercept is 0, since $y = mx + 0$ is the same as $y = mx$.

15. These equations are not direct variations since there is a constant involved in the equation. So, for example, if x doubles y will be double x + or − the constant value, not just double x. In the equation $y = 2x + 1$, if $x = 4$, $y = 9$ not 8.

16. The function $y = 5x$ crosses the y-axis at $(0, 0)$ since, at $x = 0$, $y = 5(0) = 0$. This makes sense in terms of our generalizations since the constant being added to the $5x$ term is 0 (that is, $y = 5x + 0$).

17. a) $y = -4x + 1$
Slope is -4; y-intercept is $(0, 1)$.
$y = -4x - 2$
Slope is -4; y-intercept is $(0, -2)$.

b) $y = 6x - 0.5$
Slope is 6; y-intercept is $(0, -0.5)$.
$y = 4\frac{3}{4} + 6x$
Slope is 6; y-intercept is $(0, 4\frac{3}{4})$.

c) $y = -1 + \frac{1}{2}x$
Slope is $\frac{1}{2}$; y-intercept is $(0, -1)$.
$y = \frac{1}{2}x$
Slope is $\frac{1}{2}$; y-intercept is $(0, 0)$.

16. Where does the function $y = 5x$ cross the y-axis? Why does this make sense in terms of your generalizations from above?

You have discovered that parallel lines have the same slope but different y-intercepts. The y-intercept is the point on a line where $x = 0$ (that is, where the line crosses the y-axis). For lines written in the form $y = mx + b$, m indicates the slope of the line and b indicates the y-value of the y-intercept.

When $x = 0$, $y = mx + b$ becomes $y = m(0) + b$, or $y = b$, so $y = mx + b$ crosses the y-axis at $(0, b)$.

This form of a linear equation, $y = mx + b$, is called the slope-intercept form, since by looking at the equation we can immediately recognize the slope, m, and the y-intercept, $(0, b)$.

17. Identify the slope and the y-intercept of the following equations.

a) $y = -4x + 1$ and $y = -4x - 2$

b) $y = 6x - 0.5$ and $y = 4\frac{3}{4} + 6x$

c) $y = -1 + \left(\frac{1}{2}\right)x$ and $y = \left(\frac{1}{2}\right)x$

18. a) $m = -1$, y-intercept $= (0, 0)$
The equation is $y = -1x$ or $y = -x$.

b) $m = 3$, y-intercept is $(0, -1)$.
The equation is $y = 3x - 1$.

c) $m = -\frac{1}{2}$, y-intercept is $(0, 1)$.
The equation is $y = -0.5x + 1$

d) $m = 0$, y-intercept $= (0, 3)$.
The equation is $y = 3$.

18. Find the slope and *y*-intercept of the lines graphed below. Write the equation of each line in slope-intercept form.

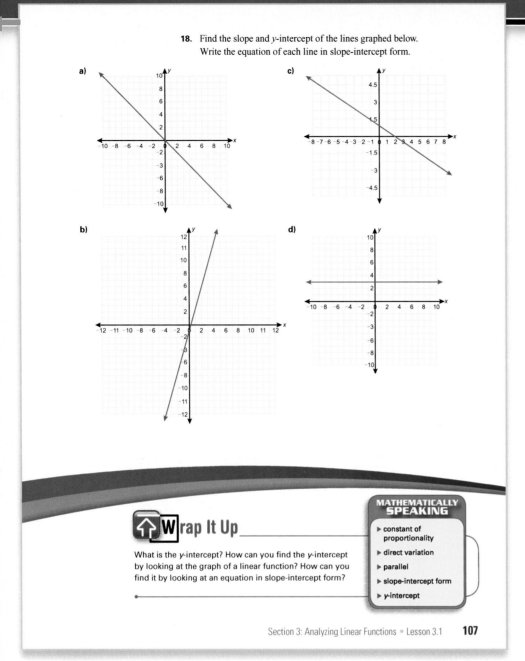

a)

c)

b)

d)

 **rap It Up**

What is the *y*-intercept? How can you find the *y*-intercept by looking at the graph of a linear function? How can you find it by looking at an equation in slope-intercept form?

MATHEMATICALLY SPEAKING

▶ constant of proportionality
▶ direct variation
▶ parallel
▶ slope-intercept form
▶ *y*-intercept

 **rap It Up**

Student responses should include the following:

- The *y*-value of the *y*-intercept is the constant that is being added to or subtracted from the *mx*-term of a function written in the form $y = mx + b$. The *y*-intercept is the point where the graph crosses the *y*-axis; it shows the value of the function when $x = 0$.

- When a linear function is written in slope-intercept form ($y = mx + b$), *b* is a constant that represents the *y*-value of the *y*-intercept. The *y*-intercept is the point $(0, b)$ on the graph.

Reflect

Use these questions to help you reflect on the lesson and plan for future instruction.

- Do students understand the equation $y = mx$ as direct variation?

- How successful were students in graphing linear equations written in slope-intercept form?

- Do students readily recognize that linear functions with the same slope are parallel?

- What are some misconceptions about the slope and *y*-intercept that need to be addressed before teaching the next lesson?

On Your Own

Write About It

1. **a)** Write the equations of three parallel lines that are different from the examples used above.

   b) Explain how you know the lines are parallel.

   c) State the slope and y-intercept of each line.

   d) Write the equations in order, as you would see them vertically, from top to bottom, on the Cartesian plane.

2. How is the slope of a line of equations in the form of $y = mx$ related to direct variation?

3. Is a situation that represents direct variation always linear? Explain.

4. **a)** Use three objects such as a cup, a round wastepaper basket and a food can. Using a ruler or tape measure, find the diameter and measure the circumference of the base of each object in centimeters.

   b) Copy the table below and fill in your measurements.

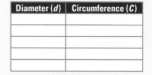

Diameter (d)	Circumference (C)

   c) Calculate to two decimal places the ratio of circumference to diameter, $\frac{C}{d}$, for each pair of numbers.

   d) Is the relationship shown in the table a direct variation? Explain. If so, what is the constant of proportionality?

   e) Using a graphing calculator, graph the paired values in the table as points. Is this relationship linear?

   f) Calculate the average of the values of $\frac{C}{d}$ for each pair of numbers.

   g) Using this value as the slope of the line, write an equation that relates the circumference to the diameter.

   h) How does this equation compare to the formula $C = \pi d$?

On Your Own

Write About It

1. Answer will vary.
   Possible response:

   a) $y = 3x$
   $y = 3x + 15$
   $y = 3x - 2$

   b) These lines are parallel because they all have the same slope. The slope can be determined by looking at the coefficient of x when the equations are written in the form $y = mx + b$, where m is the coefficient of x. In the equations above, the slope is 3.

   c) $y = 3x$ has a slope of 3 and a y-intercept of $(0, 0)$. $y = 3x + 15$ has a slope of $+3$ and a y-intercept of $(0, 15)$. $y = 3x - 2$ has a slope of 3 and a y-intercept of $(0, -2)$.

   d) The lines would be graphed in order from the one with the largest y-value of the y-intercept to the one with the smallest y-value of the y-intercept as follows:
   $y = 3x + 15$
   $y = 3x$
   $y = 3x - 2$

2. The slope is the constant of proportionality (k or m) in an equation that represents a direct variation (written as $y = kx$ or $y = mx$).

3. Yes, there is a constant rate of change, k, in every equation of the form $y = kx$.

4. a) Answers will vary.

   b) Answers will vary.

   c) The ratios should be approximately 3.14.

 Students' ratios may vary slightly due to inaccuracies in measuring.

---

   d) Yes, the ratios among the circular objects comparing circumference to diameter is a constant. The constant of proportionality is approximately 3.14.

   e) Graphs will vary. This relationship is linear. Note: Student graphs may vary slightly due to measurement inaccuracies and number rounding.

   f) The value should be 3.14.

   g) $y = 3.14x$

   h) C represents circumference and is the dependent variable, y; d represents the diameter and is the independent variable, x; and π represents the constant rate of change, or slope, 3.14.

5. a) $y = 4x + 1$

   b) $y = 4x - 5$

   c) $y = 4x + \dfrac{1}{2}$

   d) $y = 4x + 1$
      $y = 4x + \dfrac{1}{2}$
      $y = 4x - 5$

6. Definitions will vary. Possible response: intercept: (v.) to stop passage or motion in space; obstruct; intervene. (The New Shorter Oxford English Dictionary; Oxford Press, 1993). This definition relates to the *y*-intercept since it is the point on the graph where the line crosses or "intervenes" with the *y*-axis.

7. a) $y = 75x$, where *x* represents the number of people attending the banquet and *y* represents the total cost.

   b) $y = 75x - 50$, where *x* represents the number of people attending the banquet, *y* is the total cost, and -50 is the discount.

     i) The *y*-value of the *y*-intercept, for the equation $y = 75x$, is 0 and its graph will cross the *y*-axis at the point (0, 0). The *y*-value of the *y*-intercept, for the equation $y = 75x - 50$, is -50 and its graph will cross the *y*-axis at (0, -50).

     ii) No. Since the equations have the same slope, 75, the lines will be parallel, so it is impossible for them to intersect.

     iii) Since the slopes are the same, the graphs are parallel. The *y*-intercept of the line representing $y = 75x - 50$ is 50 units below the *y*-intercept of the line $y = 75x$, which is at the origin. The lines are 50 units apart from each other on the *y*-axis.

iv) There is a 75-unit (dollar) increase in *y* (the cost) for each one-unit increase in *x* (the number of people attending the banquet) for both equations. $y = 75x$, so the rate of change is $75 per additional person.

v) The slope of each line is 75.

c)

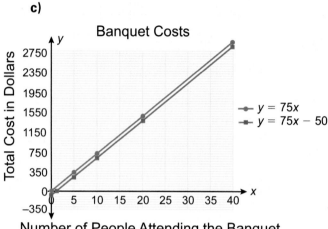

 The graph above shows the banquet cost for up to 40 guests. A smaller scale range on the *x*-axis was used to make it easier to distinguish between the two trendlines. Encourage students to use an appropriate scale on their graphs that would enable them to represent data for up to 200 guests when creating their own graphs on grid paper. Also, the trendlines on the graph were extended to show the *y*-intercepts; however, it isn't really necessary to include this information on the graph for the given real-world situation. Ask students to explain why.

5. Write the equations of lines that will be parallel to $y = 4x$ and will cross the y-axis at the following points:

   a) $(0, 1)$

   b) $(0, -5)$

   c) $(0, \frac{1}{2})$

   d) Write the equations above in order, as you would see them graphed vertically, from top to bottom, on the Cartesian plane.

6. Look up the meaning of the word *intercept*. How does it relate to the definition of y-intercept?

7. You are going to have a final banquet for your conference. You have an estimate from Corporate Caterer that the banquet will cost $75 per person.

   a) Write an equation that shows the relationship between the total cost and the number of people attending the banquet.

   b) The manager of the conference center decides to give you a $50 discount on the total cost of the banquet. Modify your equation to indicate this discount. Then, predict the following:

   i. What are the y-intercepts of the two lines described in Parts a and b above?

   ii. Will the two lines cross each other? How do you know?

   iii. Describe the relationship between their graphs.

   iv. What is the rate of change in each situation?

   v. What is the slope of each line?

   c) Graph both lines on the same coordinate plane and check your answers from Part b.

8. **a)** What is the y-intercept of the line $y = 4x$?

   b) What is the slope of the line $y = 4$?

Hint
See page 155

8. **a)** The y-intercept is 0, or the point $(0, 0)$.

   b) The slope is 0. Since y is constant, there is no change in y as x changes, so the rate of change is 0, and the line is horizontal.

9. a) $y = 4x + 2$ The slope is 4 and the y-intercept is the point $(0, 2)$.

b) $y = \frac{1}{2}x - 1$ The slope is $\frac{1}{2}$ and the y-intercept is the point $(0, -1)$.

c) $y = -x + 5$ The slope is -1 and the y-intercept is the point $(0, 5)$.

d) $y = -3$ The slope is 0 and the y-intercept is the point $(0, -3)$.

e) $y = 4 - 2x$ The slope is -2 and the y-intercept is the point $(0, 4)$.

f) $y = -\frac{1}{3}x$ The slope is $-\frac{1}{3}$ and the y-intercept is the point $(0, 0)$.

10. a) For the equation $y = 2x + 1$, the y-intercept is $(0, 1)$. Since the coefficient of x is 2, the slope is 2. Starting at the point $(0, 1)$, go up 2 units to $y = 3$ and over 1 unit to $x = 1$, and plot the point $(1, 3)$.

b)

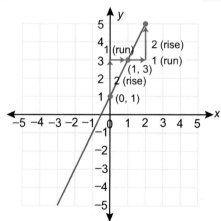

Possible new points: $(2, 5)$, $(-2, -3)$

---

9. State the slope and y-intercept of each equation.

a) $y = 4x + 2$ **d)** $y = -3$

b) $y = \frac{1}{2}x - 1$ **e)** $y = 4 - 2x$

c) $y = -x + 5$ **f)** $y = -\frac{1}{3}x$

10. a) On graph paper, graph the point that represents the y-intercept of the line $y = 2x + 1$. How can you use the slope to find another point on the line?

 Hint
See page 155

b) Plot two more points of the line, using the equation above, and then draw the line.

11. Use the method in Question 10, to graph the following:

a) $y = 4x + 2$ **b)** $y = \frac{1}{2}x - 1$ **c)** $y = -\frac{1}{3}x$

12. a) Write the equation of a line with slope -3 and y-intercept $(0, 4)$.

b) Name two points on this line.

c) Will the line pass through the origin? Why or why not?

13. a) Write the equations of two lines that are not parallel.

b) How do you know that they are not parallel without graphing them?

c) Check your answers by graphing the lines on a graphing calculator.

14. Use the graph to the right to find the slope and the y-intercept of each line. Write the equation of each line in slope-intercept form.

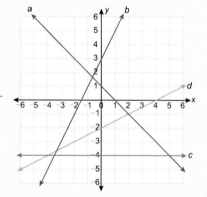

11. a) $y = 4x + 2$

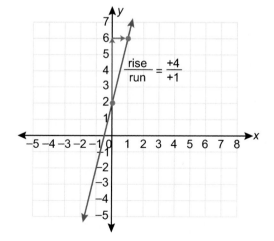

$$\frac{\text{rise}}{\text{run}} = \frac{+4}{+1}$$

15. The rooms at the conference center have different price rates. There are five floors at the center (Floors 0, 1, 2, 3 and 4). The rooms on the ground floor (Floor 0) are the most expensive. All ground floor rooms cost $100 per day. The rooms on the other floors are discounted at $10 per floor above the ground level.

    a) If x is the floor number and y is the cost of a room on that floor, write the equation that shows this relationship.

    b) Is this relationship linear? Explain.

    c) What is the slope of the line? What is the y-intercept? What does the y-intercept mean in terms of the cost of rooms?

    d) If you reserve 10 rooms on the ground floor, 6 rooms on the first floor, and 2 rooms on the fourth floor, what will be your total cost?

Think Beyond

16. You now know what the y-intercept means. What do you think the x-intercept is? Find the x-intercepts of the lines graphed in Question 15 above.

Think Back

17. In the equation $y = -16x + 21.8$, find the value of y if $x = -1.6$.

18. If $A = 4$ and $B = 2$, find the value of $AB - (A - B)^2$.

19. Sue and Bob each earn $6 per hour raking leaves. If Sue works for $1\frac{3}{4}$ hours and Bob works for $2\frac{3}{4}$ hours, what is the total amount of money they earn?

    A. $24.50
    B. $27.00
    C. $24.75
    D. $10.50

20. About 4.4 pounds of butter fat can be found in 100 pounds of whole milk. Use a proportion to calculate the amount of butter fat that can be found in 55 pounds of whole milk.

21. The People of Color Conference in Seattle had an attendance of 3,000 citizens. The ratio of adults to students participating was $2:1$. If there was one adult supervising every 10 students, how many adults attended the conference with no supervisory role?

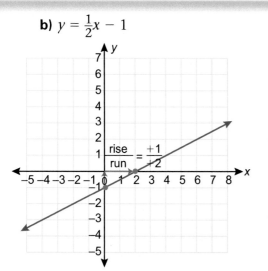

b) $y = \frac{1}{2}x - 1$

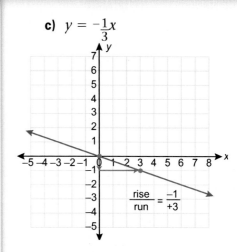

c) $y = -\frac{1}{3}x$

$\frac{\text{rise}}{\text{run}} = \frac{-1}{+3}$

12. **a)** The equation of the line is $y = -3x + 4$.

    b) Answers will vary. Possible answers: $(0, 4)$, $(1, 1)$, $(2, -2)$, $(3, -5)$

    c) No, the line will not pass through the origin. The y-intercept is $(0, 4)$ so it is impossible for the line to pass through the origin.

13. **a)** Answers will vary. The two lines should have different slopes.

    Possible response:
    $y = x + 4$ and $y = 2x$

    b) The slope can be determined by looking at the coefficient of x in the equation. Since the coefficients of x in the equations above are different, the lines do not have the same slope and, therefore, are not parallel.

    c) Graph of equations listed in Question 13a:

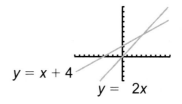

$y = x + 4$

$y = 2x$

14. a) Slope is -1. The y-intercept is $(0, 1)$.
$y = -x + 1$.

b) Slope is 2. The y-intercept is $(0, 3)$.
$y = 2x + 3$.

c) Slope is 0. The y-intercept is $(0, -4)$.
$y = -4$.

d) Slope is $\frac{1}{2}$. The y-intercept is $(0, -2)$.
$y = \frac{1}{2}x + 2$.

15. a) $y = -10x + 100$

b) Yes, the relationship is linear. There is a steady rate of change in y for every change in x over equal intervals.

c) The slope (m) is -10. The y-intercept is 100 and indicates the cost of a room on the ground floor where $x = 0$.

d) One room on the ground floor costs $100; 10 rooms on the ground floor will cost $1000.

One room on the first floor costs $90; 6 rooms on the first floor will cost $540.

One room on the fourth floor will cost $60; 2 rooms of the fourth floor will cost $120.

The total cost of the rooms will be $1000 + $540 + $120 = $1660.

16.  **Think Beyond**

The x-intercept is the point at which the line of the graph crosses the x-axis. The y-value of this point is 0. The x-intercepts for lines in Question 14 are the following:

a) $y = -x + 1$; $(1, 0)$

b) $y = 2x + 3$; $(-\frac{3}{2}, 0)$

c) $y = -4$; no x-intercept

d) $y = \frac{1}{2}x - 2$; $(4, 0)$

 Think Back

17. $y = 47.4$

18. 4

19. B. $27.00

20. $\frac{4.4}{100} = \frac{x}{55}$.
$55 \cdot 4.4 = 100x$
$x = 2.42$ lbs.

21. There were 2000 adults and 1000 students at the conference. The 1000 students required $\frac{1000}{10} = 100$ supervisors.
Adults without supervisory role:
$2000 - 100 = 1900$.

See corresponding assessments in Assessment Resources.

Table of Values for the Equation $y = 5x - 10$

x-values	y-values
−2	−20
−1	−15
0	−10
1	
2	
3	
4	

Accommodation Guide

LESSON
3.2

An Important Meeting Point

Suggested Pacing: 1 Day

In this lesson, students should polish their ability to identify and interpret the slope and y-intercept of linear functions as they work with equations written in slope-intercept form. The activities presented are designed to deepen students' understanding of the relationship between parallel and intersecting lines, and their slopes. Students will also explore how to solve a system of equations graphically by identifying the point of intersection and interpret what that point represents in relation to a given real-world situation.

LESSON OBJECTIVES

- Students will analyze linear equations written in the slope-intercept form to determine whether the lines are parallel or intersecting.
- Students will solve a system of linear equations graphically by identifying the point of intersection.
- Students will interpret the solution, or point of intersection, of a system of linear functions in relation to given real-world situations.

DAY 1	MATERIALS*	ESSENTIAL *ON YOUR OWN* QUESTIONS
Choosing the Best Deal	**In Class** ■ Graph paper ■ Graphing calculator **On Your Own** ■ Graph paper ■ Graphing calculator	Questions 1–9, 11–15

* The Think Like a Mathematician Daily Record Sheet should be used daily

---

MATHEMATICALLY SPEAKING

▶ point of intersection ▶ solution to a system of equations ▶ system of equations

⮕ Start It Off

Ted's Taxi Service	Airport Taxi
$y = 0.80x + 3$ $y = 0.80(10) + 3$ $y = \$11$	$y = x$ $y = 10$ $y = \$10$
Airport Taxi is a better deal for a 10-mile trip.	
$y = 0.80(15) + 3$ $y = \$15$	$y = 15$ $y = \$15$
Both companies cost the same for a 15-mile trip. Either one could be used.	
$y = 0.80(20) + 3$ $y = \$19$	$y = 20$ $y = \$20$
Ted's Taxi Service is the better deal for a 20-mile trip.	

TEACHING THE LESSON

Remind students of Corporate Caterer's bid for the cost of the final conference banquet. Then present Fancy Caterer's bid to students. Have students work with a partner to predict which is a better deal as they answer Question 1. Encourage students to use mathematical reasoning about the rate of change and the constant value being subtracted (the y-intercept) as they support their predictions in a class discussion.

Pair student to complete Questions 2 and 3 and discuss their responses with the class. For Question 3a, students need to apply their knowledge of parallel lines. Guide the discussion to help students recognize that these lines have different slopes and thus are not parallel. If the lines are not parallel, they must intersect at some point. Do not rush the discussion for Question 3b. Encourage students to connect this discussion with what they have already learned in Section 2 of this unit. Help students make the generalization that the line whose slope has the greater absolute value will be steeper. Ask:

- *How does the value of m in a linear equation relate to the steepness of the line?*

Choosing the Best Deal

1. Predictions may vary. The actual answer is for less than 10 people, Fancy Caterer is the better deal. For 10 people, the cost is the same. For more than 10 people, the additional one-time $100 discount that Fancy Caterer offers no longer makes a difference. Therefore, for a party of 10 or more, Corporate Caterer is a better deal because it charges $5 less per person. Since it is very likely that more than 10 people will attend the banquet, the conference organizers should use Corporate Caterer.

2. Let y be the total cost for the banquet and x be the number of people attending:
   Corporate Caterer:
   $y = 75x - 50$
   Fancy Caterer: $y = 80x - 100$

3. a) Yes. Possible response: Since the functions do not have the same slopes, m, the lines are not parallel and will intersect at a point.

   b) The graph for Fancy Caterer will be steeper. Possible response: Since the coefficient of x has a greater value, the function has a greater rate of change, meaning there is a greater change in y-values compared to the change in x-values. In the given real-world situation, the cost of the banquet increases more per person for Fancy Caterer than for Corporate Caterer.

Start It Off

As a conference planner, you need to provide transportation for conference participants to and from the airport. Ted's Taxi Service charges a flat fee of $3.00 plus $0.80 per mile. Airport Taxi charges $1.00 a mile. Which service will you choose if the conference is about 10 miles from the airport? 15 miles? 20 miles? Explain your reasoning.

Choosing the Best Deal

You have received bids for the cost of the final banquet. Corporate Caterer's bid was $75 per person plus a discount of $50 on the total cost. You have another bid from Fancy Caterer. They charge $80 per person with a $100 discount on the total cost. You must determine which option is a better deal.

With your partner:

1. Predict which caterer offers a better deal. Be prepared to explain your prediction.

2. Write equations for each bid.

3. Looking at the equations predict the following:

   a) If you graph the equations on the same coordinate grid, will the lines ever cross? How do you know?

   b) Which graph will be steeper? How do you know from looking at the equations? What does that tell you about the rate of change of the functions? What does that tell you about the situations that the functions represent?

   c) What is the y-intercept of each function?

Using Your Graphing Calculator

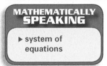

MATHEMATICALLY SPEAKING

▶ system of equations

The variables in the two equations from the example above represent the same things: the total cost of the banquet and the number of attendees. When we have two or more equations with variables that represent the same thing, we call them a system of equations. In this case, since both equations are linear, we call this a system of linear equations.

---

c) The y-intercept for Corporate Caterer is -50, or the point $(0, -50)$.

This means that a $50 discount can be deducted from the total cost of the banquet, regardless of the number of people attending.

The y-intercept for Fancy Caterer is -100, or the point $(0, -100)$.

This means that a $100 discount can be deducted from the total cost of the banquet, regardless of the number of people attending.

4. Graph the two catering bid equations using your graphing calculator. Use $x = 0$ up to $x = 20$ with an x scale $= 1$; y should range from -100 to 1500, with a y scale of 10.

5. Use the TRACE and ZOOM functions on your calculator to determine the point where the two graphs cross each other. We call this point the point of intersection.

   a) What will be the result if you substitute the x- and y-values of the point of intersection into each equation?

   b) Substitute the point of intersection into both equations and see if your prediction was correct. We call the point of intersection the solution to a system of equations. Why do you think we use this terminology?

   c) What does this point of intersection represent?

6. With your partner, determine which option is the better deal. Explain your answer.

7. Explain why the y-intercepts of each graph, $(0, -50)$ and $(0, -100)$, are not meaningful in this particular situation.

The Culinary Institute's Bid

8. The Culinary Institute has submitted a bid that when graphed is parallel to the graph of the function associated with Fancy Caterer's bid ($80 per person with a discount of $100). Write a situation and the equation that *could* represent the Culinary Institute's bid. Explain your reasoning.

9. Julian's equation for the Culinary Institute bid was $y = 80x - 200$.

   a) Could Julian's equation be correct? Explain.

   b) What are the similarities between Julian's equation and the equation for Fancy Caterer's bid?

   c) What are the differences?

   d) Predict what the graph of the Julian's equation will look like compared to the graphs of Fancy Caterer's bid and Corporate Caterer's bid.

10. a) Graph the three bids in the same window and compare the results with your prediction.

    b) Who has the best deal: Julian's bid for the Culinary Institute, Fancy Caterer's bid or Corporate Caterer's bid? Explain your answer.

Using Your Graphing Calculator

 Talk
Moves

 Have students work independently on Question 4 and compare the window graphs on their graphing calculator with a partner. Next, have student pairs determine which caterer is a better deal. Circulate as students discuss their ideas with partners. Encourage students to share their ideas in a class discussion. Use Questions 5 and 6 to further enhance the discussion. Guide students to recognize that in Question 5b, the point of intersection on the graph is a point whose coordinates satisfy both situations and is the solution to the system of linear equations. It is considered the point where the catering costs would be the same for both companies. Determining the point of intersection graphically is one way to solve a system of linear equations. In their study of algebra, students will learn to also solve a system by manipulating equations.

4.

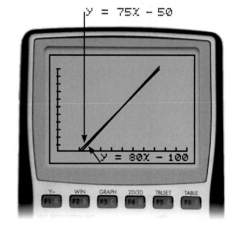

5. The graphs meet at (10, 700). See graph in Question 4.

a) Since the point satisfies both equations, both equations will be true statements when you substitute the values of the point and simplify.

b)

$y = 75x - 50$	$700 = 80(10) - 100$
$y = 80x - 100$	$700 = 700$
$700 = 75(10) - 50$	$700 = 700$

The point of intersection (10, 700) is the solution to the system of equations because when we substitute its x- and y-values into the equations, the point satisfies both.

c) It is the point where the catering cost for either company would be the same for a specific number of participants (10) attending the banquet.

6. For fewer than 10 people, Fancy Caterer is the better deal. For 10 people, the catering cost is the same for both companies. If more than 10 people attend the banquet, the additional one-time $100 discount that Fancy Caterer offers no longer makes a difference. Since it is very likely that more than 10 people will attend the banquet, the conference organizers should use Corporate Caterer.

7. The y-intercepts (0, −50) for Corporate Caterer and (0, −100) for Fancy Caterer do not make sense since they mean that if 0 people attend, the catering companies would have to pay the conference organizers money.

The Culinary Institute's Bid

Have students complete Questions 8–11 independently.

8. Answers will vary. Any equation of the form $y = 80x + b$ is correct.

9. a) Yes, The graph of this line is parallel since the coefficient of x is the same as Fancy Caterer's.

b) The per-person charge, $80, is the same as Fancy Caterer. The value of the coefficient of x is the same.

c) The discount amount, $200, is different in this situation. (This represents the constant amount that is being subtracted regardless of the number of people attending the banquet. It provides the y-intercept).

d) The graph for Culinary Institute's bid will be a line that is parallel to the graph for Fancy Caterer, but with a y-intercept located 100 units below the graph for Fancy Caterer. The y-intercept occurs at $y = -200$, or the point (0, −200). The line for Corporate Caterer will initially lie above the lines for Fancy Caterer and Culinary Institute and will intersect the line for Fancy Caterer at the point (10, 700), and will intersect the line for Culinary Institute shortly after at point (30, 2200). The line for Corporate Caterer will then remain below the graphs of the other two companies.

10. a) The prediction stated in Question 9 is correct.

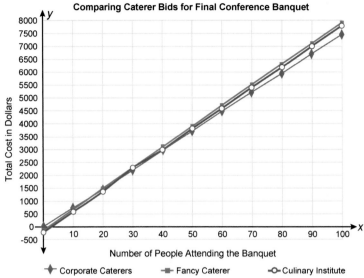

Comparing Caterer Bids for Final Conference Banquet

Legend: Corporate Caterers — Fancy Caterer — Culinary Institute

The prediction stated in Question 9 is correct.

b) If fewer than 30 participants attend the banquet, Culinary Institute is the cheapest. If more than 30 participants attend the banquet, Corporate Caterer is the best deal. If 30 participants attend, the banquet cost for both companies is the same.

Your Bid

Explain to students that they are owners of their own catering company. They will be responsible for creating a bid for the final conference banquet. Have students work independently on Questions 11–13, and then share their responses with a partner. Encourage student pairs to discuss Question 13 together as they compare their bids and graphs.

Discuss Question 14 as a class. It is important for students to notice that the slopes are different. This means that the lines are not parallel and will eventually intersect. The slope gives an indication of the steepness of a line: the greater the absolute value of the slope, the steeper the line. The y-intercept $(0, 0)$ is the same in all linear equations.

Have students complete Question 15 independently and then share their responses with the class. Guide students to recognize that although the points may differ depending on the bid students created, the points of intersection represent where the cost for the banquet will be the same as the cost for the banquet whose line it intersected.

11. Answers will vary. Possible response: Ann's Catering charges $70 per person for banquets.

a) $y = 70x$

b) The y-intercept is 0 or the point $(0, 0)$.

c) Answers will vary. Using the example above, this line will begin at $(0, 0)$, and will be graphed above the other lines initially, then intersect the lines for Fancy Caterer and Corporate Caterer at $(10, 700)$, and then lie below these lines thereafter. The line will lie below the line for Culinary Institute when there are 11 people attending the banquet. The slope of the line that represents Ann's Catering is not as steep as the other lines.

12. Answers will vary depending on the accuracy of predictions.

13. Answers will vary. Possible responses:

- Bids that have the same per-person rate as one of the given situations will be parallel to the line representing that situation.

- Bids that have a greater per-person rate than one of the given situations will have a line that is more steep than the line representing the given situation.

- Bids that have a per-person rate that is less than one of the given situations will have a line that is less steep than the line of the given situation.

All of the class' new lines will have y-intercepts of $(0, 0)$ since none offered a discount.

14. a) Answers will vary but should be of the form $y = mx$ with m as the slope.

b) Answers will vary. The slope is directly related to the number of people attending.

15. Answers will vary. The point(s) of intersection represents where the two bids yield the same catering cost for a specified number of participants.

 **W rap It Up**

The discussion should include the following key ideas:

- When equations are written in the slope-intercept form, $y = mx + b$, and the value of m (which is the coefficient of x) is the same for both equations, the lines have the same slope and are parallel. Therefore, they will not intersect.

- When the value of m is different, the lines are not parallel. Therefore, they will eventually intersect at a point.

- The point of intersection is the solution for the system of equations. The values of the x- and y-coordinates of the intersection point satisfy both equations.

Your Bid

11. Make up a bid for the banquet in which there is no discount on the total cost.

   a) Write an equation to represent your bid.

   b) What is the y-intercept for this function?

   c) Predict where the line for this equation will fall in relation to the lines you have already graphed.

12. Graph the line on your graphing calculator and see if you were correct. (You may need to change the window to be able to view the appropriate portion of the graph.)

13. Your classmates may have created different bids. However, there should be similarities among the graphs. Without looking at others' responses, predict the similarities. Share your ideas with your partner.

14. a) What is the slope of each line?

   b) How is the slope of each line related to the corresponding bid?

15. Would the graph of your equation cross any of the graphs of your classmates? If so, where? What does the intersection point represent?

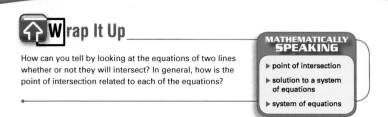 **W rap It Up**

How can you tell by looking at the equations of two lines whether or not they will intersect? In general, how is the point of intersection related to each of the equations?

> **MATHEMATICALLY SPEAKING**
> ▶ point of intersection
> ▶ solution to a system of equations
> ▶ system of equations

Reflect

Use these questions to help you reflect on the lesson and plan for future instruction.

- What strategies did students use to help them successfully predict where the lines of a given situation would be located on a graph, and whether these lines would be parallel or intersect at a point?

- How well did students interpret the point of intersection for a system of equations?

- What are some lingering misconceptions about the slope and the y-intercept of linear equations that need to be addressed before beginning the next lesson?

MATERIALS LIST
▶ Graph paper
▶ Graphing calculators

Write About It

1. Create two different bids that include no discount.

   a) Discuss the similarities and the differences between them. Use vocabulary terms, such as slope, *y*-intercept, steepness and point of intersection, in your explanation.

   b) Which of your bids was the better deal? Explain your answer.

2. Create two more banquet bids whose graphs each have a slope of 50.

   a) Name the independent and dependent variables for each bid.

   b) What does the slope represent for each bid?

   c) Predict the similarities and differences between the graphs of the lines representing these bids.

   d) Will these two lines intersect? Why or why not?

3. Suppose that Carlotta's Catering gives a discount of $75 on the total cost and that her price is better than Fancy Caterer no matter how many people attend the banquet.

   a) What is one possibility for the price Carlotta's charges per person?

   b) Write an equation for Carlotta's Catering's bid. Graph the equations of Carlotta's Catering and Fancy Caterer on the same coordinate axes.

   c) How can you tell from the two graphs that Carlotta's Catering is a better deal?

4. If two lines with different slopes are graphed on the same coordinate plane, the graphs will:

   A. always intersect in a point.

   B. never intersect.

   C. sometimes intersect in a point.

Section 3: Analyzing Linear Functions • Lesson 3.2 **115**

On Your Own

Write About It

1. Answers will vary. Students' responses should address the slope of the graphs, the *y*-intercept, the steepness of the lines and the point of intersection. The *y*-intercepts of the student bids will all be at (0, 0), but the slopes may differ.

2. Answers will vary. Possible response:

   Lin's Banquet Catering charges $50 per person with no additional discounts.
   Jon's Banquet Catering charges $50 per person and offers a one-time discount of $75.

   a) The independent variable in each situation is the number of people attending the banquet and the dependent variable is the total catering cost.

   b) The slope represents how much the catering companies charge per person.

   c) The steepness of the lines will be the same, since they have the same slopes (*m* = 50). The graphs will be lines rising from left to right.

      The lines will have different *y*-intercepts. Lin's Banquet Catering graph has a *y*-intercept of 0, or the point (0, 0). Jon's Banquet Catering graph has a *y*-intercept of ⁻75, or the point (0, ⁻75).

   d) The lines will not intersect. Since they have the same slope, they will be parallel.

3. a) Answers will vary. Student responses should state a per-person cost of less than $55.

b) Possible equation: $y = 50x - 75$.

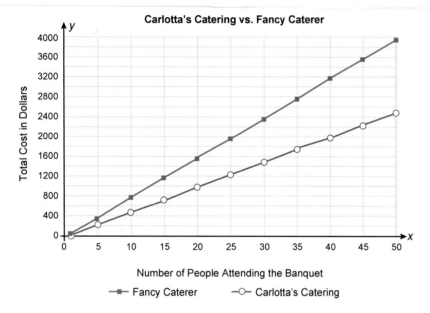

Carlotta's Catering vs. Fancy Caterer

Total Cost in Dollars

Number of People Attending the Banquet

■— Fancy Caterer   —○— Carlotta's Catering

c) The graph of Carlotta's Catering lies below the graph for Fancy Caterer, for 1 or more participants.

4. A. always intersect in a point.

5. a) In 2002, there were 40 participants from east of the Mississippi. In 2003, the number of participants increased to 60 and then decreased in 2004 back to 40. There was a small increase in number of participants in 2005 (to approximately 45). The number of participants remained the same for 2006.

b) In 2002, there were approximately 45 participants from west of the Mississippi. Attendance decreased in 2003 to 30 participants. In 2004, the number of participants increased to 40 and attendance continued to increase in 2005 to 60 participants. However, in 2006, attendance decreased to approximately 42 participants.

c) In 2004, the number of participants from east and west of the Mississippi was the same. Each area had 40 participants. The conference was possibly held in Kansas City, offering a central location for both geographic areas.

6. Connecting the points makes it easier to see trends; therefore a trendline is often used to better describe discrete data.

7. a) Line l has a y-intercept of 300, or the point (0, 300), and has a slope of 0. The line is a horizontal line. The equation of the line is $y = 300$.

b) Points will vary. Possible sets of points: (50, 300) and (100, 600); slope is
$$600 - \frac{300}{100} - 50 = 6.$$

c) Points will vary. Possible sets of points: (10, 60) and (30, 180); slope is
$$180 - \frac{60}{30} - 10 = 6.$$

5. As conference planner for Sports Mecca, you need to decide where next year's annual conference should be held. You have made a graph of where the participants from previous years have traveled from.

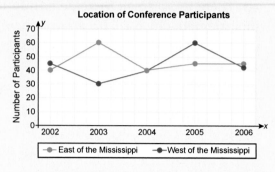

Location of Conference Participants

East of the Mississippi   West of the Mississippi

a) Describe the graph that represents the participants who traveled from east of the Mississippi River.

b) Describe the graph that represents the participants who traveled from west of the Mississippi River.

c) In which year was the number of participants from both sides of the river the same?

6. Michael asked his teacher, "I thought that discrete points should not be connected by a line. Why are the points in the graph for Question 5 connected?" If you were his teacher, how would you respond?

8. a) Line *p* represents the amount of money collected in relation to the number of tickets sold.

b) Line *l* represents the cost of the band.

c) Point *C* represents where the amount of money earned from selling tickets is the same as the cost of the band. It is the break-even point and it is the solution to the system of equations.

d) Sarah is incorrect. The amount of money earned in the sale of tickets is $900, but students must deduct the cost of the band, which is $300. Therefore, the amount of money they can donate would be $600 if 150 tickets were sold.

e) The label of the second column is $y = 300$. The values in this column represent the corresponding y-values (cost for the band) for the given x-values (number of tickets sold).

The label of the third column is $y = 6x$. The values in this column represent the corresponding y-values (amount of money collected) for the given x-values (number of tickets sold).

7.

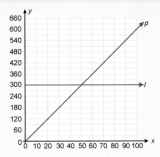

a) Describe the graph of line *l*. Write an equation for line *l*.

b) Find the slope of line *p* by using two points and by drawing a slope triangle.

c) Find the slope of line *p* by using two different points and drawing a different slope triangle.

8. Remember the students from Dodd High School, who were sponsoring a benefit for one of their classmates? They planned to have a live band and sell tickets for $6.00 each. The PTA is covering all costs except the live band, which charges $300 to perform. Their advisor told them that the graphs in Question 7 above represent the given situation.

a) Describe what line *p* represents in this situation.

b) What does line *l* represents in this situation?

c) Label the point of intersection of lines *l* and *p* as point *C*. What does point *C* represent?

d) Sarah said, "If we sell 150 tickets we will have a $900 profit." Do you agree or disagree with Sarah? Please explain.

e) The table below shows some of the *x*-values with their corresponding *y*-values, for the two functions. What are the equations for the second and third column headers? Explain what these equations mean and how they relate to the table values.

Number of Tickets	Band Cost	Ticket Sales
x	y = ?	y = ?
45	300	270
47	300	282
50	300	300
52	300	312
55	300	330

Think Beyond

9.

a) The label of the *x*-axis is Number of T-shirts. The label of the *y*-axis is Profit.

b) Line *p* represents the amount of money earned when selling T-shirts at a cost of $5 each with an initial up-front cost of 6 dozen plain T-shirts for $125.

Line *q* represents the amount of money earned when selling T-shirts in three different colors for a cost of $5 each after paying an up-front cost of $3.50 for each, thereby earning $1.50 per T-shirt sold.

c) The slope of line *q* is $\frac{75}{50}$, or 1.5.

d) The slope of line *p* is $\frac{75}{15}$, or 5.

e) It is the point at which both situations would earn the same amount of money. Profits for both situations would be the same when selling between 35 and 36 T-shirts. If less than 36 T-shirts were sold, paying $3.50 for each would be more profitable. If 36 or more T-shirts were sold, buying 6 dozen plain shirts would be more profitable.

f) The point (25, 0) means that when 25 shirts have been sold, the total amount of money earned would be $0. It is the point where the initial up-front cost of $125 for 6 dozen T-shirts has been recovered. Although no profit has been made at this point, there is no loss from paying the initial start-up cost.

LESSON
3.2
SECTION 3
On Your Own

 **Think Beyond**

9. The 8th grade class is planning to tie-dye T-shirts that come in three different colors for a class project. The class can purchase 6 dozen T-shirts that come in three different colors for $125 or buy the plain T-shirts for $3.50 each. They plan to charge $5 for each tie-dyed shirt. The graph below represents the *profit* students will make in each situation.

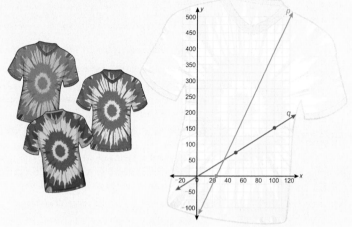

a) Label each axis appropriately.

b) Which situation does line *p* represent? Which situation does line *q* represent?

c) Find the slope of line *p*. Two points on *p* are (25, 0) and (10, −75).

d) Find the slope of line *q*. Two points on *q* are (100, 150) and (50, 75).

e) Line *p* and line *q* intersect in the point (35.71, 53.55). What does this intersection represent in terms of the situation?

f) What does the point where the *x*-value is 25 and the *y*-value is 0 mean on line *p*? What does the point (10, −75) represent?

g) Using the graph, can you tell how much more money the class will make if they sell 100 T-shirts using plan *p* instead of plan *q*? Explain your answer.

h) Which option would you advise the class to choose? Explain your answer.

 NOTE This point is the *x*-intercept and in this type of problem is called the break-even point. It is where the line crosses the *x*-axis. The point (10, 275) means that when 10 shirts have been sold, the total amount of money still owed for the start-up is $75.

---

g) Yes, you can tell from the graph. Plan *p* will yield a profit of $375 while plan *q* will yield a profit of $150. Plan *p* will earn $225 more than plan *q*. You can draw or imagine a vertical line from *x* = 100 and compare where it crosses the two lines.

h) Answers will vary. If students anticipate selling more than 35 T-shirts, students should select plan *p*. If students anticipate selling fewer than 36 T-shirts, students should select plan *q*.

 **Think Beyond**

10. First, graph the equation $y = 2x + 1$. Students should know from recent lessons that the slope is 2 and the *y*-intercept is (0, 1). Since the inequality states that *y* is "greater than" the expression, shade in the area above the line (that is, in the positive *y* direction).

Think Beyond

10. So far, we have been working with linear equations. We can also consider linear inequalities such as $y \geq 2x + 1$. This means that y can take on any value greater than or equal to $2x + 1$. What do you think the graph of this inequality will look like?

Hint
See page 155

Think Back

11. Henry needs to be at a meeting in Philadelphia for a week. He found a deal where he can stay at a hotel for 5 days at $185 per day and get the last 2 days free, or he can stay at another hotel for $129 per day. Which hotel is a better deal for a 7-day stay? By how much?

12. Henry can get a less expensive room if he is willing to stay outside the city, but then he would need to take the train to the city and back each day. The room is $110 per day, and one-way train fare is $12.35. Would staying outside the city save him money? How much would a train pass for the week have to cost to save him at least $1.00?

13. Besides cost, what other considerations might go into choosing a hotel?

14. If $5w = x - 6$ and $w = 3$, then $x =$

   A. −2   **C.** 21

   B. 11   **D.** 14

15. $30 = 1.5\%$ of _____? Show your work.

You can also check points to determine which side of the line to shade. Pick one point above the line and one point below the line.

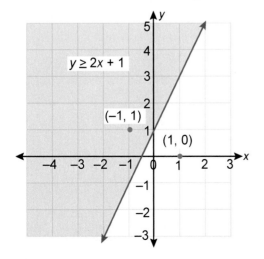

$y \geq 2x + 1$

(−1, 1)

(1, 0)

Points above the line will satisfy the equation. Points will vary. Possible response:

$(-1, 1)$ $y \geq 2x + 1$
             $1 \geq 2(-1) + 1$
             $1 \geq 2(-1)$ True

Points below the line will not satisfy the equation. Points will vary. Possible response:

$(1, 0)$ $y \geq 2x + 1$
        $0 \geq 2(1) + 1$
        $0 \geq 3$ Not true

Think Back

11. For the entire week, the first is hotel costs $925 and the second costs $909.93. The second hotel is $15.07 cheaper.

12. This would not save him money, since the round trip would be $24.70 + $110 hotel, or $134.70 per day. The hotel in Philadelphia is cheaper at $129.99 per day.

$129.99 − $110 = $19.99;
$19.99 • 7 = $139.93, which is difference in hotel prices for the week. The weekly train pass would have to be $138.93 or less to save him at least $1.

13. Answers may vary. Possible response:
The hotel outside the city would mean commuting time, and train schedules would have to be considered as well.

14. **C.** 21

15. 2000

LESSON 3.3 Graphing Systems of Equations

Suggested Pacing: 1 Day

In this lesson, students will explore a variety of linear functions with positive and negative slopes, form generalizations about lines, and consider how their graphs behave on a coordinate plane. There is less emphasis on real-world situations in this lesson. Rather, students are encouraged to focus on the mathematics behind the situations to develop a broader understanding of the key ideas that are being generalized.

LESSON OBJECTIVES

■ Students will form generalizations about the slopes of the lines in a system of linear equations and determine whether the lines intersect, coincide, or are parallel.

DAY 1	MATERIALS*	ESSENTIAL *ON YOUR OWN* QUESTIONS
Thinking Like a Mathematician	**In Class** ■ Graph paper ■ Graphing calculator **On Your Own** ■ Graph paper ■ Graphing calculator	Questions 1–10, 12–16

* The Think Like a Mathematician Daily Record Sheet should be used daily

119A   Course 3: Line It Up: Focusing on Linear Relationships

➡️ Start It Off

1. When $x = 1$, $y = -10$, for all equations.

2. When $x = 0$, $y = -8$, for all equations.

3. When $x = 5$, $y = 2$, for all equations.

Students should notice that the solutions are the same. They should examine the equations and realize that the terms in each equation are all multiples of each other. This is a precursor to help students understand when the graphs of linear functions will coincide.

 TEACHING THE LESSON

Thinking Like a Mathematician

Talk Moves — Have students work with a partner to complete Question 1, and then discuss their predictions as a class. Do not push for consensus at this time. Rather, have students offer mathematical reasoning to explain their predictions. Then, have students complete Question 2 to see if their predictions were correct. Although they are working with partners, each student should graph the lines on their own grid paper. Have students discuss as a class how their graphs compare to their predictions. Use talk moves, such as agree/disagree and why, to stimulate the discussion and enhance student understanding.

💡 Differentiation

Think Differently: For those students experiencing difficulty recognizing the slope or the y-intercept in a given equation, encourage them to create a table of values for x and y. Next, have students plot the points for each function on the coordinate plane and connect them to form lines. Students can create slope triangles to verify that the slopes are 1 and -1 for the lines that share a y-intercept of $(0, 0)$. This reinforces the connection between the equation and the graph in determining the slope and y-intercept of the function.

Have students complete Questions 3–5 with their partners and share their responses in a class discussion. For Question 5, make sure the discussion emphasizes the fact that the graphs will always intersect at a point. However, depending on the scale used or the window selected on the graphing calculator, the point of intersection may not be visible.

1. Predictions will vary. A line with a positive slope will always have a point of intersection with a line with a negative slope when graphed on the same coordinate grid.

2. **a)** Yes, the conjecture appears to be correct. The two lines intersect.

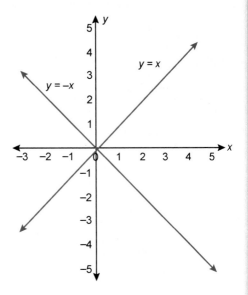

b) The graphs will intersect at (0, 0). It is the y-intercept for both lines, since it is the point they both have in common.

c), **d)** and **e)** Answers will vary, but the two lines will always intersect.

Graphing Systems of Equations

 **Start It Off**

For each of the equations below, find the value of y when $x = {}^-1$, 0 and 5.

1. $y = 2x - 8$

2. $2y = 4x - 16$

3. $4y = 8x - 32$

What do you notice about the y-values? Why do you think that is?

Thinking Like a Mathematician

As a mathematician, you should know that math is a powerful tool that can help you model real-life situations. In the first two sections of this unit, you used linear functions to solve real-life problems. To get a broader understanding of mathematics, you need to analyze the mathematical concepts themselves. Doing so, you will better understand the logical connections within mathematics and the power this gives you in solving real-life applications.

The situations you examined in the last lesson resulted in linear functions with positive slopes. When written in the form $y = mx + b$, m (the slope) was always positive. All the linear functions had positive slope because the rate of change was always positive. For example, the total cost of the banquet increased as the number of attendees increased.

In some of the On Your Own equations, you saw that m could be negative. That is, a line could have a negative slope. Let's examine what this means.

3. Isabel is incorrect. She needs to extend the lines of the graph or the table of values. Since the y-intercept for both equations is (0, 2), this is the point that the two lines have in common. So, the lines will intersect at the point (0, 2). If she extends the tables for each equation to include the x-value 0, she will find that the corresponding y-value for each graph is 2.

Isabel could have also recognized that the slope of the lines is not the same. This means that the lines are not parallel. Therefore, they will intersect.

1. Do you think that a line with a positive slope and a line with a negative slope graphed on the same coordinate plane will have a point of intersection? Talk to your partner and make a conjecture.

2. a) Using a graphing calculator, graph the lines $y = x$ and $y = -x$ in the same window. Does your conjecture appear to be correct?

   b) Name the point of intersection of the two lines.

   c) You and your partner should each write a pair of linear equations—one with a positive slope and one with a negative slope—with graphs that you think will intersect.

   d) Share your equations and predict whether or not the lines for your partner's equations will intersect.

   e) Check your prediction on a graphing calculator.

3. Isabel said she found two equations, one whose line has a positive slope and one whose line has a negative slope, that do not intersect. She created a table of values for each equation, plotted the points and graphed both equations, as shown below. She says that her graph clearly shows that the two lines do not intersect.

   How would you respond to her?

x	y = 3x + 2
1	5
2	8
3	11
4	14

x	y = -2x + 2
1	0
2	-2
3	-4
4	-6

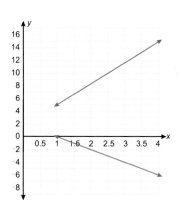

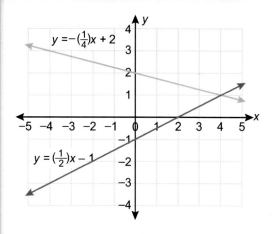

$y = \frac{1}{2}x - 1$	
x	**y**
-2	-2
-1	$-1\frac{1}{2}$
0	-1
1	$-\frac{1}{2}$
2	0
3	$\frac{1}{2}$
4	1

$y = -\frac{1}{4}x + 2$	
x	**y**
-2	$2\frac{1}{2}$
-1	$2\frac{1}{4}$
0	2
1	$1\frac{3}{4}$
2	$1\frac{1}{2}$
3	$1\frac{1}{4}$
4	1

4. Josh is incorrect. The slopes of the lines are not the same. This means that they are not parallel. Therefore, they will intersect at some point on the coordinate plane. The point of intersection is the solution to both equations. If Josh extends the tables, he will find out that for the x-value of 4, the y-value is 1 for both equations. Therefore, the point (4, 1) is the point where the lines intersect. The graph of the equations below shows the lines intersecting at the point (4, 1).

5. Yes, the graphs will always intersect. Since the slopes are different, the lines are not parallel and therefore will intersect at some point on the coordinate plane.

Lines with Negative Slopes

Have students complete Questions 6–14 independently and share their responses with a partner. Discuss any discrepancies as a class. Do not rush the discussion for Question 12, as this is an important generalization for students to develop. Encourage students to share their systems of equations for Questions 13 and 14. Although the systems will vary, it is important that students recognize what they have in common. Ask:

- *How are the systems of equations alike? How are they different?*

- *How can you tell whether the lines will intersect?*

- *How can you tell whether the lines will intersect at the origin?*

---

4. Josh thinks that Isabel's lines should intersect because they have the same y-intercept. He found two new equations below with different slopes and different y-intercepts. He is certain that these two graphs will not intersect. How would you respond to him? Use the tables below. Make a graph to help explain your answer.

x	$y = \frac{1}{2}x - 1$
-2	-2
-1	$-1\frac{1}{2}$
0	-1
1	$-\frac{1}{2}$
2	0

x	$y = -\frac{1}{4}x + 2$
-2	$2\frac{1}{2}$
-1	$2\frac{1}{4}$
0	2
1	$1\frac{3}{4}$
2	$1\frac{1}{2}$

5. Will the graphs of two equations, one with a positive slope and one with a negative slope, always intersect in one point? Explain your reasoning.

Lines with Negative Slopes

Look at the following pairs of equations with negative slopes, in Questions 6–10 below. Predict whether or not they will intersect at a point. Give a reason for your prediction.

6. $y = -x + \frac{1}{8}$ and $y = -x + 4$

7. $y = -2x + 6.2$ and $y = \frac{3}{4} - 2x$

8. $y = 8x$ and $y = -16x$

9. $y = -1.2x$ and $y = -5.3x$

10. $y = -\frac{1}{3}x + 4$ and $y = -x$

11. Use a graphing calculator and see if your predictions were correct.

12. Make a conjecture about the intersection of two lines with negative slopes.

13. a) Write a system of two linear equations that both have negative slopes and do not intersect.

    b) Explain to your partner how to do this so that he or she can do the same.

NOTE The systems of linear equations with the same values for m and b represent lines that intersect in an infinite number of points, or coincide. This will be discussed in the next part of the lesson.

---

6. No, they will not intersect. Both equations have the same slope so the lines will be parallel.

7. No, they will not intersect. Both equations have the same slope so the lines will be parallel.

8. Yes, they will intersect. The equations have different slopes so the lines will not be parallel.

9. Yes, they will intersect. The equations have different slopes so the lines will not be parallel.

10. Yes, they will intersect. The equations have different slopes so the lines will not be parallel.

11. Answers will vary depending on accuracy of predictions. The above predictions are correct.

14. a) Write a system of two linear equations that both have negative slopes and intersect at the origin.

    b) Explain to your partner how to do this so that he or she can do the same.

Looks Can Be Deceiving

Let's examine some new situations.

15. Take a look at the following three systems of equations:

System 1	System 2	System 3
$y = x + 5$	$y = -x - 4$	$y = 3x + 2$
$5y = 5x + 25$	$4y = -4x - 16$	$4y = 12x + 8$

    a) How is the second equation in each system related to the first?

    b) Predict whether or not the graphs of the two equations in each system will intersect.

    c) Graph each system by making a table of values and plotting points. Were your predictions correct?

    d) Were you surprised? Explain your answer.

16. Remember that the intersection point of two lines is the solution to the system of linear equations represented by the lines. What is the solution of each system above?

17. Create a system of two linear equations so that the graphs of the lines coincide. Graph your system and see if you were correct.

 **Wrap It Up**

When two lines are graphed on the coordinate plane, explain the possible ways they can intersect. Consider all possible situations and give examples to illustrate each.

12. When graphed in the same coordinate plane, lines with different negative slopes will intersect at a point. Lines with the same negative slopes will be parallel and will not intersect. And, in general, any two lines that have different slopes and are graphed on the same plane will intersect at a point.

13. a) Equations will vary. Possible response: $y = -3x + 1\frac{1}{2}$ and $y = -3x - 5$

    b) Write two equations in the slope-intercept form, $y = mx + b$, so that m (the coefficient of x) has the same negative value in both equations. Any two different values can be used for b, the y-intercept.

14. a) Equations will vary. Possible response: $y = -\frac{1}{4}x$ and $y = -5x$

    b) Write two equation in the slope-intercept form, $y = mx + b$, so that m (the coefficient of x) has a different negative value in each equation. The value of b should be 0 for both equations.

Looks Can Be Deceiving

Have students work with a partner to complete Questions 15–17. Circulate as students work on the problems to assess understanding. Use the Student Snapshot observational tool to record anecdotal notes. When finished, encourage students to share their responses in a class discussion.

Have students compare systems of equations to make a generalization about linear functions that coincide on a coordinate grid. Ask:

- *How can you tell whether the two equations in a system of linear equations will have graphs that coincide on a coordinate grid?*

15. a) The terms in the first equations of each system have been multiplied by a common factor to create the terms in the second equations. The systems actually represent the same equation.

    b) Predictions will vary. The graphs for each system will be exactly the same line.

c) Students might be surprised that the graph for each system are the same line. The second equation in each system represents the same equation as the first. Each of the terms in the second equation can be divided by the same factor to arrive at the first equation. For example, if each term of the equation $5y = 5x + 25$ is divided by 5, the resulting equation is $y = x + 5$. This is the same as the first equation. Students who rewrite the second equations into $y = mx + b$ form in order to graph it may recognize this relationship quicker. Students who make a table for each equation and then plot points may not immediately see the relationship within the system.

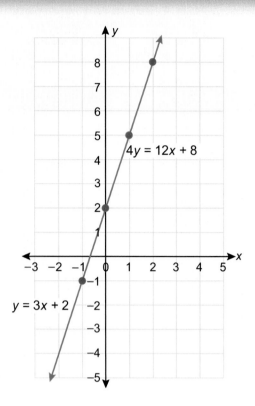

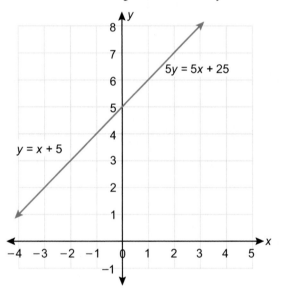

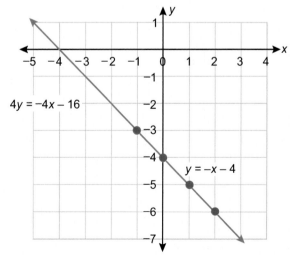

d) Students will find that the table of values is the same for each set of equations, so it makes sense that the graphs are the same line.

$y = x + 5$	
x	**y**
−1	4
0	5
1	6
2	7

$5y = 5x + 25$	
x	**y**
−1	4
0	5
1	6
2	7

$y = {}^-x - 4$	
x	**y**
−1	−3
0	−4
1	−5
2	−6

$4y = {}^-4x - 16$	
x	**y**
−1	−3
0	−4
1	−5
2	−6

$y = 3x + 2$	
x	**y**
−1	−1
0	2
1	5
2	8

$4y = 12x + 8$	
x	**y**
−1	−1
0	2
1	5
2	8

16. Since the lines coincide, the lines intersect in an infinite number of points. There are an infinite number of solutions to each system of equations.

17. Answers will vary. Possible response:
$y = 3x + 2$
$3y = 9x + 6$

 **Wrap It Up**

Responses will vary. Guide the discussion to include the following key ideas:

- Two lines that intersect at a point will have different slopes. Possible example:
  $y = 4x - 2$ and $y = -\frac{1}{2}x$

- Two lines that are parallel will have the same slope and a different y-intercept and will not intersect. Possible example:
  $y = -2x - 2$ and $y = -2x + 5$

- Two lines that coincide will intersect at an infinite number of points. The terms of one equation have been multiplied by the same factor to derive the terms of the second. Possible example:
  $y = x - 2$ and $3y = 3x - 6$

Encourage students to graph the lines on grid paper to further enhance their understanding.

Reflect

Use these questions to help you reflect on the lesson and plan for future instruction.

- Were students able to form generalizations about the slopes of the lines in a system of linear equations and determine whether the lines would intersect, be parallel, or coincide?

- What lingering misconceptions need to be addressed to solidify students' understandings about the slope of linear equations?

Write About It

1.

a) Answers will vary. Functions should have different slopes. Possible response:
$y = 3x + 1, y = -2x - 5$

b) Answers will vary. Functions should have the same slope and y-intercept. Possible response:
$y = 3x + 1, 2y = 6x + 2$

c) Answers will vary. Functions will have the same slope, but different y-intercepts.

Possible response:
$y = 3x - 1$ and $y = 3x + 10$

2. Answers will vary. The equation should have the same slope as the one in the given problem, which is $\frac{5}{8}$. Possible response:
$y = \frac{5}{8}x - 2$

3. Answers will vary. Possible response: $0.5y = 2x$. Students should state that they multiplied the coefficients of x and y by the same factor.

4. **C.** Sometimes intersect.

There are 2 possibilities when two lines with the same slope are graphed on the same coordinate plane. The lines may be parallel and not intersect, or they may coincide (intersect in an infinite number of points). Therefore, "sometimes intersect" is the correct response.

Write About It

1. Give examples of systems of two linear equations that:

   a) intersect at a single point.

   b) coincide.

   c) do not intersect.

2. Find an equation of a line that is parallel to $y = -10 + \frac{5}{8}x$. Check your answer using a graphing calculator.

3. Write an equation of a line that has the exact same points as $2y = 8x$. How did you find this equation? Check by graphing the system of equations.

4. If two lines with the same slope are graphed on the same coordinate plane, the graphs will:

   A. always intersect.

   B. never intersect.

   C. sometimes intersect.

   Explain your answer and give an example.

5. Determine if the graphs of the systems of equations below will form parallel lines, intersecting lines, or will coincide. Explain your answer.

   a) $y = 6x + 8$
   $y = 6 + 8x$

   b) $y = \frac{1}{3}x + 7$
   $y = \frac{-1}{3}x$

   c) $y = \frac{-1}{4}x$
   $y = \frac{-1}{4}x - 6$

   d) $y = 2x - 8$
   $2y = 4x - 16$

   e) $y = \frac{22}{5}x + 3$
   $y = 4.4x - 3$

6. Write an equation of a line that intersects $y = 4x - 8$ at exactly one point. Explain how you found this equation. Check your answer using a graphing calculator.

7. Find the equations of two lines that will coincide with $y = \frac{1}{2}x - 8$.

---

5. **a)** intersect in one point since the slopes (6 and 8) are different.

   b) intersect in one point, since the slopes are different.

   c) parallel, since the slopes are the same and the y-intercepts are different.

   d) coincide, since you can multiply $y = 2x - 8$ by 2 to get $2y = 4x - 16$. Slopes and y-intercepts are the same.

   e) parallel, since the slopes are the same with different y-intercepts.

8. a) Find the equation of a line that is parallel to the line graphed below.

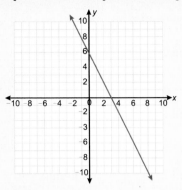

b) Find the equation of a line with a negative slope that intersects the line above at only one point.

c) Find the equation of a line with a positive slope that intersects the line above at only one point.

9. Explain to a friend how to write a system of two linear equations that both have negative slopes and intersect at only one point, different from the origin.

10. Harry claims that the two lines below are parallel. "It's obvious," he says. "Just look at them." Jocelyn disagrees and tells him that you cannot always go by the way things look. Determine who is correct. Explain your answer.

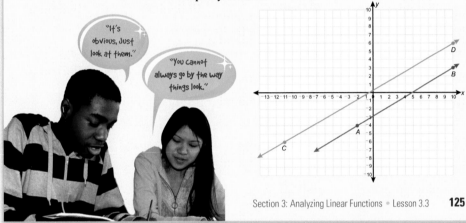

Section 3: Analyzing Linear Functions • Lesson 3.3 **125**

6. Answers will vary. The equation should have a slope that is different from the slope in the given equation. Possible response: $y = 2x - 1$

7. Answers will vary. All of the terms in the equation should be multiples of the terms in the given one.

Possible responses: $2y = x - 16$ and $3y = 1.5x - 24$.

8. Answers will vary.

a) Possible response: $y = -2x + 2$ (slope must be -2 with y-intercept different from 6.)

b) Possible response: $y = -x$. Slope should be negative and different from -2.

c) Possible response: $y = 3x + 6$.

9. The equations should have different negative coefficients of x. At least one equation should have a constant value added.

For example, $y = -2x + 6$ and $y = -3x$ would work.

10. Although the two lines may be parallel, Jocelyn is correct to not accept an answer by just looking at the graph. It is a good idea to check the slope of the lines to be sure that they are parallel. The lines must have the same slope to be parallel. Slope triangles can be used to determine the slope of each line.

The slope of line AB is $\frac{3}{5}$ and the slop of line CD is $\frac{4}{7}$. So, they are not parallel even though they appear to be.

Think Beyond

11.

a)

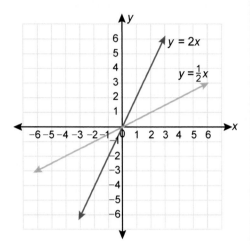

b)

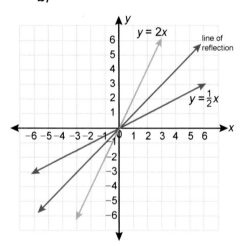

c) $y = x$

d)

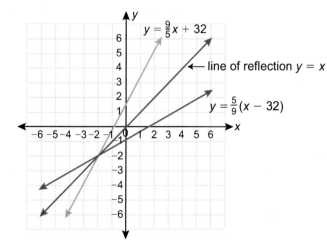

Think Beyond

11. **a)** Graph $y = 2x$ and $y = \frac{1}{2}x$.

b) The graph of $y = 2x$ can be reflected, or flipped, over another line, called the line of reflection, to match exactly with the graph of $y = \left(\frac{1}{2}\right)x$. Draw this line of reflection.

c) What is the equation of this line of reflection?

The two functions from Part a are called inverse functions, that is, one is the inverse of the other.

d) The equations for temperature conversions between Fahrenheit and Celsius degrees, $F = \frac{9}{5}C + 32$ and $C = \frac{5}{9}(F - 32)$, are additional examples of inverse functions. Graph each temperature equation on the same coordinate plane and find one line of reflection.

Think Back

12. If half of a number added to $\frac{1}{4}$ of the number is 27, what is the number?

13. If Euclid lived from 330–275 B.C.E., how old was he when he died? Jeff's math textbook has a copyright date of 2008 and uses many geometry concepts that have been credited to Euclid. How many years before the textbook's copyright date was Euclid born?

14. Simplify:

$$\frac{\frac{4}{15}}{\frac{2}{3}} \cdot \frac{1}{5}$$

? Hint
See page 155

15. Jenna needs $3\frac{1}{2}$ yards of material to make a dress. She finds a cotton cloth that costs $2.30 per yard. She also needs a zipper that costs $1.95. She pays for her items with a $20 bill. How much change will she get back?

16. The prime factorization of 18 is

  A. $2 \cdot 9$ **C.** $2 \cdot 2 \cdot 3$

  B. $3 \cdot 6$ **D.** $2 \cdot 3 \cdot 3$

Optional Technology Lesson for this section available at www.mymathinnovations.com

---

Think Back

12. 36

13. Euclid was 55 years old when he died. He was born 2,338 years before Jeff's textbook was published!

14. $\frac{2}{25}$

15. $20 - (\$8.05 + \$1.95) = \$10$

16. **D.** $2 \cdot 3 \cdot 3$

Optional Technology Lesson for this section available at www.mymathinnovations.com

Sum It Up

The Sum It Up summarizes the important mathematics students should have learned in this section. Encourage students to use this Sum It Up as they complete the Study Guide and prepare for quizzes and tests.

In this section you have learned that a linear function with the equation $y = kx$ is called a direct variation, where k is the constant of proportionality. You have also learned about the y-intercept and how it relates to the graph of a line. You have examined systems of equations and looked for points of intersection. You have also learned how to analyze two linear functions at the same time and make decisions about specific situations.

Direct Variation

A direct variation is a situation in which the two quantities, such as distance and time, both increase or decrease at the same rate. If one quantity doubles, then the other quantity doubles too. The ratio between the two quantities is a positive constant.

Direct variation is represented by the equation $y = kx$ where k is the constant of proportionality.

y-intercept

The y-intercept of a function is the point where the graph crosses the y-axis. At that point, the x-value is 0. The y-value of the y-intercept represents a constant that is being added to (or subtracted from) the mx-term in a linear function in of the form $y = mx + b$.

- In the situation graphed to the right, you pay a flat rate of $5 for shipping and handling in addition to $15 per CD. The line that represents this function crosses the y-axis at the y-intercept $(0, 5)$. The equation for the function is $y = 15x + 5$.

- The slope-intercept form of a linear equation is $y = mx + b$, where m is the slope of the line and b is the y-value of the y-intercept. In the equation above, 15 is the slope and $(0, 5)$ is the y-intercept.

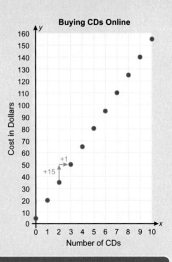

Buying CDs Online

Systems of Linear Equations

- A system of linear equations is a set of two or more linear equations.

- Two lines graphed on the same coordinate plane representing a system of two linear equations will be parallel, intersect at a single point or coincide.

- If two different lines are parallel, they will not intersect. They have the same slope but different y-intercepts. The graph below shows that $y = x$ and $y = x + 2$ are parallel lines. Both lines have the same slope, 1, but different y-intercepts. For $y = x$, the y-intercept is $(0, 0)$. For $y = x + 2$, the y-intercept is $(0, 2)$.

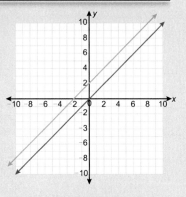

- If two lines have different slopes, they intersect at one point. The point of intersection of the two lines is the common solution to the system of two linear equations. In the graph below, the point of intersection $(2, 2)$ is the solution for the system of equations $y = x$ and $y = 2x - 2$. It is a point on the graph of both equations.

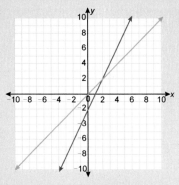

- If two lines have the same slope and same *y*-intercept, the lines will coincide. The solution to this system is all of the points on the line.

- Given two different pricing scenarios, you can determine when it is best to use one scenario instead of the other. You do this by first finding the point of intersection of the lines of the two functions. Then, examine the nearby *x* and *y*-values to make a decision. The point of intersection of the two lines indicates where the two scenarios are exactly the same in terms of the situations that are represented by the *x*- and *y*-variables.

MATHEMATICALLY SPEAKING

Do you know what these mathematical terms mean?

▸ constant of proportionality	▸ point of intersection	▸ system of equations
▸ direct variation	▸ slope-intercept form	▸ *y*-intercept
▸ parallel	▸ solution to a system of equations	

Study Guide

SECTION 3
Study Guide
Analyzing Linear Functions

MATERIALS LIST
▶ Graph paper

Part 1. What did you learn?

1. a. Slope: $\frac{4}{1}$

   y-intercept: (0, 1)

   Equation: $y = 4x + 1$
   (or equivalent)

   b. Slope: -1

   y-intercept: (0, 2)

   Equation: $y = -1x + 2$

2. a. The point (0, -1) is on the line.

   b. The points (-2, 5), (-1, 1) and (0, -3) are on the line.

   c. The points (0, 5), (1, 5) and (17, 5) are on the line.

   d. The points (2, 5), (-2, 3) and (0, 4) are on the line.

   e. The point (-3, 10) is on the line.

3. a. both positive slopes; coinciding lines; infinitely many solutions

   b. one positive slope and one negative slope; intersecting; one solution

   c. both positive, parallel lines; no solution

   d. both negative; intersecting lines; one solution

   e. both positive; intersecting lines; one solution

4. The equations $y = -8x$ $y = 8x$ and $y = 5x$ are direct variations because they are of the form $y = kx$.

1. Find the slope and y-intercept of each line. Then write the equation of the line in slope-intercept ($y = mx + b$) form.

   a.

   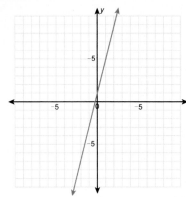

   b.

   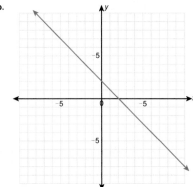

5. a. $y \, 5 \, 2x + 50$ (or equivalent)

   b. $y = 5x$ (or equivalent)

   c. Ned's equation is a direct variation since it is of the form $y = kx$.

   Songs on MP3 Player

   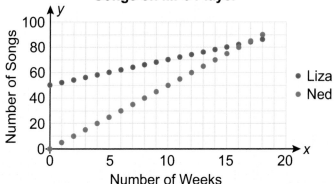

2. Which of the points are on each of the lines listed below?

   A. $y = 7x + {}^-1$ $({}^-1, 3)$ $(2, {}^-13)$ $(7, {}^-1)$ $(0, {}^-1)$

   B. $y = -4x + {}^-3$ $({}^-2, 5)$ $({}^-1, 1)$ $({}^-4, {}^-3)$ $(0, {}^-3)$

   C. $y = 5$ $(0, 5)$ $(1, 5)$ $(17, 5)$ $(5, 0)$

   D. $y = \frac{1}{2}x + 4$ $(2, 5)$ $({}^-2, 3)$ $(1, 2)$ $(0, 4)$

   E. $y = {}^-3x + 1$ $({}^-3, 1)$ $(0, {}^-3)$ $(0, {}^-1)$ $({}^-3, 10)$

3. The chart below gives five different systems of equations. Copy and complete the chart.

System of Equations	a. Description of Slopes of the Lines (both positive, both negative or one positive and one negative)	b. Description of System (coinciding lines, parallel lines, intersecting lines)	c. Number of Solutions (infinitely many, exactly one, none)
a. $y = 9x - 3$ $2y = 18x - 6$			
b. $y = {}^-8x$ $y = 8x$			
c. $y = 5x + 4$ $y = 5x$			
d. $y = {}^-3x + 4$ $y = -\frac{1}{3}x + 4$			
e. $y = 4x + 2$ $y = 2x + 4$			

4. Which of the equations in Question 3 are direct variations? How do you know?

5. Liza has 50 songs on her MP3 Player. She wants more songs and decides to use part of her allowance to download two songs per week. Ned just got an MP3 Player for his birthday. He also got money for his birthday and plans to download five songs per week.

   a. Write an equation to represent the relationship between week number and the number of songs Liza has. Use x for the independent variable and y for the dependent variable.

e. The slope of Liza's line is 2, which represents the songs she downloads each week. The y-intercept of her line is 50, which is the number of songs she had at week 0. The slope of Neil's line is 5, which represents the number of songs he downloads each week. His y-intercept is 0, which is the number of songs he had at week 0.

f. Ned will have at least as many songs as Liza after week 16. Student explanations will vary. One possible explanation: This can be seen on the graph where Ned's line crosses over Liza's line between weeks 16 and 17.

b. Write an equation to represent the relationship between week number and the number of songs Ned has. Use x for the independent variable and y for the dependent variable.

c. Is either of the equations you wrote in Parts a or b a direction variation? Why or why not?

d. Graph your two equations.

e. Find the slope and y-intercept of each line. What does each represent in this situation?

f. When will Ned have as many songs as Liza? How do you know?

6. Examine the graph below.

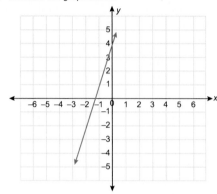

a. Write the equation of a line parallel to the line shown.

b. Write the equation of a line that coincides with the line shown.

c. Write the equations of two different lines that intersect the line shown. At least one of your lines should have a negative slope.

---

6. Student answers will vary. One possible answer:

Parallel: $y = 3x$

Coinciding: $y = 3x + 4$

Intersecting: $y = 2x + 4$, $y = -2x + 4$

7. 1st blank: A

2nd blank: B

3rd blank: C

4th blank: B and C

8. Company A: $5 per shirt

Company B: $4 per shirt

Company C: Zero rate of change:
$200 for any number of shirts

9. Company B charges a flat fee of $25.

10.

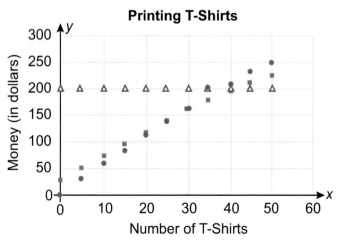

Printing T-Shirts

- Company A
- Company B
- Company C

11. Student answers will vary. One possible answer: Company A is the best buy for less than 25 t-shirts. Company B is the best buy for between 25 and 43 shirts. Company C is the best buy for more than 43 t-shirts.

7. The conference planners at Sports Mecca will print T-shirts with their logo for participants. They interviewed three companies about their price, y, for printing any number of T-shirts, x. The planners then wrote a linear function for each company's pricing plan:

Company A: $y = 5x$

Company B: $y = 4x + 25$

Company C: $y = 200$

Then, they plotted the data on one graph. They made the following notes about the graph. Use the three linear functions to fill in the blanks: Company _____ has a line that is steeper than the line for company_____.

$_1$ $_2$

The line for Company _____ is a horizontal line.

$_3$

Companies _____ have a positive y-intercept.

$_4$

8. Find the rate of change for each function in Question 7. Describe what each rate of change tells about the price of the T-shirts at each company.

Company A:

Company B:

Company C:

9. In Question 7, what does the "+ 25" tell you about the price of T-shirts at Company B?

10. Graph all three pricing plans (from Question 7) on the same coordinate grid.

11. Which company (from Question 7) has the best buy on T-shirts? Justify your choice.

12. Answers will vary. One possible answer: Mary Anne is wrong. Two lines with positive slopes can intersect and two lines with negative slopes can intersect. The pictures below show this.

As long as two lines have different slopes, they will intersect. Mary Anne might be confusing intersecting lines with perpendicular lines. Perpendicular lines must have opposite reciprocal slopes—so one slope must be positive and one must be negative. But, lines can cross at angles other than 90 degrees.

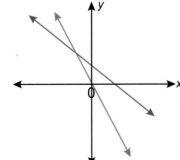

12. Mary Anne answered the following question on a recent quiz:

    How do you know by looking at two linear equations in slope-intercept form whether the lines will intersect or not?

    Mary Anne wrote, "In order for two lines to intersect, one line must have a positive slope and one line must have a negative slope. In order to intersect, the lines must be going in different directions. Lines with positive slopes go up from left to right and lines with negative slopes go down from left to right. If two lines have positive slopes, they will not intersect since they will both be going in the same direction."

    Mary Anne's teacher marked her answer wrong. Why? What could you do to help Mary Anne realize and fix her error?

13. Mauritzio answered the following multiple-choice question on his latest math quiz.

    Which one of the following is not parallel to the line represented by the equation $y = -2x + 3$?

    A. $2y = -4x + 8$ **C.** $y = -2x - 3$

    B. $y = 2x + 3$ **D.** $y = -2x$

    Mauritzio chose letter A since "The equation $2y = -4x + 8$ has a slope of -4. The line $y = -2x + 3$ has a slope of -2, and parallel lines must have the same slope." Mauritzio got this question wrong. Why? What could you do to help Mauritzio realize and fix his error?

13. Answers will vary. One possible answer: Choice A is the wrong choice because the equation $2y = -4x + 8$ is equivalent to $y = -2x + 4$. Multiply each term in $y = -2x + 4$ by 2 to get $2y = -4x + 8$. This means that this equation would create a line parallel to $y = -2x + 3$ since they have the same slope and different y-intercepts. Mauritzio should write each equation in slope-intercept form before he determines its slope. The correct choice is letter B since this equation would create a line that has the same steepness as $y = -2x + 3$ but moves in the opposite direction. This line would intersect $y = -2x + 3$ at the point $(0, 3)$, so they are not parallel.

Line It Up: Focusing on Linear Relationships

MATERIALS LIST
▶ Calculators
▶ Graph paper

Part 1. What did you learn?

SECTION 1

1. Sports Mecca is paying for travel expenses at the rate of $0.40 per mile. Suppose a participant's car gets 22 miles per gallon. Imagine that at the time of the Sports Mecca conference in Houston, Texas, gas costs $3.25 per gallon.

   a. Find the price of gas in dollars per mile. Use a calculator. Round to the nearest cent.

   b. Copy and complete the chart below.

Number of Miles	Total Cost of Gas
0	
1	
2	
3	
4	
5	
10	

   c. Write a recursive rule that shows how the cost of gas changes with each mile driven.

   d. Write an explicit rule for the cost of gas, c, and the number of miles driven, m.

   e. Is the conference payment per mile more or less than the price of gas per mile? Why?

2. In each of the following situations, determine if the number of miles is being used as the independent variable, dependent variable or neither.

   a. The distance from Stan's home to school if he lives 3 miles from school

   b. The total money paid for driving if each attendee will be paid 40 cents per mile

   c. The distance a car travels if driven at the rate of 60 miles per hour

   d. The distance Tamilynn can drive if her new car gets 30 miles to the gallon

c. *Previous* + 0.15 = *New*

d. $c = 0.15m$, where m is the number of miles and c is the total cost of gas.

e. The conference payment per mile is more than the cost of gas per mile since the payment is intended to cover any additional costs that arise from driving to the conference.

2. I. neither (number of miles between home and school is a constant)

   II. independent variable

   III. dependent

   IV. dependent

Unit Study Guide

1. a. $0.15 per mile

   $$\frac{3.25}{22 \text{ miles}} \approx \frac{\$0.15}{1 \text{ mile}}$$

   b.

Number of Miles	Total Cost of Gas ($)
0	0
1	0.15
2	0.30
3	0.45
4	0.60
5	0.75

3.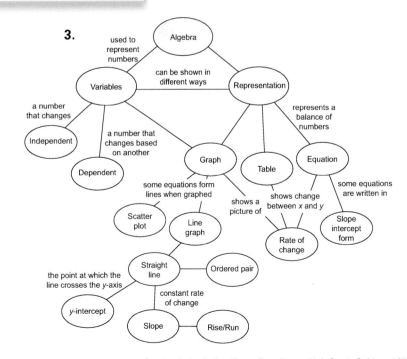

3. Add the words listed under Mathematically Speaking at the end of Section 2 to your concept map.

4. Examine the data tables below.

Table 1	
x	y
0	3
1	6
2	9
3	12
4	15

Table 2	
x	y
0	4
3	3
6	2
9	1
12	0

Table 3	
x	y
-9	-3
-6	-2
-3	-1
0	0
3	1

Find the rate of change in each table. Be sure to identify whether it is positive or negative.

5. Dominica's deli makes home-made cannolis. Each cannoli costs the same number of dollars. Three cannolis cost $9.00 and 5 cannolis cost $15.00.

   a. Make a scatter plot to show the relationship between number of cannolis and cost.

   b. Draw a trend line on your scatter plot.

   c. What is the rate of change between the cost and number of cannolis?

   d. What is the slope of the line you graphed?

6. Examine the graph to the right.

   a. Is the slope of the line positive, negative or zero?

   b. Find the slope of the line. Write the slope as a ratio.

   c. Describe the slope in words as a rate of change.

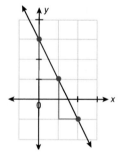

4. Table 1: $\frac{3}{1}$ (positive)

   Table 2: $-\frac{1}{3}$ (negative)

   Table 3: $\frac{1}{3}$ (positive)

5. **a.** and **b.** See below for one possible graph.

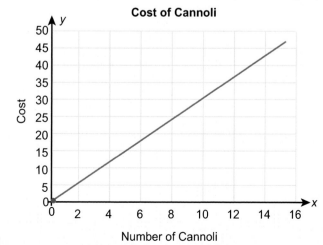

Cost of Cannoli

Cost / Number of Cannoli

c. $\frac{3}{1}$

d. $\frac{3}{1}$

6. **a.** negative

   b. $-\frac{1}{2}$

   c. The *y*-value decreases by 2 every time the *x*-value increases by 1.

7. a, g, k, n, t

   b, e, j, m, s

   c, h, i, p, r

   d, f, l, o, q

7. Match each table in the first column with a recursive rule in the second column, a graph in the third column, a slope in the fourth column, and an explicit rule in the last column.

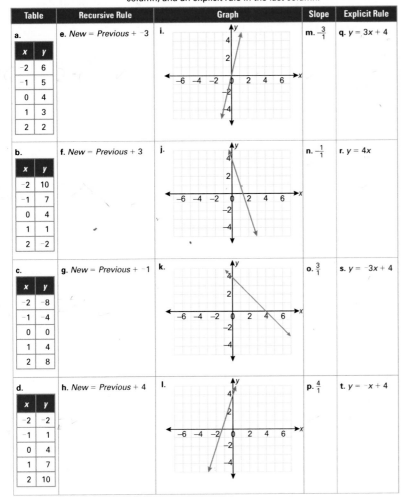

Table	Recursive Rule	Graph	Slope	Explicit Rule
a. x: -2, -1, 0, 1, 2 y: 6, 5, 4, 3, 2	**e.** New = Previous + -3	**i.**	**m.** $-\frac{3}{1}$	**q.** $y = 3x + 4$
b. x: -2, -1, 0, 1, 2 y: 10, 7, 4, 1, -2	**f.** New = Previous + 3	**j.**	**n.** $-\frac{1}{1}$	**r.** $y = 4x$
c. x: -2, -1, 0, 1, 2 y: -8, -4, 0, 4, 8	**g.** New = Previous + -1	**k.**	**o.** $\frac{3}{1}$	**s.** $y = -3x + 4$
d. x: -2, -1, 0, 1, 2 y: -2, 1, 4, 7, 10	**h.** New = Previous + 4	**l.**	**p.** $\frac{4}{1}$	**t.** $y = -x + 4$

Unit Study Guide   **137**

8. Answers will vary. One possible answer: The rate of change of a situation is the ratio of the change in the dependent variable to the corresponding change in the independent variable. For example, the rate of change for the gas mileage reimbursement problem is $0.40 for each mile driven. The slope of a line is rate of change as displayed on a graph. The slope of a line shows the ratio of the change in the dependent variable changes to the corresponding change in the independent variable. So, for the gas mileage situation, the slope of the graph correspondings to moving up 0.40 each time you move over 1.

8. How is the slope of a line related to the rate of change of a situation? Explain.

9. Use two different slope triangles to find the slope of the line below.

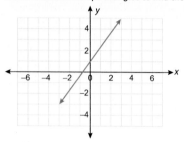

10. Add the words listed under Mathematically Speaking at the end of Section 3 to your concept map.

9. Answers will vary. The slope of the line is $\frac{4}{3}$.

10.

11. **a.** s vi

    b. w $\times$

    c. u $viii$

    d. v ix

    e. t vii

    f. x xi

    g. r $\checkmark$

    h. n i

    i. q iv

    j. y xii

    k. z $xiii$

    l. o ii

    m. p iii

11. Match each word to its definition or description.

a. slope	**i.**	$y = mx + b$	vi)
b. function	**ii.**	the output variable; the y-coordinate of a point on the graph; the result of performing an operation on the independent variable	ii
c. y-intercept	**iii.**	the point of intersection of two lines in a system of equations	p
d. decreasing function	**iv.**	a function where the y-value increases as the x-value increases	q
e. line graph	**v.**	a graph of discrete data points	r
f. ratio	**vi.**	the ratio of the change in the y-variable to the change in the x-variable over the same interval	s
g. scatter plot	**vii.**	a graph of a continuous set of points	t
h. slope-intercept form	**viii.**	the point where a graph crosses the y-axis	u
i. increasing function	**ix.**	a function where the y-value decreases as the x-value increases	v
j. linear function	**x.**	a rule that describes how one variable relates to another variable	w
k. independent variable	**xi.**	a comparison of two measures or quantities	x
l. dependent variable	**xii.**	a function in which the y-variable changes at a constant rate per unit increase in the x-variable	y
m. solution to a system of equations	**xiii.**	the input variable, the x-coordinate of a point on a graph, and the variable which you perform an operation on as part of the function rule	z

13. a. The distance to the storm is the independent variable. The number of seconds between lightening and thunder is the dependent variable.

b.

x	y
0	0
1	$\frac{1}{5}$
2	$\frac{2}{5}$
3	$\frac{3}{5}$
4	$\frac{4}{5}$
5	1
10	2

c. $y = \frac{1}{5}x$ where x (the independent variable) is the number of seconds and y (the dependent variable) is the distance

12. Blank 1: linear

Blank 2: intercept

Blank 3: slope

Blank 4: y-intercept

Blank 5: negative

Blank 6: down

Blank 7: one

Blank 8: two

Blank 9: run

Blank 10: rise

Blank 11: negative

Blank 12: negative

Blank 13: decreasing

14. Charts Tables A and B show direct variations. The constant of proportionality for Chart A is −5 and the equation is $y = -5x$. The constant of proportionality for Chart B is 3 and the equation is $y = 3x$.

15. a. The slope is −2.
The y-intercept is 3.

b.

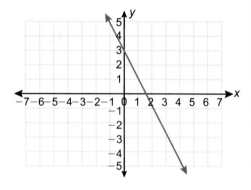

c.

x	y
−3	9
−2	7
−1	5
0	3
1	1
2	−1

d. The rate of change in the table is the slope of the line.

e. The y-intercept of the line is the entry (0, 3) in the table.

---

12. Examine the graph below. Then fill in the blanks using the words listed under "Mathematically Speaking" at the end of Sections 1, 2 and 3.

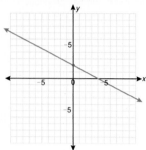

The equation $y = -\frac{1}{2}x + 2$ is a _____ equation
                                                          1
written in slope-_____ form. The _____
                              2   3
of the line is $-\frac{1}{2}$ and the_____ is (0, 2). Since the
                                        4
slope is _____ , the line moves _____
              5   6
as you read the graph from left to right. The slope is $-\frac{1}{2}$
because you can move down _____ units and
                                          7
over _____ units to move from one point to the
          8
next on the line. The slope is not $-\frac{2}{1}$, but that is a common
error. People who think the slope is $-\frac{2}{1}$ have confused
_____ with _____. Another common
      9   10
error is recording that the slope is $\frac{1}{2}$. The slope is not $\frac{1}{2}$
because the slope is _____. A _____
                              11   12
slope also indicates that this is a _____ function.
                                              13

13. Reba taught her little sister Mandy how to figure out the distance between them and a lightening storm. Reba said to Mandy, "If we see lightening 5 seconds after we hear thunder, we are 1 mile away. If we see lightening 10 seconds after we hear thunder, we are 2 miles away." The relationship between the distance to a storm and time between lightening and thunder is a direct variation.

a. State the independent and dependent variables.

b. Create a chart showing the relationship between time and distance for 0, 1, 2, 3, 4, 5, and 10 seconds.

c. Write a function rule for the relationship between distance and time.

16. Answers will vary. One possible answer:

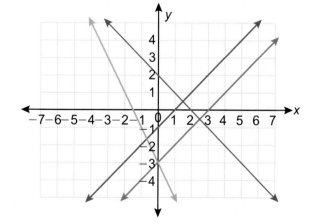

14. Determine which of the tables below show a direct variation. For each direct variation you find, identify the constant of proportionality and write the explicit equation for the variation.

Table A	
x	y
-2	10
-1	5
0	0
1	-5
2	-10

Table B	
x	y
1	3
2	6
3	9
4	12
5	15

Table C	
x	y
2	5
4	6
6	7
8	8
10	9

15. The equation $y = -2x + 3$ is a linear equation in slope-intercept form.

   a. Identify the slope and the y-intercept of the line.

   b. Make a graph of the equation.

   c. Make a table of x and y values for the equation.

   d. How is the rate of change in the table related to the line?

   e. How is the y-intercept of the line related to the table?

16. On the same piece of graph paper, draw four lines that meet the following descriptions:

   • Two lines that have the same rate of change.

   • Two lines that have the same y-intercept.

   • Two lines that have slopes with the same absolute values, but are not equal.

17. For each line you drew in Question 16, make a chart of x- and y-values for $x = -2, -1, 0, 1$ and 2.

17. Answers will vary. One possible answer:

A.

x	y
-2	-3
-1	-2
0	-1
1	0
2	1

B.

x	y
-2	4
-1	3
0	2
1	1
2	0

C.

x	y
-2	-5
-1	-4
0	-3
1	-2
2	-1

D.

x	y
-2	1
-1	-1
0	-3
1	-5
2	-7

18. a. Slope: $\frac{2}{1}$ (or equivalent) y-intercept: (0, 1)
   Equation: $y = 2x + 1$ (or equivalent)

   b. Slope: $\frac{-2}{1}$ (or equivalent) y-intercept: (0, 1)
   Equation: $y = -2x + 1$ (or equivalent)

   c. Slope: $-\frac{3}{2}$ (or equivalent) y-intercept: (0, 1)
   Equation: $y = -\frac{3}{2}x + 1$ (or equivalent)

18. Find the slope and y-intercept of each line below. Then, write the equation of the line in slope-intercept ($y = mx + b$) form.

a.
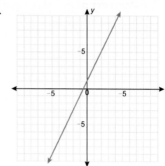

b.
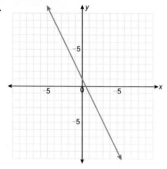

c.
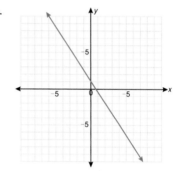

19. The equations $y = 4x + 3$ and $y = 4x - 1$ represent two linear functions in a system of equations.

a. Fill in the table for each linear function.

$y = 4x + 3$

x	y
−2	
−1	
0	
1	
2	

$y = 4x - 1$

x	y
−2	
−1	
0	
1	
2	

19. a.

x	y
−2	−5
−1	−1
0	3
1	7
2	11

x	y
−2	−9
−1	−5
0	−1
1	3
2	7

b.

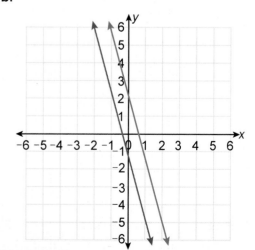

c. Parallel

d. Zero solutions

Explanations will vary. One possible explanation: The solution to a system of linear equations is the point where the two lines intersect. Since these lines will never intersect, there is no solution.

b. Graph both functions on the coordinate grid below.

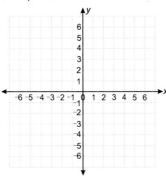

c. Are the lines you graphed in Part b parallel, coinciding or intersecting?

d. Does this system of equations have zero solutions, one solution or infinitely many solutions? Explain your answer.

20. Examine the graph showing a system of equations. Then, determine whether each statement below is true or false.

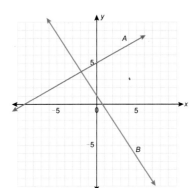

a. The solution to the system of equations is (0, 5).

b. The solution to the system of equations is (–2, 4).

c. The y-intercept of Line A is 5

d. The y-intercept of Line B is 0

e. The slope of Line A is positive.

f. The slope of Line B is positive.

g. The system of equations has more than one solution.

20. **a.** False

b. True

c. True

d. False

e. True

f. False

g. False

21. Answers will vary. One possible answer: In the equation $y = 4x - 6$, 4 is equal to the ratio $\frac{4}{1}$. So, this line has a slope of $\frac{4}{1}$ meaning for every vertical change of 4 units, there is a horizontal change of 1 unit.

21. Calvin learned in class that slope is the ratio of vertical change to horizontal change. He also learned that the value of m in the equation $y = mx + b$ identifies the slope of a line. For homework, Calvin was asked to find the slope of the line represented by the equation $y = 4x - 6$. But he is confused since 4 is not a ratio. Is there a mistake in the homework or is there another reason why the slope is written as a whole number?

22. Donatella's friend told her that she could find the slope of a line by looking at a table of (x, y) values for points on that line. But Donatella is confused. She doesn't know which row of the table will tell her the slope. For example, she asked her friend which row in the table below is the slope. What should her friend tell her?

x	y
−2	4
0	5
2	6
4	7

23. On her homework last night, Maureen wrote that the slope of the line pictured below is $\frac{2}{1}$, and she drew a slope triangle to show this. The next day in class, Maureen's teacher said the answer was $\frac{3}{2}$. Is Maureen wrong or did the teacher read the wrong answer?

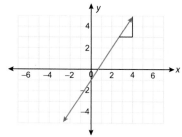

22. Answers will vary. One possible answer: The slope cannot be found by looking at one row. Instead, the change of corresponding values between the rows in the table indicates the slope of the line. In the table given, the y-value increases by 1 every time the x-value increases by 2. So, this means the rate of change is $\frac{1}{2}$ so the slope of the line will be $\frac{1}{2}$.

23. Answers will vary. One possible answer: Maureen is wrong. The slope of the line is $\frac{3}{2}$ because you must move down 3 units and then left 2 units to move from one point on the line to another on the grid. After Maureen moves down 2 units, she moves more than 1 unit to the left in order to hit the line again, which should show her that the slope is not $\frac{2}{1}$.

24. Al was asked to answer the following multiple-choice question on a recent quiz.

To pick apples at the U-Pick-It apple orchard, you pay $10 for the bag plus $0.10 per apple. Which rule shows the cost, y, to pick any number of apples, x?

A. $y = 10x + 0.10$ **C.** $y = 10 + 0.10x$

B. $y = 10x + 0.10x$ **D.** $y = 10 + 0.10$

Al picked Letter A but his answer was marked wrong. Why? What could you do to help Al find and fix his error?

25. Laura wrote that the slope of the line graphed below was $\frac{4}{1}$. Her teacher told her that this was not correct. What error did Laura make? How could you help her fix her error?

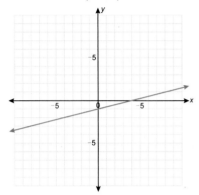

24. Student answers will vary. One possible answer: Al's answer is wrong because the rule he chose shows that the cost is $10 per apple, which is not accurate. For example, if someone picks 5 apples they do not pay 10(5) or $50 for those apples! Since the cost per apple is $0.50, 0.50x tells the cost for the apples. The $10 is a constant or flat fee so it will be added to the cost for the apples. So, the correct choice is letter B.

25. Answers will vary. One possible answer: The slope is $\frac{1}{4}$ since the ratio of rise to run is 1 to 4. Laura needs to remember that slope is the ratio of the vertical change to the horizontal change. Laura can find the slop by drawing slope triangles on the graph or making a table of (x, y) values.

See corresponding assessments in **Assessment Resources.**

compression bar A zig-zag line on one of the axes of a coordinate system indicating the absence of a portion of that axis.

Example:

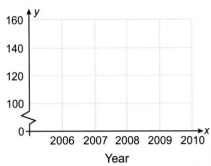

Year

concept map A diagram consisting of nodes and links depicting the relationships among and between concepts.

Example:

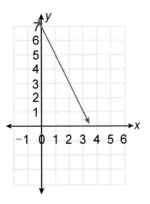

constant of proportionality The constant (numerical value) that is equivalent to the ratio of two proportional quantities.

Example:

If x and y are proportional, $\frac{y}{x} = k$, and $y = kx$, where k is the constant of proportionality.

The circumference, C, and radius, r, of a circle are proportional. $C = 2\pi r$ and $\frac{C}{r} = 2\pi$. Therefore, the constant of proportionality is 2π.

decreasing function A function in which an increase in the value of the independent variable results in a decrease in the value of the dependent variable.

Example:

Input (x)	Output (y)
0	7
1	5
2	3
3	1

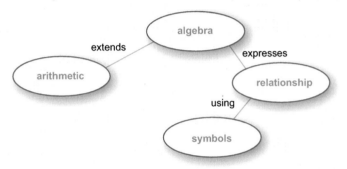

dependent variable A variable whose value is determined by the value of one or more other variables.

Example:
Let d be the distance traveled at 40 miles per hour in t hours: $d = 40t$.

  t is the independent (input) variable.
  d is the dependent (output) variable.

Distance, d, depends on the number of hours, t.

---

direct variation A relationship between two quantities such that one is a constant multiple of the other. The two quantities in a direct variation are proportional.

Example:
A cashier works for a constant wage of $8.50 per hour. There is a direct variation between the cashier's pay, P, and the number of hours worked, H.

$P = 8.50 \cdot H$ and $\frac{P}{H} = 8.50$.

---

discrete Distinct; separate.

Examples:
The set $\{1, 3, 6, 8, 10\}$ is a set of discrete numbers as shown on the number line:

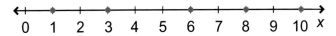

The set of points in the interval $x > 2$ is not a discrete set (it is continuous) as shown on the number line:

The points on the graph below are discrete. The line on the graph is continuous (not discrete).

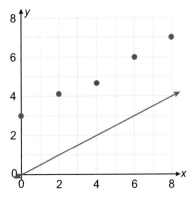

---

explicit rule A rule that directly defines the output variable in terms of the input variable.

Example:
Situation: I open a savings account with $10, and then deposit $50 each month.

Explicit Rule: $A = 10 + 50n$; A is the amount in account after n months of deposits. A is the output variable and n is the input variable.

function A relationship between two variables, in which each value of the independent (input) variable is matched to only one value of the dependent (output) variable.

Example:

Function: $y = 2x + 3$

Input (x):	-2	-1	0	1	2	3
Output (y):	-1	1	3	5	7	9

For each input value there is only one output value.

increasing function A function in which an increase in the value of the independent variable results in a increase in the value of the dependent variable.

Example:

Input (x)	Output (y)
0	1
1	4
2	7
3	10

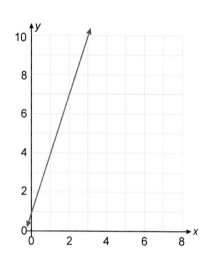

independent variable A variable whose value is not determined by the value of any other variable.

Example:

Let d be the distance traveled at 40 miles per hour in t hours: $d = 40t$.

    t is the independent (input) variable.

    d is the dependent (output) variable.

The number of hours, t, is chosen freely and does not depend on the value of any other variable.

input variable The variable in an expression or function whose value is not influenced by any other factor; the value of the input variable determines the value of the expression or function.

Example:

Let s be the length of the sides of a square, an input variable. The side length, s, can be any number greater than zero. Once chosen, s determines a square's area, A, by the equation $A = s^2$.

line graph A graph of a set of ordered pairs where the points are connected by line segments.

Example:

Year	Population
1931	4000
1941	5000
1951	9000
1961	15000
1971	18000
1981	23000
1991	27000

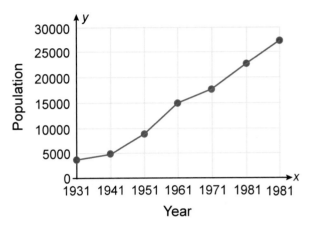

linear function A function whose ordered pairs form a straight line when graphed. The explicit rule representation is the equation of a line. The recursive rule representation shows addition or subtraction of a constant at each step. When presented in a table, a linear function will have a constant ratio of change in output to change in input.

Example:
Graph

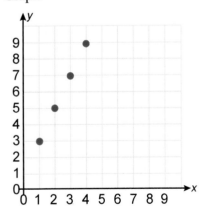

Explicit: $y = 2x + 1$

Recursive: *Next = Previous + 2*

Table

Input (x)	Output (y)
1	3
2	5
3	7
4	9

links (of a concept map) A line connecting and describing the relationship between two nodes of a concept map.

Example:
See concept map.

---

nodes (of a concept map) The concepts or ideas included in a concept map.

Example:
See concept map.

---

numerical coefficient The number multiplying a variable in an algebraic expression.

Example:

$10x = 50$ The coefficient of x is 10.

$5p + 3 \approx 20$ The coefficient of p is 5.

$3D = 7u$ The coefficient of D is 3 and the coefficient of u is 7.

---

output variable The variable representing the value of an expression or function; the value of the output variable is determined by evaluating the expression or function using the value of the input variable.

Example:
Let A be the area of a square, an output variable. The area, A, depends upon the length of the sides, s, and is determined by the equation $A = s^2$.

---

parallel Everywhere equidistant (the same distance apart). Two lines in the same plane with the same slope are parallel.

Example:
$y = 2x + 4$ and $y = 2x + 10$ are equations of parallel lines. The opposite sides of a rectangle are parallel.

---

point of intersection The point where the graphs of two or more equations cross or meet. This point is a solution to each of these equations.

Example:
Equations: $y = x + 4$ and $y = 3x$

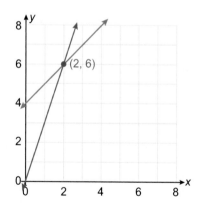

The point (2, 6) is a solution to each equation and the point of intersection of the two lines.

---

rate A ratio that compares two quantities usually measured in different units.

Examples:
The average rate of a car that traveled 60 miles in 2 hours was $\frac{60\text{mi}}{2\text{hr}} = 30$ miles per hour.

The water in the dam fell over the spillway at a rate of $\frac{1000}{3}$ cubic feet per hour.

rate of change The ratio of the change in one variable with respect to the change in a second variable; usually the ratio of the change in the dependent variable with respect to the change in the independent variable. A linear function has a constant rate of change.

Example:
Equation: $y = 3x$

The rate of change of this line is constant and is also the slope, $m = 3$. As the value of y increases by 3, the value of x increases by 1.

ratio A comparison of two quantities, a and b, stated as "a to b" and represented as $a : b$ or $\frac{a}{b}$.

Examples:
The ratio representing the number of cars in a parking lot to the number of wheels is $\frac{1}{4}$.

In a recipe calling for 3 cups of flour and 2 cups of sugar, the ratio of flour to sugar is $3 : 2$.

recursive rule A rule that is applied to the result of a previous applications of itself; the input value is a previous output value of the rule.

Example:
Situation: I open a savings account with $10 and deposit $50 each month. Therefore, each month my balance is $50 more than the previous month.

Recursive Rule: *New = Previous* + 50; initial amount of $10.

$\frac{rise}{run}$ (read "rise over run") The ratio describing the change in vertical distance to the change in horizontal distance on a graph; the slope of a line; the rate of change of a linear function.

Example:
This graph uses slope triangles to show the ratio of $\frac{rise}{run}$ as $\frac{2}{1} = \frac{-2}{-1} = 2$.

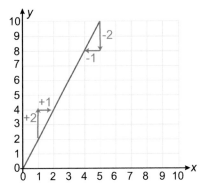

scale (on a coordinate axes system) The range of values being presented on the axes of a coordinate system. Adjusting the scale of the x- and y-axes may better illustrate graphed data, as well as impact the interpretation of the graph.

The following graphs represent the same data with different y-axis scales.

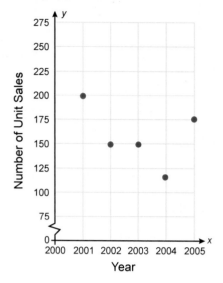

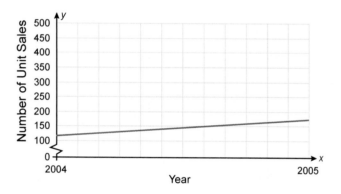

scatter plot The graph of a set of ordered pairs on a coordinate plane.

Example:

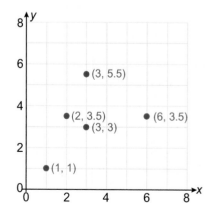

slope The "steepness" of a line; the physical representation of the rate of change. The slope is the ratio of $\frac{\text{rise}}{\text{run}}\left(\frac{\text{change in } y\text{-value}}{\text{change in } x\text{-value}}\right)$ between two points on a graph.

Example:

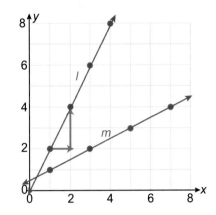

Line l is steeper, and therefore has a greater positive slope, than line m.

The slope of line l connecting the points (1, 2) and (2, 4) is $\frac{4-2}{2-1} = \frac{2}{1} = 2$.

---

slope-intercept form (of a line) The form of the equation of a line written as $y = mx + b$, where m is the slope of the line, b is the y-value of the y-intercept, x is the independent variable, and y is the dependent variable.

Example:
Equation: $y = 3x + 10$
Slope: 3
y-intercept: (0, 10)

---

solution A number (or set of numbers) that produces a true statement when substituted for a variable (or variables) in a mathematical sentence (equation or inequality). The answer to a mathematical problem.

Examples:
Problem: $5x = 10$
Solution: $x = 2$

Problem: $3x > 15$
Solution: $x > 5$

---

solution to a system of equations The variable values that simultaneously solve all equations in a system of equations. When graphed, the equations will intersect at the point which is the solution.

Example:
System: $y = 2x + 1$
$\qquad\quad\; y = x + 4$

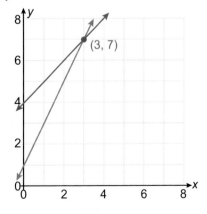

(3, 7)

The solution to this system is the point (3,7); $x = 3$ and $y = 7$.

system of equations Any group of two or more equations.

Example:

System: $y = 3x + 2$

$\qquad y = x + 1$

unit rate A comparison of two quantities or measures where the second has a value of 1. A rate that when expressed as a fraction has a denominator of 1.

Examples:

45 mph represents a unit rate of 45 miles per 1 hour.

Three cases of soda contain 36 cans of soda. The unit rate is 12 cans per 1 case.

variable A letter or other symbol used to represent a number or set of numbers in an expression or an equation.

Examples:

$10x = 50$ The variable is x.

$5p + 3 \approx 20$ The variable is p.

$3\triangle + 5 > 7\square$ The variables are $\triangle$ and $\square$.

x-axis The horizontal axis in the Cartesian (coordinate) plane.

y-axis The vertical axis in the Cartesian (coordinate) plane.

y-intercept A point where a line or curve intersects the y-axis.

Example:

Equation: $y = mx + b$

y-intercept: $(0, b)$

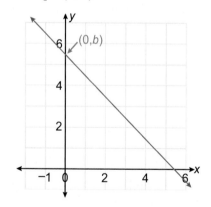

Lesson 1.3

From Graphs to Tables

Page 20. Question 6: Label one column Year and the other Sales.

Page 20. Question 8: Are there any outside factors that might contribute to sales remaining steady or decreasing?

Lesson 1.4

Mileage Reimbursement

Page 28. Question 6: As the number of miles increases, what happens to the amount of money received?

Lesson 1.4

On Your Own

Page 31. Question 3: One way to figure this out is to use a map or road atlas. Find the scale of the map so that you know how many miles 1 inch represents. Take a compass and extend it so that its radius will be the equivalent of 450 miles. Now put the point of the compass on Houston, Texas and then draw a circle on the map using this radius. Find all cities that lie on this circle. Heather will be 450 miles away from Houston. Use a similar procedure for Mike.

Lesson 1.5

Jogging Bonus

Page 39. Question 12b: One way to find this is to set up a proportion. $\frac{225}{100} = \frac{?}{?}$

Page 40. Question 13: Use the recursive rule you found for the number of calories burned for every 1 pound to help you.

On Your Own

Page 41. Question 3b: To find the explicit rule, find the cost of lunch for each person.

Page 41. Question 3c: Use the number of miles jogged per hour to find the explicit rule.

Lesson 2.3

Page 75. Question 3: Think about how slope is related to the rate of change.

Staying the Same

Page 79. Question 9a: Since the number of days does not matter, x is not needed in the equation.

On Your Own

Page 82. Question 9b: Can you divide by zero?

Lesson 3.1

On Your Own

Page 109. Question 8b: You can graph this line and find the rate of change between two points on the graph.

Page 110. Question 10a: $\frac{\text{rise}}{\text{run}} = \frac{\text{up } 2}{\text{over } 1}$

Lesson 3.2

On Your Own

Page 119. Question 10: First, graph the equation $y = 2x + 1$. You should know from recent lessons that the slope is 2 and the y-intercept is at (0, 1). Since the inequality states that y is "greater than" the expression, shade in the area above the line (in the positive y direction). You can also check points to determine which side of the line to shade. Pick one point above the line and one point below the line.

Lesson 3.3

On Your Own

Page 126. Question 14: Rewrite this as a division problem first and then solve.

Index

predicting function (See also *estimate*)

    graph 29, 30, 31, 38

    linear functions 31

prime factorization 126

Q

questioning techniques T7 (See also *discussion techniques, Five Ws and an H*)

    focusing T7

    funneling T7

R

rate 150

rate of change T29, 51, 52A, 53, 54, 82, 92, 133, 136, 141, 151 (See also *ratio, unit rate*)

    constant and varying 54, 56, 59, 60, 68, 93, 97

    direct variation and 102, 105

    graph 58, 104

    linear functions and 80, 82, 92, 93, 98, 105

    linear relationships and 53, 55

    negative 83E

    ratio and 67

    slope 66, 79, 88, 95

ratio 139, 151 (See also *rate*)

    circumference 108

    diameter 108

    estimate , of area 25

    fraction form 51

    rate of change and 67, 97

    rise over run 73, 85 (See also *slope*)

    slope as 95, 97, 144

reflection (of line) 126

relationships

    predicting linear 43

recursive rule 91, 135, 151 (See also *explicit rule*)

    difference between explicit rule and 35, 40

    functions 41

    for linear function 38

    rate of change and 53

    slope and 77, 80

    using tables 39, 44

repeat/rephrase T5 (See also *discussion techniques*)

representation

    graphical/pictorial T24

    numerical/tabular T23

S

symbolic/analytic T25

    written (and verbal) T26

    revoicing T5 (See also *discussion techniques*)

    rise over run 73–75, 85, 99 151 (See also *slope*)

    rounding

        decimals 25 (See also *fractions*)

    rule(s)

        explicit 35, 38 (using graphing calculator), 39, 40 (See also *recursive*)

        function 28, 30, 38, 46

        recursive 35, 38 (using graphing calculator), 39, 40, 44 (See also *explicit*)

        slope and 77, 91

        writing , as equation 28

scaffold learning 8

scale(s)

    and tables/graphs 16B, 17, 21, 22

    changing to mislead 22 (See also *graphs, tables*)

    on *x*- and *y*-axes 17, 23, 37, 152

scatter plot (graph) 36, 53, (vs. line) 58, 93, 96, 97, 139, 152 (See also *discrete set*)

shapes, concept map of 2

sign, equal T20

slope 51, 63–92, 68, 82A, 86A, 92, 103, 130, 139, 153

    changes in 75

    comparing 86, 104, 115

    coordinate plane and 82

    decreasing function 85

    equation 66, 101, 108, 109, 110

    explicit rule 65

    finding 78

    horizontal line 78

    -intercept form T28, 72, 106, 107, 110, 129, 130, 139–141, 153

    line 111, 118

    parallel lines 91A

    point of intersection 129

    positive and negative 85, 87, 88, 95, 120, 121, 122, 123, 125, 137

    rate of change 66, 79, 95

    rise over run 73–75, 85, 99, 144

    triangles 74, 75, 77, 81, 89, 92, 95, 97, 117, 138

    vertical line 82A

    zero 94

systems of equations T29, 112, 123, 124, 128, 130, 142, 154

    solution to 114, 129, 139